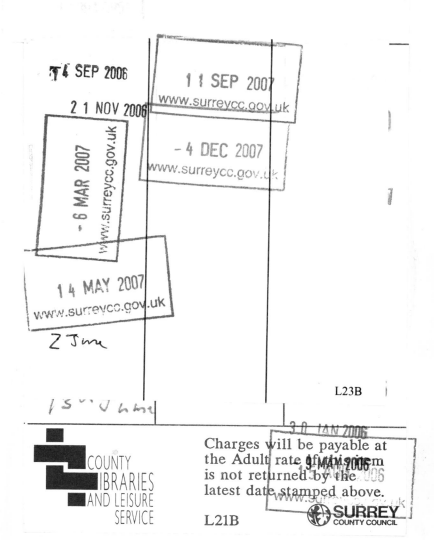

ROMAN SILVER COINS

Vol. V

CARAUSIUS TO ROMULUS AUGUSTUS
A.D. 286–476

ROMAN SILVER COINS

BY

C. E. KING

with valuations by
DAVID R. SEAR

VOL. V
CARAUSIUS TO
ROMULUS AUGUSTUS
Arranged according to *Cohen*

London

© Seaby Publications Ltd
First published 1987
Reprinted 1990
Photography by P. Frank Purvey

Published by B. A. Seaby Ltd
7 Davies Street, London W1Y 1LL

Distributed by B. T. Batsford Ltd
P.O. Box 4, Braintree, Essex CM7 7QY
also by agents in
The United States of America
Canada
Australia
South Africa

ISBN 0-900652-80-2

Typeset by
Latimer Trend & Company Ltd., Plymouth
and printed at
Biddles Ltd, Guildford & Kings Lynn

CONTENTS

INTRODUCTION

The purpose of this volume, like that of its predecessors, is to give collectors and dealers a brief and handy guide to help them to identify their silver coins and to put a value on them. For this reason the coins have been arranged alphabetically by type in the catalogue and not by series and, although an alphabetical arrangement is far from ideal, it has the merit of being easy to consult by the non-specialist. A schematic arrangement of issues in simplified form has also been included in the hope it will give some idea of the evolution of the silver coinage in this period.

Where possible the coins have been arranged according to Cohen numbers and where entries are incorrect I have corrected them and indicated this by the use of a † (dagger symbol) after the Cohen numbers. The expansion of the mint system in the later empire frequently resulted in the same reverses being produced at a number of different mints, or at the same mint with different marks. I have treated these as varieties and have added an a, b, c, etc. to the Cohen numbers. I have omitted pieces which Cohen has listed as silver but which are clearly silvered billion. Where Cohen has not recorded a type I have adopted the number of the piece which would have preceded it and added a capital letter, e.g. 318A. In the fifth century Cohen listed coinages for the Western emperors because he felt the Eastern emperors had been adequately treated in Sabatier's study. In consequence, coins of Western emperors have been given Cohen numbers, those of Eastern emperors Sabatier numbers.

Obverses

Obverse legends precede each section and are given in capital letters A, B, C, etc. Busts are also listed and given lower case letters.

Diadems

Silver coins minted by the tetrarchy normally had laureate heads and this practice continued into the next period. By about 310 Constantine was occasionally represented wearing a helmet but by the later stages of his reign he was frequently portrayed wearing a diadem. Bare, laureate, and diademed heads are also found for the Caesars. The earliest diadems seem to have been plain (Fig. 1, nos. 1a and 1b) but by the end of Constantine I's reign and during that of his successors, the pearl diadem, rosette diadem, and laurel and rosette diadem had been introduced. These were not always represented in the same way and indeed may themselves originally been of different types. (Fig. 1, nos. 2a and 2b, 3a, 36 and 4). There can be a problem in distinguishing the rosette diadem from the laurel and rosette diadem since the laurel leaves can lose their characteristic elliptical shape and become rather more circular which is the way in which the beads (pearls?) between the rosettes are represented on the rosette diadem. RIC VIII has distinguished the various types of diadem with great care and I have preserved its classification. This has made for a proliferation of entries under the relevant Cohen number as Cohen himself did not classify diadems in a detailed fashion.

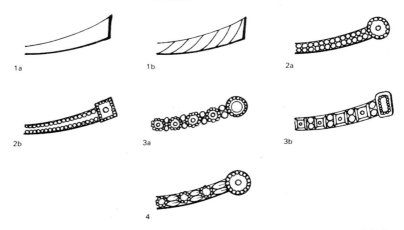

Fig. 1   Types of diadems: 1a plain diadem; 1b plain diadem; 2a pearl diadem; 2b pearl diadem; 3a rosette diadem; 3b rosette diadem; 4 laurel and rosette diadem.

Rarity

The rarity of late Roman silver coins is problematic. In the case of Carausius, for instance, the amount of variation in obverse and reverse legends, engraving mistakes, etc., suggest that no system operated by which a properly controlled and standardized coinage could be produced. As a result, many pieces vary only slightly from the main types and appear to be much rarer than they would seem if they were to be considered together with the types from which they derive. It is also extremely difficult to distinguish between regular and irregular pieces of Carausius since many of the obviously blundered pieces, nonetheless, conform in weight and fineness with those of better workmanship. For this reason, and because barbarous pieces were almost certainly produced in Britain and were contemporary with the more obviously genuine coins, a number of what are almost certainly ancient copies have been listed and designated as irregular.

By comparison, the coinage of Diocletian and his co-rulers Maximian, Constantius, and Galerius is so standard as to appear monotonous at first glance. Its survival rate has been low and, again, the notion of rarity is enhanced by the diversity of mints and issue marks. Silver output remained scanty until the mid-fourth century and at all times multiples and the larger denominations were much less common that the siliqua.

During the seond half of the fourth century silver output increased significantly, particularly in the West, and many of the siliquae are relatively common although the larger pieces tend to be much rarer. It is important to bear in mind that certain types with particular mintmarks are much commoner than others and that output varied between issues and mints.

Production slowed down abruptly in the last years of the fourth century and during the fifth century was sporadic and issues were small. Many coins appear to be very rare although this notion is enhanced by the absence of any systematic publication of fifth-century silver and there may be more surviving specimens than at first sight appear to exist.

Mints (Table A)

During the course of the later third century the Roman imperial mint system underwent a dramatic expansion. Regional mints were established at a number of centres on both a temporary and longer-term basis and, by the beginning of the fourth century, they existed in virtually every diocese (the administrative entity which loosely replaced the older provincial units which had been subdivided as a result of Diocletian's administrative reforms). Any mint could produce coins in gold, silver and bronze but in practice the issues of precious metals were often but not always restricted to those centres where the emperor resided or was visiting. Thus not all mints produced silver and while some did at certain periods, they did not at others. Nor did every silver-producing mint participate in every issue. Some issues were exclusive to individual mints and others seem to have been regional in character. Even those issues which were produced more-or-less contemporaneously in all parts of the empire very rarely included every mint currently in operation. Mints could be closed for short periods of time, for much longer periods or even permanently and new mints could be established. Thus the mint system in the later empire was a remarkably flexible one with the authorities able to dictate when and where mints were situated, what metals they could coin in, how large issues should be and which mints were to be the most important. It is therefore not surprising that output was not constant and that issues in all metals were of varying duration and size. Throughout the period covered by this volume the mint and monetary system were evolving and the appearance of either at one point in time could be significantly different from that at another.

TABLE A: Silver Mints

Alexandria	Colchester (?)	London	Sirmium
Antioch	Constantinople	Lugdunum	Siscia
Aquileia	Cyzicus	Nicomedia	Thessalonica
Arelate	Heraclea	Ravenna	Ticinum
Barcino	Ostia	Rome	Trier
Carthage	Milan	Serdica	

Identification of mints and rulers

On the whole it is not difficult to determine the mint to which a given coin belongs in this period since it is usually marked with letters which abbreviate the mint name which makes it obvious where it was produced. However, problems of various sorts can arise, e.g. some issues (particularly those minted early in the Tetrarchy) are unmarked, are marked with symbols, or with letters designating only the workshop which made them and not the mint. Attribution of such pieces is made on stylistic grounds and only experience and familiarity with the coinage make it possible to assign these pieces with confidence to the proper mint.

Problems can also arise in distinguishing rulers. Some have the same names and titles (e.g. IMP MAXIMIANVS AVG) which could refer equally well to Maximian or Galerius after 305; more than one ruler had the same name (e.g. Constantius I, Constantius II, and Constantius Gallus, Constantine I and Constantine II, etc.), or names so similar as to be easily confused with those of other rulers (Maximianus and Maximinus). Usually the distinction is easy to make but in some cases it is harder. Galerius and Maximian can be identified by the difference in their physical

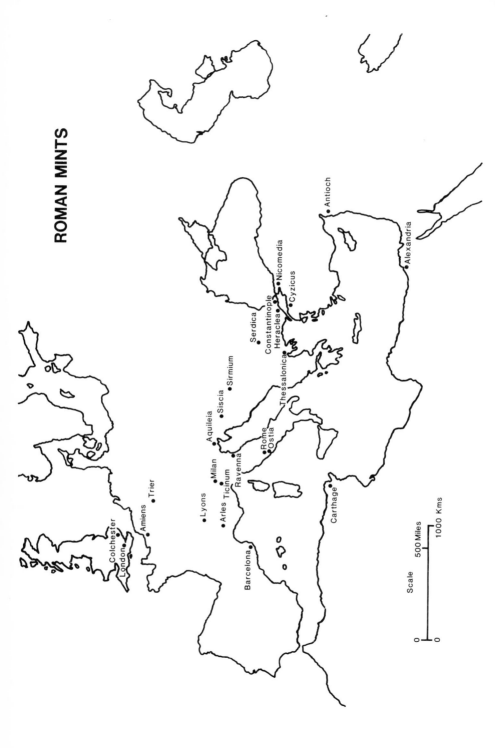

ROMAN MINTS

Colchester
London
Amiens
Trier
Lyons
Arles
Ticinum
Ravenna
Milan
Barcelona
Aquileia
Siscia
Sirmium
Rome
Ostia
Serdica
Constantinople
Heraclea
Thessalonica
Nicomedia
Cyzicus
Antioch
Alexandria
Carthage

Scale
500 Miles
0
1000 Kms
0

appearance; Maximian has an upturned nose and Galerius has not. Late portraits of Constantine I as Augustus and early ones of Constantine II as Augustus with anepigraphic portraits have been distinguished on similar grounds. Disputed attributions will be discussed more fully in the section on issues.

Mint and series marks

Mint Designation

As noted above, mints usually signed their products with a letter or letters abbreviating the name of the mint city. Table B lists these abbreviations for mints producing silver during the period covered by this volume. Some mints used more than one combination of letters for no very obvious reason, although the change from ARL to CONS at Arelate and L to AVG at London reflects a change in the name of both cities. In some instances the same letter was used by more than one mint. For example C is found at Colchester (?) under Carausius and at Constantinople and Cyzicus but usually the other components of the mint mark allow the mint in question to be readily identified.

Mint designations appear on the reverse of the coin, usually in the exergue. While these letters may stand alone and often do, especially on the issues of precious metals, they also commonly occur in conjunction with other combinations of letters in the field and the exergue, the total of which equal the mintmark. (Fig. 2.)

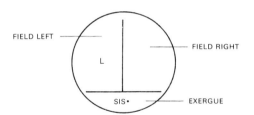

FIELD LEFT

FIELD RIGHT

L

SIS·

EXERGUE

Fig. 2   Diagrammatic reverse of a coin.

The conventional method of representing the mintmark schematically is to divide the field in half by a vertical line and to delineate the exergue by a horizontal one ($\perp$). This allows the relative positions of letters and symbols to be easily represented (e.g. $\frac{S|F}{PTR}$).

The letters M or SM often precede or follow the letters designating the mint of origin. These letters can be expanded to MONETA and SACRA MONETA and simply mean mint. Thus the basic core of the mintmark is made up of the mint abbreviation ($\overline{C}$, $\overline{TR}$, $\overline{H}$, $\overline{TS}$, etc.) to which the letters M or SM are commonly appended ($\overline{CM}$, $\overline{SMTR}$, $\overline{SMH}$, $\overline{MTS}$, etc.).

Officina Marks

In addition to the mint signature most issues of silver coins in this period had a letter or letters designating which workshop (officina) made them. The number of

TABLE B: Mint Abbreviations

ALE	Alexandria	L, RSR, AVG	London
ANT, AN	Antioch	LVG, LG, LVGD, LA,	Lugdunum
AQ	Aquileia	LD	(Lyons)
ARL, AR, CON, CONT,		N, NIK	Nicomedia
CONST, KONSAI,	Arelate	RV	Ravenna
KONT, KA		R, ROMA, RM	Rome
BA, B	Barcino	SD	Serdica
None — Workshop	Carthage	SIRM	Sirmium
letter only		SIS, SISC	Siscia
C	Colchester (?)	TS, THES, T̂S∈, TES,	
C, K, KV	Cyzicus	TE, THS	Thessalonica
C, CONS, CP, CN	Constantinople	T	Ticinum
H, HE	Heraclea	TR	Trier
OST	Ostia		
MD	Mediolanum (Milan)		

workshops varied from mint to mint and often within the same mint since the number could be expanded or contracted and was at different times. Workshops usually signed using Latin letters (P, S, T, Q, V, VI) or Greek letters (A, B, Γ, Δ,). Table C lists the commonest of these letters. These letters could precede or follow the mint signature, e.g. $\overline{\text{SMSDA}}$, $\overline{\text{PTR}}$, etc. On the whole the Eastern mints tended to have a larger number of workshops than those in the West. Although coins were often produced in all workshops, in some issues this does not seem to have occurred and they were limited to one or two workshops. In the catalogue the number of workshops for a given issue has not been specified, only the first letter is given. *It is therefore extremely important when reading a mintmark to remember that a variation in the letters listed in the catalogue may be no more than a reflection of the fact that a different workshop produced the coin and it is not a new or variant mintmark.* For example, $\overline{\text{CONSA}}$ and CONSIA belong to the same issue from Constantinople; the A refers to Workshop One, the IA to Workshop Eleven. The full range of workshops for each issue is given in the appropriate volume of RIC.

TABLE C: Workshop Designations

LATIN

P	*Prima*	(Workshop One)	H	Workshop Eight
S	*Secunda*	(Workshop Two)	Θ	Workshop Nine
T	*Tertia*	(Workshop Three)	I	Workshop Ten
Q	*Quarta*	(Workshop Four)	IA	Workshop Eleven

GREEK

A	Workshop One
B	Workshop Two
Γ	Workshop Three
Δ	Workshop Four
E	Workshop Five
S	Workshop Six
Z	Workshop Seven

SYMBOLS

$\star$	Star
⸕	Branch
·	Dot
Ϙ	Wreath
⋺⋸	Thunderbolt
∪	Crescent
∪	Dot within crescent

Symbols

Occasionally neither the workshop nor the mint is represented by a letter and the issue is marked with a symbol, e.g. the tetrarchic issue of argentei signed with a club. Symbols are also found in conjunction with the letters forming the mint signature in the exergue or in the field of the coin, e.g. $\overline{\text{·SIS·}}$, $\overline{\text{*ANT*}}$, $\frac{*|*}{\text{PR}}$. The precise meaning of these symbols is unclear although different combinations most probably reflect different issues. Some mints commonly used them as part of the mint mark, some rarely did, and some never.

Other letters marked on silver coins (Table D)

Some silver coins seem to have been marked with letters suggesting what their denominational value was meant to be. A group of argentei minted at Rome, Ticinum and Aquileia had in place of a conventional reverse legend, the Roman numeral XCVI inscribed within a wreath. This is interpreted to mean that the weight of the coin was equal to 1/96th of the Roman pound. The numeral L found in the field on some pieces of the silver issue with the VOTA ORBIS ET VRBIS SEN ET PR XX/XXX MVL FEL reverse (p. 102) has been construed as meaning that they were struck at 1/50th of the Roman pound, but the number of these coins now extant is far too small to validate this assumption. Some heavy miliarenses struck at Aquileia in the name of Constans and Magnentius bear the mark LX, which may refer to the fact that they were intended to be struck at 1/60th of the Roman pound. Silver minted after the financial reforms of Valentinian I and Valens between 365 and 368 were commonly marked PS or PV (*Pusulatum*) referring to the fact that they were struck from refined or purified bullion.

TABLE D: Letters commonly found with mint designation and workshop

L	Fifty
LX	Sixty
M	*Moneta* (mint)
PS, PV	*Pvslatvm* (refined, purified silver)
SM	*Sacra moneta*
XCVI	Ninety-six

Silver denominations and metrology

Carausius, who was the first emperor to issue 'pure' silver coins after the collapse of the antoninianus, minted denarii which had a considerable variation in weight (2.36–5.74g.) but which averaged *c.* 3.6g. which suggests a theoretical standard of 1/84th of the pound (3.75g.). The actual average weights are equivalent to the standard of Nero's pre-reform denarius and considerably higher than the Tetrarchic post-reform silver which had an average weight of 3.1g. in the Sisak hoard. The coins marked XCVI (96) minted by the Tetrarchy suggest that the theoretical standard was 1/96th of the pound, which would give a theoretical average weight of 3.38g. The silver coins of Carausius are traditionally called denarii for want of a better term while the Tetrarchic pieces are usually labelled argentei, although this term has been rejected by some since there is no historical support for its ever having been the actual name of a coin. Later pieces on the same weight standard are called siliquae and this term, which is attested in the earlier fourth century, remained in general use thereafter. The weight of the siliqua was reduced under Constantius II between 355 and 360 to *c*. 1.9g. It has been argued that the theoretical standard was 1/144th of the Roman pound, but this would give a theoretical standard of 2.26g. approximately. If the theoretical standards are correct, then it was common practice to mint low-weight coins, which is certainly possible. The weight of the siliqua was again reduced late in the fourth century to *c*. 1.3g.

Between 315 and 337 Constantine not only minted siliquae but coins of other denominations as well. There were multiples, such as the DN CONSTANTINVS MAX TRIVMF AVG, which may have been issued at 1/20th of the pound although the numbers known are too few to admit of any real certainty as to their weight standard. Various other multiples may have been intended as two-siliqua pieces (e.g. SALVS REIPVBLICAE at Ticinum; MONETA AVGG ET CAESS NN at Aquileia, and VOTA POPVLI ROMANI at Rome). Constantine also seems to have introduced the miliarensis which appears to have been struck at 1/60th and at 1/72nd of the pound. His successors continued to mint the miliarensis on two weight standards, a heavier at 1/60th of the pound and a lighter at 1/72nd of a pound. The heavier piece had a theoretical weight standard of *c*. 5.41g., the lighter 4.51g. Unfortunately the rarity of all these heavy pieces makes it difficult to do more than suggest a weight standard since there are not enough specimens available for a valid statistical analysis.

In this catalogue the silver coins of Carausius are labelled denarii; those of the Tetrarchy up to 337 as argentei or multiples, thereafter the denominations are listed as follows: Mult. (multiple); Heavy Mil. (heavy miliarensis); Light Mil. (light miliarensis); Red. Sil. (reduced siliqua), and Half Sil. (half-siliqua). The unreduced siliqua is not specifically labelled. After 364 the siliqua produced at 1/96th of the pound has been labelled Arg. (Argentevs).

The important thing to remember about the Roman denominational system is that coins were usually struck at a given number to the Roman pound and thus could be easily related to one another on the basis of weight when coins were exchanged.

Between 337 and 395 the weight of the siliqua was reduced twice, the first time late in the reign of Constantius (355) when it fell from *c*. 3g. to *c*. 1.9g., and again in the West in the 380s during the usurpation of Magnus Maximus, when it was lowered to *c*. 1.6g. The weight of the miliarenses, however, remained constant. The unreduced siliqua continued to be minted after the weight reduction in 355 relatively frequently in the East and much less so in the West. To distinguish it from its lighter successor, the heavier piece has been labelled argenteus in the catalogue.

In the fifth century the Eastern empire continued to produce silver issues on the traditional denominational system: heavy and light miliarenses, siliquae and, more rarely, half-siliquae. In the West multiples, heavy and light miliarenses, siliquae and half-siliquae were struck under Honorius but thereafter issues were restricted to siliquae and half-siliquae, except for Priscus Attalus.

Fifth-century weight standards are difficult to establish given the relatively small number of specimens known. However, in the East it would appear that for the first half of the century at least heavy miliarenses were still struck at 1/60th and 1/72nd of the pound. Siliquae in Italy and the East seem, again, in the earliest part of the century (*c*. 410–450), to have been minted at *c*. 1.9g. while those of the Gallic usurpers were struck on a lower standard *c*. 1.6g.

Issues

The catalogue listing of coins in alphabetical order of reverse type under each ruler has made for ease in locating a given specimen but has tended to obscure the chronological development of the silver coinage. One of the more interesting aspects of the silver coinage of the later empire is the extent to which mints functioned individually, regionally, or globally in producing given issues of coins. Therefore, issues have been arranged by period and, insofar as possible, chronologically within that period in a schematic fashion to emphasize the ways in which the coinage evolved. Frequently issues with the same types and legends which may have been minted at two (or more) separate intervals have been grouped as one. This has admittedly somewhat oversimplified the picture but has the advantage of allowing the major issues of lines of development of the coinage to be readily distinguished. A brief commentary on each period has also been included.

The silver issues of Carausius

Carausius' silver was almost certainly issued early in his reign and virtually all of it was minted at London. The existence of die-links between coins marked R̄S̄R̄ and the unmarked pieces led Norman Shiel to conclude that not only were they produced at the same mint but that the unmarked pieces immediately preceded the R̄S̄R̄ group. There are two coins with the M̄L̄ mark, one with a doubtful mintmark and an early portrait and the other from the same dies as a gold piece with a late portrait (p. 75, no. 35) which may be suspect. There are also very few coins mintmarked C either in the field or the exergue of the coin which seem to have been produced at a second mint (again early in the reign on stylistic grounds) which is traditionally thought to be Colchester.

Silver Issues of 294–305 (Table E)

Despite Carausius' short-lived attempt to produce a silver coinage of high quality, it was not until Diocletian's reform c. 294 that a systematic attempt to produce silver coins of high fineness on a well-controlled weight standard took place. The post-reform silver consisted of a single denomination which weighed c. 3.1g. and had a silver fineness in excess of 90%. In RIC VI it was argued that the reform did not occur simultaneously at every mint, which may well be the case. However, the fundamental unity of the coinage of this period emerges very quickly if the coins are arranged on the basis of their reverse types (not legends). There are two major reverse types with minor variants:

1. Four princes at sacrifice before a camp gate (the camp gate has a varying number of turrets).
2. A camp gate with three or four turrets (with or without doors, and with or without a star over the door).

The earlier type is that of the four princes and the first issues are arguably the unmarked ones at Trier, Ticinum, Rome, and Siscia (Group 1).

Three standard reverse legends are coupled with this type: VIRTVS MILITVM, VICTORIA SARMAT, (at all mints) and PROVIDENTIA AVGG at Rome and Siscia. The unmarked issue was followed by two groups of marked coins with the same reverse type and legends except at Siscia, which has a new reverse legend (VICTORIA AVGG), (Groups 2 and 3), Eastern mints first appear in Group 2. Group 4 continues the four princes reverse type but the legends are in the dative case and the issue is restricted to Eastern mints. In Group 5 the legends are again in the dative case but a new reverse type has been introduced: a four-turreted camp gate with the doors flung

TABLE E: Silver Issues 294–305

1 Unmarked: Trier; Ticinum; Rome; Siscia.
Reverse type: Four princes at sacrifice before camp gate: (Fig. 3, a and b).

Reverse legends:	TR	TIC	R	SIS
VIRTVS MILITVM	X	X	X	X
VICTORIA SARMAT	X	X	X	X
VICTORIA SARM	—	—	X	—
VICTORIA SARMA	—	—	X	—
VICTORIA SARMATI	—	—	X	—
VICTORIA SARMATIC	—	—	X	X
VICTORIA SARMATICA	—	—	X	X
PROVIDENTIA AVGG	—	—	X	X
Obverse legends				
— AVG	X	X	X	X
— PF AVG	—	—	X	—
IMP—— AVG	X	—	—	—
— CAES	—	—	X	X
— CAESAR	—	X	—	—
— NOB C	X	—	—	—
ON—— NC (dative)	—	—	X	—

2 Marked issues (Group 1): Trier (C̄); Rome (R̄); Siscia (S̄IS̄); Heraclea (H̄Ē), (H̄Ā); Cyzicus (C̄M̄).
Reverse type: Four princes at sacrifice before camp gate: (Fig. 3, b and c).

Reverse legends:	TR	TIC	R	SIS	HER	CYZ
VIRTVS MILITVM	X	—	X	X	X	X
VICTORIA SARMAT	X	—	X	—	X	—
VICTORIA SARMATICA	X	—	—	—	X	X
PROVIDENTIA AVGG	—	—	X	—	X	X
VICTORIA AVGG	—	—	—	X	—	—
Obverse legends:						
— AVG	X	—	X	X	X	X
— CAES	—	—	—	X	—	—
— CAESAR	—	—	X	—	X	X
— NC	X	—	—	—	—	—
— NOB C	X	—	—	—	—	—

3 Marked issues (Group 2): Trier (CLUB); Rome (Ā); Siscia (*S̄IS̄), (*SIS.).
Reverse type: Four princes at sacrifice before camp gate: (Fig. 3, b and c).

Reverse legends:	TR	TIC	R	SIS
VIRTVS MILITVM	X	—	X	X
VICTORIA SARMAT	X	—	X	X
VICTORIA SARM	—	—	X	—
VICTORIA AVGG	—	—	—	X
Obverse legends;				
— AVG	X	—	X	—
— PF AVG	—	—	X	—
— CAES	—	—	X	—
— NC	X	—	—	—
— NOB C	—	—	—	X

4 Marked issues (Group 3): Reverse legends in dative case: Heraclea (H̄Ā); Nicomedia (S̄MNΓ̄); Antioch ($\frac{*|B}{ANT}$); Alexandria ($\frac{|B–\Delta}{ALE}$, $\frac{\Delta|}{ALE}$).
Reverse type: Four princes at sacrifice before camp gate: (Fig. 3, b, c and d).

Reverse legends:	HER	NIC	CYZ	ANT	ALE
VIRTVTI MILITVM	X	X	—	X	X
VICTORIAE SARMATICAE	X	X	—	X	X
PROVIDENTIAE AVGG	X	X	—	X	X
Obverse legends:					
— AVG	X	X	—	X	X
— CAESAR	X	X	—	X	—

5 Marked issues (Group 4):
Reverse legends in dative case:
Thessalonica ($\overline{\cdot\text{T}\cdot\text{S}\cdot\text{A}\cdot}$); Nicomedia
($\overline{\text{SMN}\Gamma}$).
Reverse type: Four-turreted camp gate,
doors flung back (Fig. 3, f—star
above gate; e—no star).

Reverse legends:	e	e	f
	THES	NIC	NIC
VIRTVTI MILITVM	—	X	X

	e	e	f
	THES	NIC	NIC
VICTORIAE SARMATICAE	X	X	X
PROVIDENTIAE AVGG	—	X	X
Obverse legends:			
— AVG	X	X	X
— CAESAR	—	X	X
— NOB C	X	—	—

6 Marked issues (Group 5):
Reverse legends in nominative case:
Siscia (SIS); Thessalonica ($\overline{\cdot\text{TS}\cdot\text{A}\cdot}$, $\overline{\text{TSA}}$.
Reverse type: Four-turreted camp gate,
doors flung back (Fig. 3, f—star
above gate; e—no star).

Reverse legends:	e	f
	SIS	THES
VIRTVS MILITVM	X	X

	SIS	THES
PROVIDENTIA AVGG	—	X
VICTORIA AVGG	X	—
CONCORDIA MILITVM	—	X
Obverse legends:		
— AVG	X	X
— PF AVG	X	—
— NOB C	X	—

7 Marked issues (Group 6): Rome
($\dfrac{\text{RF}}{\Gamma}$); Siscia ($\overline{\ast\text{SIS}}$); Serdica
($\overline{\cdot\text{SM}\cdot\text{SDA}\cdot}$); Thessalonica ($\overline{\text{TS}\cdot\text{A}\cdot}$,
$\overline{\cdot\text{T}\cdot\text{S}\cdot\text{A}\cdot}$, $\overline{\text{TS}\cdot\text{A}\cdot}$); Antioch ($\dfrac{\text{H}}{\text{ANT}}$, $\overline{\text{ANT}\cdot\text{H}}$, $\overline{\ast\text{ANTH}}$ $\overline{\ast\text{ANTH}\ast}$); Alexandria ($\dfrac{\text{A}}{\text{ALE}}$, $\dfrac{\text{A}}{\text{ALE}}$, $\overline{\text{ALE}}$).

Reverse type: Three-turreted camp
gate, no doors (Fig. 3, g).

	R	SIS	SERD	THESS	ANT	ALE
Reverse legends:						
VIRTVS MILITVM	X	X	X	X	X	X
VICTORIA SARMAT	X	—	—	—	—	—
VICTORIA AVGG	—	X	—	—	—	—
Obverse legends:						
— AVG	—	X	X	X	X	X
— PF AVG	—	X	—	—	—	—
— CAESAR	—	—	—	—	X	X
— NOB C	—	X	X	X	—	—
— CAES	X	—	—	—	—	—

8 Marked Issues (One unmarked):
Ticinum ($\overline{\text{T}}$); Aquileia ($\overline{\text{AQ}}$); Rome
(unmarked, PR).
Reverse type: Wreath.

Reverse legend:	TIC	AQ	R
XCVI	X	X	X

Obverse legends:	TIC	AQ	R
— AVG	X	—	X
— PF AVG	—	X	—
— CAES	X	—	X
— CAESAR	X	X	—

**9 Marked issue exclusive to
Carthage** ($\overline{\text{P}}$)
Reverse type: Africa standing facing
wearing elephant-skin head-dress,
holding standard and tusk, lion at
feet to left with captured bull.

Reverse legends:
F ADVENT AVGG NN
FEL ADVENT AVGG NN
FELIX ADVENT AVGG NN
Obverse legends:
— PF AVG
— NOB C

**10   Unmarked issue of fractions
     exclusive to Trier**

Reverse type: Wreath.
Reverse legends:
VOT · X SIC XX

VOT XX SIC XXX
Obverse legends:
— PF AVG
— P AVG
— AVG

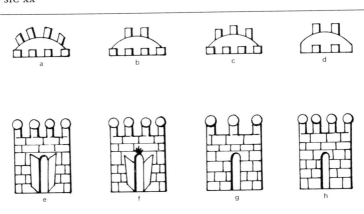

Fig. 3   Camp gates.

back. Group six continues the new reverse type but a new reverse legend
CONCORDIA MILITVM appears at Thessalonica. Group 7 introduces a three-turreted
camp gate with no doors which was minted at Rome, Siscia, Serdica, Thessalonica,
Antioch and Alexandria. The final three groups consist of the XCVI issue minted at
Ticinum, Aquileia and Rome, an issue of fractions exclusive to Trier and an issue
exclusive to Carthage. It should be noted that I have reassigned the unmarked XCVI
pieces attributed to Carthage in RIC VI to Rome on the basis of style and the fact
that a signed specimen P̄R̄ has since been found at Carnuntum. Thus the bulk of the
post-reform silver from 295–305 was issued with two 'military' reverses and three
main reverse legends which are found with both types. In addition, there are other
issues particular to an individual mint or region.

Silver Issues 305–315 (Table F)
Silver issues of this period are very much less abundant than those of 295 to 305.
Initially conservatism continued to dominate the choice of reverse types and
legends. VIRTVS MILITVM with a four-turreted or three-turreted camp gate is found
on the earliest issues of silver at Trier and Rome which are linked to the usurpations
of Constantine I and Maxentius and the return from abdication of Maximian
(Groups 1 and 2). At mints not under their control these rulers are not recognized
on the very rare silver coins but only Galerius, Severus, and Maximinus Daia
(Groups 1 and 3). Thereafter silver coinage ceased in the Eastern half of the empire
but continued sporadically at Trier and Rome. There was a brief issue in the name
of Constantine I at Carthage known from a single specimen in Paris (Group 8). At
Trier, Constantine minted a series of silver fractions with vota reverses in his own
name only before he took the title of Augustus late in 307 (Group 4). He also minted

TABLE F: Silver Issues 305–315

1 Marked issue: Trier ($\overline{\text{PTR}}$); Rome ($\overline{\text{RS}}$); Siscia ($\overline{\text{SIS}}$).
Reverse type: Four-turreted camp gate, doors thrown back (Fig. 3, e).

Reverse legends:	TR	R	SIS
VIRTVS MILITVM	X	X	—
VICTORIA AVGG	—	—	X

Obverse legends:			
— PF AVG (GAL)	X	—	—
— AVG (GAL)	—	—	X
— SEN PF AVG(MH)	—	X	—
— NOB C (C_1)	X	—	—

2 Marked issue: Trier ($\overline{\text{PTR}}$); Rome ($\overline{\text{RS}}$).
Reverse type: Four-turreted camp gate, no doors (Fig. 3, h).

Reverse legends:	TR	R
VIRTVS MILITVM	X	X

Obverse legends:		
— PF AVG (GAL)	X	—
— SEN PF AVG (MH)	X	X
— NOB C (C_1)	X	X

3 Marked issue: Rome ($\overline{\text{RS}}$); Serdica (·SM·SDA·); Antioch (*ANTH*).
Reverse type: Three-turreted camp gate, no doors (Fig. 3, g).

Reverse legend:
VIRTVS MILITVM

Obverse legends:	R	SERD	ANT
IMP MAXIMIANVS PF AVG (MH)	X	—	—
MAXIMIANVS AVG (MH)	X	—	—
MAXIMIANVS AVG (GAL)	—	—	X
SEVERVS AVG	—	X	—
CONSTANTINVS NOB C	X	—	—
MAXENTIVS PRINC INVICT	X	—	—

4 Unmarked issue of fractions exclusive to Trier.
Reverse type: Wreath.
Reverse legends:
HAEC VOTA MVLT ANN
PLVR NATAL FEL
VOT X FELICITER
Obverse legends:
FL VAL CONSTANTINVS NOB C
FL VAL CONSTANTINVS NC

5 Marked issue of fractions exclusive to Trier ($\overline{\text{TR}}$). Group 1.
Reverse type: Four-turreted camp gate, doors thrown back (Fig. 3, e).
Reverse legend:
VIRTVS MILITVM
Obverse legends:
IMP CONSTANTINVS PF AVG
IMP CONSTANTINVS AVG

6 Marked issue of fractions exclusive to Trier (T̄R̄). Group 2.
Reverse type: Four-turreted camp gate, no doors (Fig. 3, h).
Reverse legend:
VIRTVS MILITVM
Obverse legends:
IMP CONSTANTINVS AVG
IMP CONSTANTINVS PF AVG
IMP MAXIMIANVS PFS AVG (MH)
IMP MAXIMIANVS PV AVG (MH)
IMP MAXIMIANVS PV AVG (GAL)
MAXIMINVS NOB CAES

7 Marked issue of fractions exclusive to Trier (T̄R̄). Group 3.
Reverse type: Venus seated left, hldg. Globe and palm.
Reverse legend:
VENVS FELIX
Obverse legend:
FAVSTAE NOBILISSIMAE FEMINAE

8 Unmarked issue exclusive to Carthage.
Reverse type: Carthage standing facing in hexastyle temple.
Reverse legend:
CONSERVATOR KART SVAE XCVI (in exergue)
Obverse legend:
CONSTANTINVS NOB C

9 Marked issue of Maxentius at Rome (R̄S̄) and Ostia (POSTΔ̄, MOSTA̅).

Reverse legends:	*Reverse types:*	R	OST
CONSERVATOR VRBIS SVAE	Rome seated in temple	X	—
FELIX PROCESS CONSVLAT AVG N	Emp. togate, stg. facing	X	—
MARTI PROPAG IMP AVG N	Mars stg. r extending hand to woman, Wolf and Twins bet.	X	X
MARTI PROPAGATORI AVG N	Mars stg. l. giving Victory on globe to Emp.	—	X
TEMPORVM FELICITAS AVG N	Wolf and Twins r.	X	—
TEMPORVM FELICITAS AVG N	Wolf and Twins l.	—	X
Obverse legends:			
IMP MAXENTIVS PF AVG		X	—
MAXENTIVS PF AVG		X	X

10 Marked issue of base silver exclusive to Trier (P̄T̄R̄).

Reverse legends:	*Reverse types:*	Ruler
IOVI CONSERVATORI	Jupiter seated on eagle	LIC. I
SOLI INVICTO COMITI	Sol in facing quadriga	DAIA
VICTORIAE LAETAE PRINC PERP	Two Victories stg. facing	
VOT PR	hldg. incribed altar	C.I.
Obverse legend:		
IMP — AVG		

the four-turreted camp gate with and without doors with the VIRTVS MILITVM reverse legend as a fraction in which he recognized Galerius and Maximinus Daia as well as Maximian (Groups 5 and 6). His last issue of silver in this period was much debased (c. 25% silver) and featured three new reverses: IOVI CONSERVATORI for Licinius; SOLI INVICTO COMITI for Daia, and VICTORIAE LAETAE PRING PERP VOT PR for himself (Group 10). This last type was later to be repeated as a billon issue in his own name only.

Maxentius minted silver with an imaginative set of reverse types and legends at Rome and Ostia relatively late in his reign (Group 9). From about 310 to about 315 no silver was minted anywhere in the empire.

Silver Issues 315–337 (Table G)
Between 315 and 324 Licinius produced no silver and the earliest issues of Constantine c. 315 seem to have consisted of very small emissions of multiples restricted to individual mints and known today in only a handful of examples (Groups 1 and 2).

TABLE G: Silver Issues 315–337

1 Unmarked issue: Ticinum—multiple (2 sil.).
Reverse: SALVS REIPVBLICAE – Emperor stg. left on platform being crowned by Victory, surrounded by soldiers.

Obverse legend:
IMP CONSTANTINVS PF AVG

2 Marked issue: Aquileia ($\overline{\text{MAQ}}$)—multiple (2 sil.).
Reverse: MONETA AVGG ET CAESS NN—Three Monetae stg. left.
Obverse legend:
FL IVL CRISPVS NOB CAES

3 Marked issue: Rome ($\frac{*|*}{\text{PR}}$); Ticinum ($\frac{\text{L}|}{\text{SMT}}$); Aquileia ($\frac{*|*}{\text{AQS}}$, $\frac{\text{L}|}{\text{AQ}}$); Siscia ($\frac{*|*}{\text{SIS}}$)—heavy mil. (?).
Reverse type: Altar on square base: a. with flame; b. without flame.

Reverse legends:	b R	a TIC	a AQ	b AQ	a SIS	b SIS
VOTA ORBIS ET VRBIS	—	X	X	X	X	—
SEN ET PR XX/XXX MVL FEL						
VOTA POPVLI ROMANI	X	—	—	—	—	—

Obverse legends:	R	TIC	AQ	SIS
CONSTANTINVS MAX AVG	X	—	—	—
IMP CONSTANTINVS MAX AVG	—	X	X	—
IMP CONSTANTINVS PF AVG	—	—	X	—
IMP LICINIVS PIVS FELIX AVG	—	—	X	—
FL IVL CRISPYS NOB C	—	—	X	X
— IVN NOB C	—	—	—	X

4 Marked issue of siliquae exclusive to Sirmium $\overline{\text{SIRM}}$.

Reverse legends:	*Reverse types:*
PRINCIPI IVVENTVTIS	Prince stg. left hldg. standard and sceptre, second standard behind.
VIRTVS AVG ET CAES	Trophy, two spears and four shields at base.

Obverse legends:
IMP — AVG
FL IVL — NOB C

5 Marked issue of light miliarenses: Rome $\overline{\text{SMR}}$; Nicomedia $\overline{\text{SMN}}$; Cyzicus $\overline{\text{SMK}}$.

Reverse type: Emperor standing under arch with three sons.
Reverse legend:

	R	NIC	CYZ
FELICITAS ROMANORVM	X	X	X
Obverse legends:			
— MAX AVG	—	X	—
DN CRISPVS NOB CAESAR	—	X	—
— IVN NOB C	X	—	X
CONSTANTIVS NOB CAES	—	—	X

6 Marked issue of light miliarenses: Trier $\overline{\text{PTR}}$; Sirmium $\overline{\text{SIRM}}$; Thessalonica $\overline{\text{THES}}$; Heraclea $\overline{\text{HER}}$; Nicomedia $\overline{\text{SMN}}$.

Reverse type: Emperor standing under arch with two sons.
Reverse legend:

	TR	SIRM	THESS	HER	NIC
FELICITAS ROMANORVM	X	X	X	X	X
Obverse legends:					
— MAX AVG	—	X	—	X	—
— MAX PF AVG	—	—	X	—	—
FL IVL CONSTANTIVS NOB CAESAR	—	—	—	—	X
FL IVL CRISPVS NOB CAES	—	—	X	—	—
— IVN NOB CAES	X	—	X	—	—
DN — IVN NOB CAES	—	—	—	—	X

7 Marked issue of heavy miliarenses in base silver exclusive to Sirmium $\overline{\text{SIRM}}$.

Reverse type: bareheaded busts of two Caesars facing one another.
Reverse legend: CRISPVS ET CONSTANTINVS CC
Obverse legend: — MAX AVG

8 Marked issue of heavy miliarenses in base silver: Thessalonica $\overline{\text{MTS}}$; Constantinople $\overline{\text{CONS}}$.

Reverse type: Busts of two Caesars, draped, cuirassed, hldg. Victory on globe.
Reverse legend:

	THES	CONS
NOB CAESS	X	X
Obverse legend:		
— MAX AVG	X	X

9 Marked issue exclusive to Rome $\overline{\text{SMR}}$—multiple.

Reverse: GENIVM PR	Genius stg. left hldg. globe and cornucopiae.

Obverse legend:
— AVG

10   Marked issue exclusive to Rome $(\overline{\text{PR}})$—heavy mil.
Reverse: FIDIS MILITVM (sic)   Three standards.
Obverse legend:
— IVN NOB C

11   Marked issue exclusive to Constantinople $\dfrac{\text{A}|}{(\text{CONS})}$—sil.
Reverse: CONSTANTINIANA DAFNE   Victory seated left on cippus.
Obverse legend:
— MAX AVG

12   Marked issue exclusive to Constantinople $(\overline{\text{MCONSA}})$—multiple (5 sil. ?).
Reverse: DN CONSTANTINVS MAX TRIVMF
AVG   Tyche seated facing on throne.
Obverse legend:
No legend (C$_1$)

13   Marked issue exclusive to Constantinople $(\overline{\text{CONS}})$—sil.
Reverse: FELICITAS PVBLICA   Euphrates reclining left.
Obverse legend:
FL ANNIBALIANO REGI

14   Marked issue exclusive to Trier $(\overline{\text{SMTR}})$—sil.
Reverse: CONSTANTINVS AVG   Emperor in mil. dress stg. left hldg.
                                       vexillum and sceptre.
Obverse legend:
No legend (C$_1$)

15   Marked issues of light miliarenses: Thessalonica ($\overline{\text{TS}}$, $\overline{\text{TS}\in}$); Constantinople ($\overline{\text{CONSA}}$, $\overline{\text{C·A}}$).
Reverse legends: *Types:*
GLORIA EXERCITVS   Female stg. left, leaning on column.
VIRTVS EXERCITVS   Soldier stg. left hldg. spear and shield.
Obverse legends:

	THES	CP
— MAX AVG	X	X
— IVN NOB C	X	X
No legend (C$_S$)	X	—
FL IVL CONSTANTIVS NOB C	—	X

16   Marked issue of light miliarenses: Trier ($\overline{\text{SMTR}}$); Arelate ($\overline{\text{CONST}}$); Ticinum ($\overline{\text{SMT}}$); Siscia ($\overline{\text{SIS}}$); Thessalonica ($\overline{\text{SMTS}}$, $\overline{\text{TS}\in}$); Heraclea ($\overline{\text{SMH}}$); Constantinople (·$\overline{\text{CONSA}}$·, $\overline{\text{CONSA}}$); Nicomedia ($\overline{\text{SMN}}$).
Reverse type: Four standards.

Reverse legends:	TR	ARL	TIC	SIS	THES	HER	CP	NIC
CONSTANTINVS AVG	X	—	X	X	X	X	X	X
CONSTANTINVS MAX AVG	—	—	—	—	X	—	—	—
CONSTANTINVS CAESAR	X	X	—	—	—	X	X	—
CONSTANTINVS IVN NOB C	—	—	—	—	—	X	—	—
CONSTANTIVS CAESAR	X	X	—	X	—	—	X	X
CONSTANTIVS CAES	—	—	—	—	—	—	X	—
CONSTANS CAESAR	X	—	—	—	—	—	—	—
Obverse legends:								
No legend (c.I)	—	—	X	—	X	X	X	X
CONSTANTINVS MAX AVG	X	—	—	X	—	—	X	—

No legend (c.ii)	—	X	—	—	—	X	X	—
CONSTANTINVS IVN NOB C	—	X	—	—	—	—	X	—
No legend (C$_S$)	—	—	—	—	—	—	—	X
DN CONSTANTIVS NOB CAES	—	—	—	X	—	—	—	—
FL IVL CONSTANTIVS NOB CAES	X	—	—	—	—	—	X	—
FL IVL CONSTANTIVS NOB C	X	—	—	X	—	—	X	—
CONSTANTIVS NOB CAES	X	—	—	—	—	—	—	—
CONSTANTIVS NOB C	—	—	—	X	—	—	—	—
FL IVL CONSTANS NOB CAES	X	—	—	—	—	—	—	—

17 Marked issue of siliquae: Rome ($\overline{\text{R}}$); Ticinum ($\overline{\text{MT}}$); Thessalonica ($\overline{\text{TS}}$); Nicomedia ($\overline{\text{N}}$); Antioch ($\overline{\text{SMAN}}$).
Reverse type: Three palm branches, star above.
Reverse legends:

	R	TIC	THES	NIC	ANT
CRISPVS CAESAR	—	—	—	—	X
CONSTANTINVS CAESAR	X	X	X	—	—
CONSTANTIVS CAESAR	X	—	—	—	—
CONSTANTIVS NOB CAES	—	—	—	X	—
Obverse legends:					
No legend (C$_{II}$)	X	X	X	—	—
No legend (Crispus)	—	—	—	—	X
No legend (C$_S$)	X	—	—	X	—

18 Marked issue of siliquae: Siscia ($\overline{\text{SIS}}$); Thessalonica ($\overline{\text{MTS}}$).
Reverse type: Victory walking left holding wreath and palm.

Reverse legends:	SIS	THES
VICTORIA CAESAR NN	—	X
VICTORIA CAESARVM	X	—
VICTORIA CONSTANTINI AVG	—	X
Obverse legends:		
CONSTANTINVS MAX AVG	—	X
CONSTANTINVS IVN NOB CAES	—	X
CONSTANTINVS IVN NOB C	X	—
FL IVL CONSTANTIVS NOB C	X	—

19 Marked issue of siliquae: Aquileia ($\overline{\text{SMAQ}}$); Rome ($\overline{\text{R}}$); Thessalonica ($\overline{\text{SMTS}}$, $\overline{\text{TS}}$, $\overline{\text{TS}\epsilon}$); Heraclea ($\overline{\text{SMH}}$); Constantinople ($\overline{\text{CONS}}$, $\cdot\overline{\text{CONSA}}\cdot$, $\overline{\text{CONSA}}$, $\frac{\text{M}|}{\text{CONSA}}$, C·A); Nicomedia ($\overline{\text{N}}$, $\overline{\text{SMA}}$, $\overline{\text{SMN}}\cdot$); Antioch ($\overline{\text{SMAN}}$).
Reverse type: Victory walking left holding wreath and palm.

Reverse legends:	AQ	R	SIS	THES	HER	CP	NIC	ANT
CONSTANTINVS AVG	X	—	X	X	X	X	X	X
CONSTANTINVS CAESAR	—	X	—	X	—	X	—	X
CONSTANTINVS CAES	—	—	—	—	—	X	—	—
CONSTANTIVS CAESAR	—	—	—	X	X	X	—	—
CONSTANTIVS CAES	—	—	—	—	—	X	—	—
CONSTANS CAESAR	—	—	—	—	—	—	—	X
CONSTANS NOB CAESAR	—	—	—	—	—	X	—	—
DELMATIVS CAESAR	—	—	—	—	X	X	X	—
DELMATIVS NOB CAESAR	—	—	—	X	—	—	—	—
Obverse legend:								
No legend	X	X	X	X	X	X	X	X

20   Unmarked and marked issue of multiples: Trier ($\overline{\text{TR}}$); Lugdunum ($\overline{\text{LVG}}$); Arelate (CONST); Aquileia (AQ); Siscia (SIS); Thessalonica (TSϵ); Constantinople (unmarked); Nicomedia (unmarked).
Reverse type: Wreath.

Reverse legends:

	TR	LVG	ARL	AQ	SIS	THES	CP	NIC
CAESAR	—	X	X	—	X	X	X	X
XX	X	X	X	X	X	—	—	—

Obverse legends

	TR	LVG	ARL	AQ	SIS	THES	CP	NIC
AVGVSTVS (C_I)	X	X	X	—	X	X	X	X
CAESAR (C_{II})	—	X	X	X	X	—	—	—

During the years 315 to 325 silver production was initially limited to the mints of Ticinum, Rome, Aquileia and Siscia and was later extended to Sirmium. Group 3 was the first issue to have been produced at several mints with the same reverse type (an altar set on a square base) and the same reverse legend (except at Rome). Sirmium put out an issue of siliquae not found elsewhere (Group 4) and an issue of base silver which may have been heavy miliarenses with a reverse type echoed by a similar issue at Thessalonica (Groups 7 and 8).

After 324 silver began to appear at Eastern mints which Constantine now controlled and in larger quantities. Two issues of light miliarenses were minted (Groups 5 and 6) with similar reverses (the emperor standing under an arch with two or three sons), and the former appeared at mints ranging from Trier to Nicomedia. Although special issues of siliquae continued to be struck at single mints (Groups 9 to 15) to commemorate specific events, individuals, or for less obvious reasons, towards the end of this period silver began to be struck more systematically at a number of mints with the same reverses. Groups 16 to 19 illustrate this trend very clearly. The four standards series and three palms issue of light miliarenses are found at a large number of mints in conjunction with the same set of reverse legends: CONSTANTINVS AVG; CONSTANTINVS CAESAR; CONSTANTIVS CAESAR, etc. (Groups 16 and 17). These two groups may, in fact, mask more than one issue since there is no reason to believe they were struck simultaneously at all mints and, indeed, good reason for believing that they were not. Nonetheless, even if that were the case, then it suggests that the type had become standardized and that the conservatism of the Tetrarchic tradition was reasserting itself. Group 19 has the same type of reverse legends but the denomination was a siliqua and it may have been for that reason that the type was different (Victory walking left holding a wreath and palm). Another group of siliquae (Group 18), which had a different set of reverse legends, had the same type as Group 19, which may offer some support for this notion. There is no doubt that these were the largest and most important issues of silver produced by Constantine (Groups 16–19).

What was almost certainly the last issue of Constantine (Group 20) consisted of a group of multiples equivalent in weight to four siliquae. There were two reverse types: CAESAR centred in a wreath and XX centred in a wreath. The obverse consisted of a portrait of the emperor and AVGVSTVS for the former and a portrait of a Caesar and CAESAR for the latter. Since neither the Augustus or Caesar are named, considerable discussion has ensued over which rulers were represented. More recent opinion has opted on stylistic grounds and the mint signature of Arles for Constantine I and Constantine II. Although these pieces are extremely rare they were produced at no less than eight mints. The Trier piece is a hybrid.

Silver issues of 337–364

After the death of Constantine I the empire was divided among his three sons. As a result, the unity which had characterized the silver issues of Constantine I's later years was broken and his successors pursued quite independent courses in regard to the types and denominations they chose to strike, although the denominational system and weight standards were the same in all parts of the empire.

The silver coinage of these years has been subdivided chronologically in RIC VIII into a number of periods which have, on the whole, been adopted in this discussion. The first period, 337–340, ends with the death of Constantine II; the second, 340–350, with that of Constans. The coinage of the usurpers Vetranio, 350–351, and Magnentius and Decentius, 350–353, have been treated separately. Between 350 and 360 Constantius II controlled the whole of the empire (after the defeat of the usurpers) and from 350 to 355 Constantius Gallus Caesar was associated with him while between 355 and 360 the Caesar Julian was his colleague. Julian's reign as Augustus, 360–363, has been treated separately, as has that of Jovian, 363–364.

Owing to the lack of uniformity in the choice of denominations and types minted by Constantine's sons, the coinage has also been subdivided geographically. Thus Eastern and Western issues have been tabulated separately except for the years when Constantius controlled the whole empire. The coinage of the years 337–350 has been divided into Western, Central, and Eastern mints.

The silver coinage for the remainder of the fourth and the fifth centuries can also be divided into two main streams typologically:

1. what can be termed the regular issues and
2. the vota series.

The vota pieces commemorated specific anniversaries of an emperor's reign, usually in multiples of five years but sometimes ten, beginning with his accession. The interpretation of the vota so often found as part of the coin legend signifies prayers offered for a prosperous reign and carried overtones of the public festivities promised to ensure their fulfilment. Thus coins bearing the legend VOT V refer to the fifth year anniversary of an emperor's accession, those with VOT X to his tenth anniversary, etc. Sometimes the coins have a longer legend, e.g. VOT V MVLT X, which again refers to the fifth year anniversary and expresses the fact that the vows and promises of the first five years have been fulfilled and those of the next five years undertaken. A glance at the accompanying tables gives an indication of the flexibility of the form in which vota could be expressed, but the concept remained the same whether the vows were expressed in units of five or ten.

It is often tempting to try and date issues of vota coins by equating the stated year (five, ten, etc.) with the actual year with which it coincided in an emperor's reign, but this can be both misleading and dangerous. Not only could the celebrations fall in a year other than that specified on the coin, but it was possible to mint vota coins in anticipation of the event or afterwards. Thus while the purpose of the vota coinage is clear—that the emperor was expected to make payments to his subjects on the occasion of his anniversary, caution should be exercised in trying to date these issues too precisely.

Vota coins commonly carried no more than a brief inscriptional reference to the emperor's anniversary in a wreath but they could also take more elaborate forms with more complicated legends or types in which the reference to the vota forms only a small part of the whole (e.g. VICTORIAE DDNN AVGG VOT X MVLT XV). The commonest vota coins are siliquae but multiples, heavy and light miliarenses were also produced.

What I have chosen to describe as the regular coinage consists of all those pieces which make no reference to imperial anniversaries. Throughout this period and throughout the remainder of the century there is a tendency for the repertory of reverse types to become progressively more static. The main images are of the emperor as a soldier and Victories carrying wreaths, palms, and/or trophies. The emphasis on military themes suggests the content of the types may have been dictated to some extent by its intended recipients, the army.

337–340 Tables 1A, 1B, 1C.

Constantine II minted silver only at Trier during his brief reign and he produced no vota coins either in his own name or in those of his co-rulers. His types continued those of his father and, apart from the light miliarensis with the four standards reverse, all of his silver coins were siliquae (Table 1A).

Constans continued many of the types of his father although he was more adventurous in his range of denominations and types than Constantine II or Constantius II. His silver production was largely restricted to Siscia and Thessalonica in these years although Rome and Aquileia did produce siliquae (Table 1B). He minted heavy miliarenses with three different reverses, siliquae with two, and light miliarenses with one. He also minted a vota coinage in his own name and those of his brothers in four denominations: multiples, heavy and light miliarenses, and siliquae with the GAVDIVM POPVLI ROMANI reverse and multiples and siliquae with the FELICITAS PERPETVA reverse.

In the East Constantius limited himself almost exclusively on his silver issues to minting siliquae and the only exception is a group of extremely rare light miliarenses in his own name only with the four standards reverse at Constantinople (Table 1C). Again, his types continue those of his father.

340–350 Tables 2A and 2B.

After the fall of Constantine II, Constans controlled both the Western and central mints and while it might have been expected that his silver issues would begin to show more uniformity in type and legend at his various mints, quite the opposite is true. Although the reverse types on the regular coinage were extremely limited in concept, consisting almost entirely of the emperor in military dress or Victory walking left, there is a great deal of variation in minor details (e.g. the attributes of the Victory, or what the emperor is holding) which is paralleled by the large number of different legends for individual types. As a result it is rare for the same combination of reverse type and legend to occur at more than one mint and even when they do, the obverses may be different. This suggests that, whatever else mint policy at the highest level was concerned with, absolute conformity of type and legend at all mints did not have priority in this period. Constans' vota coinage reflects the same pattern, or rather lack of it, as the regular issues. Mints on the whole functioned independently of one another and even when legend and type were issued at more than one mint, the denominations were often different.

In the East silver production under Constantius was much more limited in scope and quantity (Table 2C). The only denominations other than siliquae which he produced were heavy and light miliarenses at Cyzicus. All the rest of his coins were siliquae with vota types. The issue of these pieces with the same legend at two or more mints gives the impression of a more unified production pattern than that from the Western and Central mints.

Vetranio Table 3.

During the brief period of his usurpation Vetranio minted silver largely in Siscia, although there is an issue of heavy miliarenses at Thessalonica. His types continued those of Constans with the emperor in military dress holding a standard with a *chi-*

rho inscribed on the banner being used on the heavy miliarenses and three variants of the victory type on light miliarenses and siliquae minted at Siscia. The only vota coin was a heavy miliarenses also minted at Siscia which continued the type of Constans.

Magnentius and Decentius Table 4.

Initially Magnentius controlled only the Gallic mints although he later moved into Italy and produced silver at Aquileia. The dominant mint in Gaul at first was Trier which minted multiples, heavy miliarenses, light miliarenses and siliquae, all of which had the emperor in military dress type. Some new types were introduced, namely Aequitas and Securitas on multiples. Siliquae with a victory reverse type and the legend FELICITAS PERPETVA were produced at Lugdunum, Arelate and Aquileia, the only reverse to be so widely minted. Vota coins were minted at Lugdunum, Arles and Aquileia in heavy and light miliarenses with the wreath type or Victory in two variants.

350–360 Tables 5 and 6.

After Constantius had control of the whole of the empire, his silver production expanded but only his vota siliquae were issued at a large number of mints, eleven between 350 and 355 and nine between 355 and 360. The regular coinage was much more restricted, as were issues of miliarenses and multiples except for the light miliarenses with the VIRTVS EXERCITVS legend and the helmeted soldier type which was minted at Rome, Siscia, Thessalonica, Constantinople and Cyzicus between 350 and 355 but only at Arles and Thessalonica in the next period. The range of types and mints was more diverse between 350 and 355 than between 355 and 360. In the West, Arles superseded Trier as the dominant mint producing silver and was the only one to mint the heavier denominations. Rome, Aquileia, Siscia, Sirmium and Thessalonica were active between 350 and 355 and struck both regular and vota issues while in the East, Constantinople, Nicomedia, Cyzicus and Antioch minted both heavier and lighter denominations. Activity at the central and Eastern mints was much more curtailed in the years 355 to 360 than between 350 and 355. Cyzicus produced no silver and Nicomedia minted only vota siliquae. At Constantinople, Thessalonica and Antioch issues of specific types tended to be limited to individual mints with the exception of the vota siliquae. New types were introduced, namely the emperor and Caesar in military dress standing facing under an arch and the anepigraphic star in wreath.

360–363 Table 7.

Once Julian had become Augustus, his Western mints began producing silver coins almost immediately and in some cases, e.g. the reduced weight vota siliquae at Trier, Lugdunum and Arles, in large quantities. Lugdunum and Arles also minted heavy and light miliarenses as did Sirmium and Antioch while Rome produced an issue of regular siliqae and Trier one of half-siliquae. The geographical distribution of Julian's coinage suggests that its production can often, if not always, be correlated with the emperor's presence. No new types were introduced.

Table 1A: Silver Issues 337–340
Western Mints—Regular Coinage

1 TRIER: *Light miliarenses*
Reverse Legends:
CONSTANTINVS AVG
CONSTANTIVS AVG
CONSTANS AVG

Obverse legends:
CONSTANTINVS AVG
FL IVL CONSTANTIVS AVG
FL IVL CONSTANS AVG

2 TRIER: *Siliquae*
a. *Reverse type:* Victory walking left hldg. wreath and palm.
Reverse legends:
VICTORIA AVGVSTI
VICTORIA AVGG NN
Obverse legends:
IMP CONSTANTINVS AVG
FL IVL CONSTANTIVS AVG
b. *Reverse type:* Emperor in military dress stg. l. hldg. standard with chi-rho on banner
Reverse legend:
PAX AVGVSTORVM

Obverse legends:
IMP CONSTANTINVS AVG
FL IVL CONSTANTIVS AVG
FL IVL CONSTANS AVG
c. *Reverse type:* Emperor in military dress stg. r. hldg. spear and globe, spurning captive with l. foot.
Reverse legend:
PRINCIPI IVVENTVTIS
Obverse legends:
IMP CONSTANTINVS AVG
FL IVL CONSTANTIVS AVG
FL IVL CONSTANS AVG

Table 1B: Silver Issues 337–340
Central Mints—Regular Coinage

1 Heavy miliarenses

a. *Reverse type:* Four standards.

Reverse legends:	R	AQ	SIS	TH
GLORIA EXERCITVS	—	—	—	X
CONSTANS AVG	—	—	X	—
Obverse legends:				
CONSTANS PF AVG	—	—	—	X
FL IVL CONSTANS PF AVG	—	—	X	—

b. *Reverse type:* Pax stg. facing, head l., hldg. branch and sceptre leaning l. elbow on column.

Reverse legend:	R	AQ	SIS	TH
PAX AETERNA	—	—	X	—
Obverse legend:				
CONSTANTINVS PF AVG	—	—	X	—

c. *Reverse type:* Helmeted soldier in military dress, stg. facing, head r., hldg. Spear in r. hand, resting l. on shield.

Reverse legend:	R	AQ	SIS	TH
VIRTVS EXERCITVS	—	—	—	X
Obverse legends:				
FL CL CONSTANTINVS PF AVG	—	—	—	X
FL IVL CONSTANTIVS PF AVG	—	—	—	X
FL IVL CONSTANS PF AVG	—	—	—	X

2 Light miliarenses

Reverse type: Three standards.

Reverse legends:	R	AQ	SIS	TH
CONSTANTINVS PF AVG	—	—	—	X
CONSTANTIVS PF AVG	—	—	—	X
CONSTANS PF AVG	—	—	—	X
Obverse legends:				
FL IVL CONSTANTINVS PF AVG	—	—	—	X
FL IVL CONSTANS PF AVG	—	—	—	X

3 Siliquae

a. *Reverse type:* Victory advancing l. hldg. wreath and palm.

Reverse legends:	R	AQ	SIS	TH
CONSTANTINVS AVG	X	—	X	—
VICTORIA DD NN AVGG	—	X	—	X
Obverse Legends:				
No legend (C.$_{II}$)	X	—	X	—
CONSTANTINVS PF AVG	—	X	X	X
CONSTANTINVS MAX AVG	—	—	X	—
CONSTANTIVS PF AVG	—	—	—	X
CONSTANS PF AVG	—	—	—	X

b. *Reverse type:* Three palm branches, star above.

Reverse legends:	R	AQ	SIS	TH
CONSTANTIVS AVG	X	—	X	—
CONSTANS AVG	—	—	X	—
Obverse legends:				
No legend (C$_S$)	X	—	—	—
CONSTANTIVS PF AVG	—	—	X	—
CONSTANS PF AVG	—	—	X	—
FL IVL CONSTANS PF AVG	—	—	X	—

Vota Coinage

4 Multiple denominations

Reverse type: Wreath.

Reverse legends:	SIS				TH			
	MUL	HM	LM	S	MUL	HN	LM	S
GAVDIVM POPVLI ROMANI SIC V SIC X	X	X	X	X	X	—	X	X
GAVDIVM POPVLI ROMANI SIC X SIC XX	X	X	—	X	X	—	—	—
GAVDIVM POPVLI ROMANI SIC XX SIC XXX	—	X	—	X	—	—	—	—
Obverse legends:								
CONSTANTINVS PF AVG	—	X	—	X	—	—	—	—
CONSTANTIVS PF AVG	X	X	—	X	—	—	—	—
FL IVL CONSTANS PF AVG	X	X	X	X	—	—	X	X
FL IVL CONSTANTIVS PIVS FELIX AVG	—	—	—	—	X	—	—	—
FL IVL CONSTANS PIVS FELIX AVG								
FL IVL CONSTANTIVS P F AVG	X	—	—	—	—	—	—	—

5 *Reverse type:* Three emperors enthroned, facing.

Reverse legend	SIS				THES			
FELICITAS PERPETVA VOT V	X	—	—	—	—	—	—	X
Obverse legend:								
FL IVL CONSTANS PF AVG	X	—	—	—	—	—	—	X

Table 1C: Silver Issues 337–340
Eastern Mints—Regular Coinage

1 Light miliarenses

Reverse type: Four standards.

Reverse legend:

	HER	CP	NIC	CYZ	ANT	ALE
CONSTANTINVS AVGVSTVS	—	X	—	—	—	—

Obverse legend:

	HER	CP	NIC	CYZ	ANT	ALE
No legend (C$_S$)	—	X	—	—	—	—

2 Siliquae

a. *Reverse type:* Victory walking l. hldg. wreath and palm.

Reverse legends:

	HER	CP	NIC	CYZ	ANT	ALE
CONSTANTINVS AVGVSTVS	—	X	—	—	—	—
CONSTANTIVS AVGVSTVS	—	X	—	—	—	—
CONSTANS AVGVSTVS	—	X	—	—	—	—
CONSTANTIVS AVG	X	—	X	X	—	—
CONSTANTINVS AVG	—	—	—	X	—	—
CONSTANS AVG	X	—	—	—	—	—

Obverse legends:

	HER	CP	NIC	CYZ	ANT	ALE
No legend (C$_{II}$)	—	X	—	X	—	—
No legend (C$_S$)	X	X	X	X	—	—
No legend (C$_N$)	X	X	—	—	—	—

b. *Reverse type:* Wreath

Reverse legends:

	HER	CP	NIC	CYZ	ANT	ALE
CONSTANTINVS AVG	—	—	—	—	X	X
CONSTANTIVS AVG	—	—	—	—	X	X
CONSTANS AVG	—	—	—	—	—	X

Obverse legends:

	HER	CP	NIC	CYZ	ANT	ALE
No legend (C$_{II}$)	—	—	—	—	X	X
No legend (C$_S$)	—	—	—	—	X	X
No legend (C$_N$)	—	—	—	—	—	X

Vota Coinage

3 Siliquae

Reverse type: Wreath.

Reverse legend:

	HER	CP	NIC	CYZ	ANT	ALE
VOTIX XV MVLTIS XX	—	—	—	—	X	—

Obverse legend:

	HER	CP	NIC	CYZ	ANT	ALE
No legend (C$_S$)	—	—	—	—	X	—

Table 2A: Silver Issues 340–350
Western Mints—Regular Coinage
CONSTANTIUS II AND CONSTANS

GROUP ONE

1 Multiples and heavy miliarenses

a. *Reverse type:* Emperor in mil. dress stg. l. hldg. standard in r. hand with wreath on banner.

Reverse legend:	TRIER		LVG		ARL	
	MUL	HM	MUL	HM	MUL	HM
TRIVMFATOR GENTIVM BARBARARVM	X	X	—	—	—	—
Obverse legends:						
FL IVL CONSTANTIVS PIVS FELIX AVG	X	X	—	—	—	—
FL IVL CONSTANS PIVS FELIX AVG	X	—	—	—	—	—

b. *Reverse type:* Emperor in mil. dress stg. r., head l., hldg. standard in r. hand with wreath on banner.

Reverse legend:	TRIER		LVG		ARL	
	MUL	HM	MUL	HM	MUL	HM
TRIVMFATOR GENTIVM BARBARARVM	X	—	—	—	—	—
Obverse legends:						
FL IVL CONSTANTIVS PIVS FELIX AVG	X	—	—	—	—	—
FL IVL CONSTANS PIVS FELIX AVG	X	—	—	—	—	—

2 Siliquae

Reverse type: Emperor in mil. dress stg. l. hldg. standard with chi-rho on banner.

Reverse legend:	TR	LVG	ARL
PAX AVGVSTORVM	X	—	—
Obverse legend:			
FL IVL CONSTANTIVS PF AVG	X	—	—

GROUP TWO

3 Heavy miliarenses

a. *Reverse type:* Emperor in mil. dress stg. l., hldg. standard in r. hand with chi-rho on banner.

Reverse legend:	TR	LVG	ARL
VIRTVS DD NN AVGG	X	—	—
Obverse legends:			
FL IVL CONSTANTIVS PF AVG	X	—	—
FL IVL CONSTANS PF AVG	X	—	—

b. *Reverse type:* Emperor in mil. dress stg. facing, head l. hldg. standard in l. hand with chi-rho on banner.

Reverse legend:	TR	LVG	ARL
VIRTVS DD NN AVGG	X	—	—
Obverse legend:			
FL IVL CONSTANS PF AVG	X	—	—

c. *Reverse type:* Emperor in mil. dress stg. facing, head l., hldg. standard with chi-rho on banner in r. hand, resting l. on shield.

Reverse legend:	TR	LVG	ARL
VIRTVS DD NN AVGG	—	X	—
Obverse legend:			
FL IVL CONSTANS PF AVG	—	X	—

Table 2B: Silver Issues 340–350
Central Mints—Regular Coinage
CONSTANTIUS II AND CONSTANS

1 Multiples

Reverse type: Emperor stg. l. in mil. dress hldg. standard with chi-rho on banner and transverse spear or sceptre.

Reverse legend:	R	AQ	SIS	TH
TRIVMFATOR GENTIVM BARBARARVM	—	X	X	—
Obverse legends:				
CONSTANTIVS PF AVG	—	X	—	—
FL IVL CONSTANTIVS PF AVG	—	—	X	—
FL IVL CONSTANS PIVS FELIX AVG	—	X	—	—
FL IVL CONSTANS PF AVG	—	—	X	—

2 Light miliarenses

a. *Reverse type:* Victory walking l. hldg. wreath and palm.

Reverse legend:	R	AQ	SIS	TH
VICTORIA AVGVSTORVM	—	—	X	—
Obverse legends:				
CONSTANTIVS PF AVG	—	—	X	—
FL IVL CONSTANS PF AVG	—	—	X	—

b. *Reverse type:* Four standards, those in centre inscribed A and ω, chi-rho above.

Reverse legend:	R	AQ	SIS	TH
VIRTVS EXERCITVM	X	—	—	—
Obverse legend:				
DN CONSTANS PF AVG	X	—	—	—

3 Multiples heavy miliarenses, and light miliarenses

Reverse type: Emperor in mil. dress stg. l. hldg. standard and resting l. hand on shield.

Reverse legend:	R M	HM	LM	AQ M	HM	LM	SIS M	HM	LM	TH M	HM	LM
TRIVMFATOR GENTIVM BARBARARVM	—	—	—	—	—	—	—	—	—	X	X	X
Obverse legends:												
FL IVL CONSTANTIVS PIVS FELIX AVG	—	—	—	—	—	—	—	—	—	X	—	—
FL IVL CONSTANS PIVS FELIX AVG	—	—	—	—	—	—	—	—	—	X	—	—
FL IVL CONSTANTIVS PF AVG	—	—	—	—	—	—	—	—	—	—	X	X
FL IVL CONSTANS PF AVG	—	—	—	—	—	—	—	—	—	—	X	X

Silver Issues 340–350
Western and Central Mints
CONSTANTIUS II AND CONSTANS

1 **Siliquae**

a. *Reverse type:* Victory walking l. hldg. wreath and palm.

Reverse legends:	TR	LVG	AR	R	AQ	SIS	TH
VICTORIA DD NN AVGG	X	—	X	—	—	—	—
VICTORIA AVGG NN	—	—	X	—	—	—	—
FELICITAS PERPETVA	—	—	—	—	X	—	—
VICTORIA AVGVSTORVM	—	—	—	—	—	X	—
Obverse legends:							
FL IVL CONSTANTIVS PF AVG	X	—	—	—	—	—	—
FL IVL CONSTANS AVG	X	—	—	—	X	X	—
FL IVL CONSTANTIVS PF AVG	—	—	X	—	—	—	—
CONSTANTIVS PF AVG	—	—	X	—	X	X	—
CONSTANS PF AVG	—	—	X	—	—	—	—
DN CONSTANS PF AVG	—	—	X	—	—	—	—
DN CONSTANTIVS PF AVG	—	—	X	—	—	—	—

b. *Reverse type:* Victory walking l. hldg. wreath and trophy.

Reverse legends:	TR	LVG	AR	R	AQ	SIS	TH
VICTORIA DD NN AVG	—	X	—	—	—	—	X
FELICITAS PERPETVA	—	—	—	—	X	—	—
VICTORIA AVGVSTORVM	—	—	—	—	—	X	—
Obverse legends:							
CONSTANTIVS PF AVG	—	X	—	—	X	X	X
CONSTANS PF AVG	—	X	—	—	—	—	X
DN CONSTANTIVS PF AVG	—	—	—	—	X	—	—
DN CONSTANS PF AVG	—	—	—	—	X	—	—
FL IVL CONSTANS PF AVG	—	—	—	—	X	X	—

c. *Reverse type:* Victory walking l. hldg. palm and trophy.

Reverse legend:	TR	LVG	AR	R	AQ	SIS	TH
VICTORIA AVGVSTORVM	—	—	—	—	—	X	—
Obverse legends:							
CONSTANTIVS PF AVG	—	—	—	—	—	X	—
FL IVL CONSTANS PF AVG	—	—	—	—	—	X	—

d. *Reverse type:* Victory walking l., head r., hldg. wreath and palm, captive behind.

Reverse legends:	TR	LVG	AR	R	AQ	SIS	TH
VICTORIA DD NN AVGG	—	—	—	X	—	—	—
FL IVL CONSTANS PF AVGG (sic)	—	—	—	X	—	—	—
Obverse legends:							
FL IVL CONSTANTIVS PF AVG	—	—	—	X	—	—	—
FL IVL CONSTANS PF AVG	—	—	—	X	—	—	—

2 Half siliquae

Reverse type: Victory walking l. hldg. wreath and palm.

Reverse legend:	TR	LVG	AR	R	AQ	SIS	TH
VICTORIA DD NN AVGG	X	—	—	—	—	—	—
Obverse legends:							
CONSTANTIVS PF AVG	X	—	—	—	—	—	—
DN CONSTANS PF AVG	X	—	—	—	—	—	—

Vota Coinage

3 Light miliarenses

a. *Reverse type:* Inscribed standard flanked by two seated captives.

Reverse legends:	TR	LVG	AR	R	AQ	SIS	TH
GAVDIVM ROMANORVM VOT V							
MVLT X	X	—	—	—	—	—	—
GAVDIVM ROMANORVM VOT X							
MVLT XX	X	—	—	—	—	—	—
GAVDIVM ROMANORVM VOT XX							
MVLT XXX	X	—	—	—	—	—	—
Obverse legends:							
FL IVL CONSTANTIVS PF AVG	X	—	—	—	—	—	—
FL IVL CONSTANS PF AVG	X	—	—	—	—	—	—

b. *Reverse type:* Inscribed standard flanked by two seated captives, captive on l. wears pointed hat.

Reverse type:	TR	LVG	AR	R	AQ	SIS	TH
GAVDIVM ROMANORVM VOT X							
MVLT XX	X	—	—	—	—	—	—
Obverse legends:							
FL IVL CONSTANTIVS PF AVG	X	—	—	—	—	—	—
FL IVL CONSTANS PF AVG	X	—	—	—	—	—	—

c. *Reverse type:* Wreath

Reverse legends:	TR	LVG	AR	R	AQ	SIS	TH
FELICITAS PERPETVA VOT X							
MVLT XX	—	—	—	—	X	—	—
FELICITAS PERPETVA VOT XX							
MVLT XXX	—	—	—	—	X	—	—
Obverse legend:							
CONSTANTIVS PF AVG	—	—	—	—	X	—	—

4 Heavy and light miliarenses

a. *Reverse type:* Victory seated r. on cuirass and shield, supporting inscribed shield on l. knee.

Reverse legend:	TR		LVG		AR		R		AQ		SIS		TH	
	HM	LM	HM	LM	HM	LM	HM	LM	HM	LM	HM	LM	HM	LM
VICTORIAE DD NN AVGG VOT X MVLT XV	—	—	—	—	—	—	—	—	X	—	—	—	—	—
VICTORIAE DD NN AVGG VOT X MVLT XX	—	—	—	—	—	—	—	—	X	X	—	—	—	—
Obverse legends:														
DN CONSTANS PF AVG	—	—	—	—	—	—	—	—	X	X	—	—	—	—
FL IVL CONSTANS PF AVG	—	—	—	—	—	—	—	—	X	—	—	—	—	—

5 Multiples, heavy miliarenses, light miliarenses, and siliquae.

Reverse type: Wreath.

Reverse legends:	TR				AQ				SIS				TH			
	M	HM	LM	S	M	HM	LM	S	M	HM	LM	S	M	HM	LM	S
GAVDIVM POPVLI ROMANI VOT V MVLT X	—	—	—	—	X	—	—	—	—	—	—	—	—	—	—	—
GAVDIVM POPVLI ROMANI SIC X SIC XX	—	—	—	X	—	—	—	—	—	X	X	—	—	—	—	—
GAVDIVM POPVLI ROMANI SIC XX SIC XXX	—	—	—	—	—	—	—	—	X	X	—	—	X	—	—	—
Obverse legends:																
FL IVL CONSTANS PF AVG	—	—	—	X	—	—	—	—	—	X	X	—	—	—	—	—
FL IVL CONSTANS PIVS FELIX AVG	—	—	—	—	X	—	—	—	—	—	—	—	X	—	—	—
FL IVL CONSTANTIVS PF AVG	—	—	—	—	—	—	—	—	X	—	—	—	—	—	—	—
CONSTANTIVS PF AVG	—	—	—	—	—	—	—	—	X	—	—	—	—	—	—	—
FL IVL CONSTANTIVS PIVS FELIX AVG	—	—	—	—	—	—	—	—	—	—	—	—	X	—	—	—

6 Siliquae

a. *Reverse type:* Two victories facing one another hldg. inscribed wreath.

Reverse legends:	TR	LVG	AR	R	AQ	SIS	TH
VICTORIAE DN AVG VOT V MVLT X	X	—	—	—	X	—	—
VICTORIAE DN AVG VOT V MVLT XV	X	—	—	—	X	—	—
VICTORIAE DN AVG VOT V MVLT XX	X	—	—	—	—	—	—
Obverse legends:							
FL IVL CONSTANS PF AVG	X	—	—	—	X	—	—
CONSTANTIVS PF AVG	—	—	—	—	X	—	—

b. *Reverse type:* Victory stg. r. with l. foot on globe, inscribing shield held by kneeling figure.

Reverse legends:	TR	LVG	AR	R	AQ	SIS	TH
FEL TEMP REPARATIO VOT XX	—	—	—	X	—	—	—
Obverse legends:							
FL IVL CONSTANTIVS PF AVG	—	—	—	X	—	—	—
FL IVL CONSTANS PF AVG	—	—	—	X	—	—	—

Table 2C: Silver Issues 340–350
Eastern Mints—Regular Coinage
CONSTANTIUS AND CONSTANS

1 Heavy miliarenses
Reverse type: Three standards.

Reverse legend:	HER	CP	NIC	CYZ	ANT
VIRTVS EXERCITVS	—	—	—	X	—
Obverse legend:					
FL IVL CONSTANS PERP AVG	—	—	—	X	—

2 Light miliarenses
Reverse type: Emperor stg. facing, head r., hldg. transverse spear, resting l. hand on shield.

Reverse legends:	HER	CP	NIC	CYZ	ANT
VIRTVS EXERCITVS	—	—	—	X	—
Obverse legend:					
DN CONSTANTIVS PF AVG	—	—	—	X	—

Vota Coinage

3 Siliquae
Reverse type: Wreath.

Reverse legends:	HER	CP	NIC	CYZ	ANT
FELICITAS REI PVBLICE VOT XX MVLT XXX	X	X	X	—	—
FELICITAS REI PVBLICE VOT XV MVLT XX	—	X	X	—	—
VOTIS XXV MVLTIS XXX	—	X	X	X	X
VOTIS XX MVLTIS XXX	—	—	—	—	X
Obverse legends:					
DN CONSTANTIVS AVG	X	X	—	—	—
DN CONSTANTIVS PF AVG	—	X	X	X	X
DN CONSTANS PF AVG	—	—	X	—	—
No legend (C$_s$)	—	—	X	—	—

Table 3: Vetranio 350–351
Central Mints—Regular Coinage

1. Heavy miliarenses
Reverse type: Emperor in mil. dress stg. facing, hldg. standard with chi-rho on banner, resting l. hand on shield.

	SIS	TH
Reverse legend		
VIRTVS EXERCITVM	—	X
Obverse legend:		
DN VETRANIO PF AVG	—	X

2. Light miliarenses
Reverse type: Victory walking l. hldg. wreath and palm.

	SIS	TH
Reverse legend		
VICTORIA AVGVSTORVM	X	—
Obverse legend:		
DN VETRANIO PF AVG	X	—

3. Siliquae
a. *Reverse type:* Victory walking l. with wreath and trophy.

	SIS	TH
Reverse legend:		
VICTORIA AVGVSTORVM	X	—
Obverse legends:		
DN VETRANIO PF AVG	X	—
CONSTANTIVS PF AVG	X	—

b. *Reverse type:* Victory walking l. with palm and trophy.

	SIS	TH
Reverse legend:		
VICTORIA AVGVSTORVM	X	—
Obverse legends:		
DN VETRANIO PF AVG	X	—
CONSTANTINVS PF AVG	X	—

Vota Coinage

4   Heavy miliarenses
Reverse type: Wreath.

	SIS	TH
Reverse legend:		
GAVDIVM POPVLI ROMANI VOT V MVL X	X	—
Obverse legend:		
DN VETRANIO PF AVG	X	—

Table 4: Magnentius and Decentius
350–353—*Regular Coinage*

1. Multiples

a. *Reverse type:* Securitas stg. facing, head l., l. elbow on column r. hand on head.

Reverse legend:	TR	LVG	ARL	R	AQ
SECVRITAS REIPVBLICAE	X	—	—	—	—
Obverse legends:					
IM CAE MAGNENTIVS AVG	X	—	—	—	—
DN MAGNENTIVS PF AVG	X	—	—	—	—

b. *Reverse type:* Emperor stg. l. hldg. standard with chi-rho on banner, and transverse spear.

Reverse legend:	TR	LVG	ARL	R	AQ
TRIVMFATOR GENTIVM BARBARARVM	—	—	—	—	X
Obverse legend:					
DN MAGNENTIVS PF AVG	—	—	—	—	X

2 Heavy miliarenses

Reverse type: Aequitas st. l. hldg. balance and cornucopiae.

Reverse legend:	TR	LVG	ARL	R	AQ
AEQVITAS AVG NOSTRI	X	—	—	—	—
Obverse legends:					
DN MAGNENTIVS PF AVG	X	—	—	—	—
DN DECENTIVS FORT CAES	X	—	—	—	—

3 Light miliarenses

a. *Reverse type:* Emperor in mil. dress stg. l., hldg. globe and transverse sceptre, kneeling captive before him.

Reverse legend:	TR	LVG	ARL	R	AQ
VIRTVS AVG NOSTRI	X	—	—	—	—
Obverse legend:					
IM CAE MAGNENTIVS AVG	X	—	—	—	—

b. *Reverse type:* Emperor in mil. dress walking r. hldg. transverse spear and globe.

Reverse legends:	TR	LVG	ARL	R	AQ
PRINCITI IVVENTVTIS (sic)	X	—	—	—	—
PRINCIPI IVVENTVTIS	X	—	—	—	—
Obverse legends:					
DN MAGNENTIVS PF AVG	X	—	—	—	—
DN DECENTIVS NOB CAES	X	—	—	—	—
DN DECENTIVS FORT CAES	X	—	—	—	—

4   Siliquae

a. *Reverse type:* Helmeted soldier stg. facing, head r., hldg. spear in r. hand, resting l. on shield.

Reverse legend:	TR	LVG	ARL	R	AQ
VIRTVS EXERCITI	X	—	—	—	—
Obverse legends:					
IM CAE MAGNENTIVS AVG	X	—	—	—	—
DN MAGNENTIVS AVG	X	—	—	—	—
DN DECENTIVS FORT CAES	X	—	—	—	—

b. *Reverse type:* Victory walking l. hldg. wreath and trophy.

Reverse legend:	TR	LVG	ARL	R	AQ
FELICITAS PERPETVA	—	X	X	—	X
Obverse legends:					
DN MAGENTIVS PF AVG	—	X	—	—	—
FL MAGNENTIVS PF AVG	—	—	—	—	X
DN MAGNENTIVS AVG	—	—	X	—	—

Vota Coinage

5   Heavy miliarenses

a. *Reverse type:* Wreath

Reverse legend:	TR	LVG	ARL	R	AQ
FELICITAS PERPETVA VOT V MVLT X	—	—	—	—	X
Obverse legend:					
DN MAGNENTIVS PF AVG	—	—	—	—	X

b. *Reverse type:* Victory seated r. on cuirass, inscribing shield.

Reverse legend:	TR	LVG	ARL	R	AQ
VICTORIAE DD NN AVGG					
VOT V MVLT X	—	—	X	—	—
Obverse legend:					
DN MAGNENTIVS PF AVG	—	—	X	—	—

6   Light miliarenses

a. *Reverse type:* Victory seated r. on cuirass inscribing wreath.

Reverse legend:	TR	LVG	ARL	R	AQ
VICTORIAE DD AVGG VOT V MVLT X	—	X	—	—	X
Obverse legend:					
DN MAGNENTIVS PF AVG	—	X	—	—	X

b. *Reverse type:* Two victories facing one another hldg. inscribed wreath.

Reverse legend:	TR	LVG	ARL	R	AQ
VICTORIAE DD NN AVG ET CAE					
VOT V MVL X	—	—	X	—	—
Obverse legends:					
DN MAGNENTIVS PF AVG	—	—	X	—	—
DN DECENTIVS CAESAR	—	—	X	—	—

Table 5: Silver issues 350–355
CONSTANTIUS II AND GALLUS—*Regular Coinage*

1 Heavy miliarenses

a. *Reverse type:* Three standards.

Reverse legends:	TR	LVG	AR	R	AQ	SIS	SIR	TH	CP	NIC	CYZ	ANT
VIRTVS EXERCITVS	—	—	X	—	—	—	—	X	—	—	X	—
Obverse legends:												
DN CONSTANTIVS NOB CAES	—	—	X	—	—	—	—	X	—	—	—	—
DN CONSTANTIVS PF AVG	—	—	—	—	—	—	—	X	—	—	—	—
DN FL CL CONSTANTIVS NOB CAES	—	—	—	—	—	—	—	—	—	—	X	—

b. *Reverse type:* Four standards.

Reverse legends:	TR	LVG	AR	R	AQ	SIS	SIR	TH	CP	NIC	CYZ	ANT
CONSTANTIVS AVG	—	—	—	X	—	—	—	—	—	—	—	—
GLORIA EXERCITVS	—	—	—	—	—	—	—	—	—	X	—	—
Obverse legends:												
DN CONSTANTIVS MAX AVG	—	—	—	X	—	—	—	—	—	—	—	—
DN CONSTANTIVS NOB CAES	—	—	—	—	—	—	—	—	—	X	—	—

2 Light miliarenses

a. *Reverse type:* Helmeted soldier stg. l, head r., hldg. inverted spear in r. hand, resting l. on shield.

Reverse legend:	TR	LVG	AR	R	AQ	SIS	SIR	TH	CP	NIC	CYZ	ANT
VIRTVS EXERCITVS	—	—	—	X	—	X	—	X	X	—	X	—
Obverse legends:												
DN CONSTANTIVS PF AVG	—	—	—	X	—	X	—	X	X	—	X	—
DN CONSTANTIVS MAX AVG	—	—	—	X	—	—	—	—	—	—	—	—
FL IVL CONSTANTIVS NOB CAES	—	—	—	—	—	—	—	X	—	—	—	—
DN CONSTANTIVS NOB CAES	—	—	—	—	—	—	—	X	—	—	—	—

b. *Reverse type:* Emperor and Caesar in mil. dress stg. facing under arch hldg. spear (sometimes reversed).

Reverse legend:	TR	LVG	AR	R	AQ	SIS	SIR	TH	CP	NIC	CYZ	ANT
FELICITAS ROMANORVM	—	—	—	—	X	—	X	—	—	X	—	X
Obverse legends:												
DN CONSTANTIVS PF AVG	—	—	—	—	X	—	X	—	—	X	—	X
DN CONSTANTIVS NOB CAES	—	—	—	—	—	—	X	—	—	—	—	—
DN FL CL CONSTANTIVS NOB CAES	—	—	—	—	—	—	—	—	—	X	—	—

c. *Reverse type:* Emperor in mil. dress stg. facing, head r., hldg. spear and globe; Victory moves l. towards him, hldg. wreath and palm; both stg. beneath arch.

Reverse legend:	TR	LVG	AR	R	AQ	SIS	SIR	TH	CP	NIC	CYZ	ANT
VICTORIA ROMANORVM	—	—	—	—	—	—	—	—	—	—	—	X
Obverse legends:												
DN CONSTANTIVS PF AVG	—	—	—	—	—	—	—	—	—	—	—	X
DN CONSTANTIVS NOB CAES	—	—	—	—	—	—	—	—	—	—	—	X

3 Siliquae

a. *Reverse type:* Star in wreath.

Reverse legend:	TR	LVG	AR	R	AQ	SIS	SIR	TH	CP	NIC	CYZ	ANT
No legend	—	X	X	X	—	—	—	—	—	—	—	X
Obverse legends:												
DN CONSTANTIVS NOB CAES	—	X	X	X	—	—	—	—	—	—	—	X
DN FL CL CONSTANTIVS NOB CAES	—	—	—	X	—	—	—	—	—	—	—	—

b. *Reverse type:* Victory walking l. hldg. wreath and palm.

Reverse legends:	TR	LVG	AR	R	AQ	SIS	SIR	TH	CP	NIC	CYZ	ANT
VICTORIA AVGVSTI	—	—	—	X	—	—	—	—	—	—	—	—
VICTORIA AVG N	—	—	—	X	—	—	—	—	—	—	—	—
VICTORIA AVGVSTORVM	—	—	—	—	—	X	—	—	—	—	—	—
Obverse legends:												
DN CONSTANTIVS PF AVG	—	—	—	X	—	X	—	—	—	—	—	—
CONSTANTIVS PF AVG	—	—	—	X	—	—	—	—	—	—	—	—

c. *Reverse type:* Victory advancing l. hldg. palm and trophy.

Reverse legend:	TR	LVG	AR	R	AQ	SIS	SIR	TH	CP	NIC	CYZ	ANT
VICTORIA CAESARIS	—	—	—	—	—	X	—	—	—	—	—	—
Obverse legend:												
DN CONSTANTIVS IVN NOB C	—	—	—	—	—	X	—	—	—	—	—	—

d. *Reverse type:* Victory walking l. hldg. wreath and palm, spurning captive with r. foot.

Reverse legend:	TR	LVG	AR	R	AQ	SIS	SIR	TH	CP	NIC	CYZ	ANT
VICTORIA DN AVG	—	—	—	—	—	—	—	X	—	—	—	—
Obverse legend:												
CONSTANTIVS PF AVG	—	—	—	—	—	—	—	X	—	—	—	—

Vota Coinage

4 Multiples

Reverse type: Rome and Constantinople stg. facing hldg. inscribed shield.

Reverse legend:	TR	LVG	AR	R	AQ	SIS	SIR	TH	CP	NIC	CYZ	ANT
GLORIA ROMANORVM VOT XXX MVLT XXXX	—	—	—	X	—	—	—	—	—	—	—	—
Obverse legends:												
FL IVL CONSTANTIVS PERP AVG	—	—	—	X	—	—	—	—	—	—	—	—
DN CONSTANTI AVGVSTI	—	—	—	X	—	—	—	—	—	—	—	—

5   Heavy miliarenses

Reverse type: Wreath.

Reverse legend:	TR	LVG	AR	R	AQ	SIS	SIR	TH	CP	NIC	CYZ	ANT
GAVDIVM POPVLI ROMANI VOTIS XXX MVLTIS XXX	—	—	—	—	—	—	X	—	—	—	—	—

Obverse legend:	TR	LVG	AR	R	AQ	SIS	SIR	TH	CP	NIC	CYZ	ANT
DN CONSTANTIVS PF AVG	—	—	—	—	—	—	X	—	—	—	—	—

6   Siliquae

Reverse type: Wreath.

Reverse legends:	TR	LVG	AR	R	AQ	SIS	SIR	TH	CP	NIC	CYZ	ANT
VOTIS XXX MVLTIS XXXX	—	X	X	—	X	—	X	X	X	X	X	X
VOTIS V MVLTIS X	—	—	—	—	X	X	X	X	X	X	—	—
VOT V MVLT X	—	—	—	—	—	X	—	—	—	—	—	—
VOT XXX MVLT XXXX	—	—	—	—	—	X	—	—	—	—	—	—
VOT XXX MVLTIS XXXX	—	—	—	X	—	—	—	—	—	—	—	—
VOTIS V	—	—	—	—	—	—	—	—	—	—	—	X

Obverse legends:	TR	LVG	AR	R	AQ	SIS	SIR	TH	CP	NIC	CYZ	ANT
DN CONSTANTIVS PF AVG	—	X	X	X	X	X	X	X	X	X	X	X
DN CONSTANTIVS NOB CAES	—	—	—	—	X	—	X	X	—	X	—	X
DN CONSTANTIVS IVN NOB C	—	—	—	—	—	X	—	—	—	—	—	—
DN FL CL CONSTANTIVS NOB CAES	—	—	—	—	—	—	—	—	X	X	—	—

Table 6: Silver Issues 355–360
CONSTANTIUS II AND JULIAN—*Regular Coinage*

1   Heavy miliarenses

a.   *Reverse type:* Four standards.

Reverse legends:	TR	LVG	ARL	R	AQ	SIS	SIR	TH	CP	NIC	CYZ	ANT
CONSTANTIVS AVG	—	—	X	—	—	—	—	—	X	—	—	—

Obverse legends:	TR	LVG	ARL	R	AQ	SIS	SIR	TH	CP	NIC	CYZ	ANT
DN CONSTANTIVS MAX AVG	—	—	—	—	—	—	—	—	X	—	—	—
DN CONSTANTIVS PF AVG	—	—	X	—	—	—	—	—	—	—	—	—
FL IVL CONSTANTIVS PERP AVG	—	—	X	—	—	—	—	—	—	—	—	—

b. *Reverse type:* Three standards.

Reverse legends:

	TR	LVG	ARL	R	AQ	SIS	SIR	TH	CP	NIC	CYZ	ANT
VIRTVS EXERCITVS	—	—	—	—	—	—	—	X	—	—	—	—
DN IVLIANVS CAES	—	—	X	—	—	—	—	—	—	—	—	—
DN IVLIANVS NOB CAES	—	—	X	—	—	—	—	—	—	—	—	—

Obverse legends:

	TR	LVG	ARL	R	AQ	SIS	SIR	TH	CP	NIC	CYZ	ANT
DN CONSTANTIVS PF AVG	—	—	—	—	—	—	—	X	—	—	—	—
DN CL IVLIANVS NOB CAES	—	—	—	—	—	—	—	X	—	—	—	—
FL CL IVLIANVS NOB CAES	—	—	X	—	—	—	—	—	—	—	—	—

2 Light miliarenses

a. *Reverse type:* Helmeted soldier stg. r., head r., hldg. inverted spear in r. hand, resting l. on shield.

Reverse legend:

	TR	LVG	ARL	R	AQ	SIS	SIR	TH	CP	NIC	CYZ	ANT
VIRTVS EXERCITVS	—	—	X	—	—	—	—	X	—	—	—	—

Obverse legends:

	TR	LVG	ARL	R	AQ	SIS	SIR	TH	CP	NIC	CYZ	ANT
DN CONSTANTIVS PF AVG	—	—	X	—	—	—	—	X	—	—	—	—
FL CL IVLIANVS NOB CAES	—	—	X	—	—	—	—	X	—	—	—	—

b. *Reverse type:* Helmeted soldier stg. l., head r. hldg. inverted spear in r. hand, resting l. on shield.

Reverse legend:

	TR	LVG	ARL	R	AQ	SIS	SIR	TH	CP	NIC	CYZ	ANT
VIRTVS EXERCITVS	—	—	X	—	—	—	—	—	—	—	—	—

Obverse legend:

	TR	LVG	ARL	R	AQ	SIS	SIR	TH	CP	NIC	CYZ	ANT
DN CONSTANTIVS PF AVG	—	—	X	—	—	—	—	—	—	—	—	—

c. *Reverse type:* Emperor in mil. dress stg. facing, head r., hldg. spear and globe, Victory moves l. towards him, both stg. beneath arch.

Reverse legend:

	TR	LVG	ARL	R	AQ	SIS	SIR	TH	CP	NIC	CYZ	ANT
VICTORIA ROMANORVM	—	—	—	—	—	—	—	—	—	—	—	X

Obverse legends:

	TR	LVG	ARL	R	AQ	SIS	SIR	TH	CP	NIC	CYZ	ANT
DN CONSTANTIVS PF AVG	—	—	—	—	—	—	—	—	—	—	—	X
DN IVLIANVS NOB CAES	—	—	—	—	—	—	—	—	—	—	—	X

3 Siliquae

a. *Reverse type:* Star in wreath.

Reverse legend:

	TR	LVG	ARL	R	AQ	SIS	SIR	TH	CP	NIC	CYZ	ANT
No legend	—	—	X	—	—	—	—	—	—	—	—	X

Obverse legends:

	TR	LVG	ARL	R	AQ	SIS	SIR	TH	CP	NIC	CYZ	ANT
FL CL IVLIANVS NOB CAES	—	—	X	—	—	—	—	—	—	—	—	—
DN IVLIANVS NOB CAES	—	—	X	—	—	—	—	—	—	—	—	X

b. *Reverse type:* Victory walking l. hldg. wreath and palm.

Reverse legend:	TR	LVG	ARL	R	AQ	SIS	SIR	TH	CP	NIC	CYZ	ANT
VICTORIA AVGVSTI	—	—	—	X	—	—	—	—	—	—	—	—
Obverse legend:												
DN CONSTANTIVS												
PERP AVG	—	—	—	X	—	—	—	—	—	—	—	—

c. *Reverse type:* Emperor helmeted in mil. dress stg. l. hldg. globe and spear.

Reverse legend:	TR	LVG	ARL	R	AQ	SIS	SIR	TH	CP	NIC	CYZ	ANT
SPES REIPVBLICE	—	—	—	—	—	—	—	X	—	—	—	—
Obverse legend:												
DN CONSTANTIVS												
PF AVG	—	—	—	—	—	—	—	X	—	—	—	—

Vota Coinage

4   Heavy miliarenses

Reverse type: Victory stg. facing, head l. hldg. wreath in r. hand, inscribed shield in l.

Reverse legend:	TR	LVG	ARL	R	AQ	SIS	SIR	TH	CP	NIC	CYZ	ANT
VICTORIA AVGVSTI												
VOT XXXX	—	—	—	—	—	—	—	—	X	—	—	—
Obverse legend:												
DN CONSTANTIVS												
MAX AVG	—	—	—	—	—	—	—	—	X	—	—	—

5   Siliquae

Reverse type: Wreath.

Reverse legends:	TR	LVG	ARL	R	AQ	SIS	SIR	TH	CP	NIC	CYZ	ANT
VOTIS XXX												
MVLTIS XXXX	—	—	X	X	—	X	X	X	X	X	—	X
VOTIS XXXV												
MVLTIS XXXX	—	—	—	—	X	—	—	—	—	—	—	—
VOT XXXX	—	—	—	—	—	—	—	—	X	—	—	—
VOTIS V MVLTIS X	—	—	—	—	—	—	—	X	—	—	—	—
VOTIS V	—	—	—	—	—	—	—	—	—	X	—	—
Obverse legends:												
DN CONSTANTIVS												
PF AVG	—	—	X	X	X	X	X	X	X	X	—	X
FL CL IVLIANVS												
NOB CAES	—	—	—	—	—	—	—	—	—	—	—	—
DN IVLIANVS												
NOB CAES	—	—	X	—	—	—	—	—	—	X	—	—
DN IVLIANVS												
NOB C	—	—	—	—	—	—	—	X	—	—	—	—
DN CL IVLIANVS												
NOB CAES	—	—	—	—	—	—	—	X	—	—	—	—

Table 7: Silver Issues 360–363
Julian—*Regular Coinage*

1 Heavy miliarenses

Reverse type: Two standards, pole between with eagle on top.

Reverse legend:

	TR	LVG	AR	R	AQ	SIS	SIR	THES	HER	CP	NIC	CYZ	ANT
FIDES EXERCITVM	—	—	X	—	—	—	—	—	—	—	—	—	—

Obverse legend:

	TR	LVG	AR	R	AQ	SIS	SIR	THES	HER	CP	NIC	CYZ	ANT
DN FL CL IVLIANVS PF AVG	—	—	X	—	—	—	—	—	—	—	—	—	—

2 Light miliarenses

a. *Reverse type:* Helmeted soldier stg. l., head r., hldg. inverted spear in r. hand, resting l. on shield.

Reverse legends:

	TR	LVG	AR	R	AQ	SIS	SIR	THES	HER	CP	NIC	CYZ	ANT
VIRTVS EXERCITVS	—	X	—	—	—	—	X	—	—	—	—	—	—
VIRTVS EXERCITVM	—	—	X	—	—	—	—	—	—	—	—	—	—

Obverse legends:

	TR	LVG	AR	R	AQ	SIS	SIR	THES	HER	CP	NIC	CYZ	ANT
DN CONSTANTIVS PF AVG	—	X	X	—	—	—	—	—	—	—	—	—	—
FL CL IVLIANVS PERP AVG	—	X	—	—	—	—	—	—	—	—	—	—	—
FL CL IVLIANVS PP AVG	—	—	—	—	—	X	—	—	—	—	—	—	—
DN IVLIANVS PF AVG	—	—	X	—	—	—	—	—	—	—	—	—	—

b. *Reverse type:* Helmeted soldier stg. r., head r., hldg. inverted spear in r. hand, resting l. on shield, eagle to r.

Reverse legend:

	TR	LVG	AR	R	AQ	SIS	SIR	THES	HER	CP	NIC	CYZ	ANT
VIRTVS EXERCITVS	—	—	X	—	—	—	—	—	—	—	—	—	—

Obverse legend:

	TR	LVG	AR	R	AQ	SIS	SIR	THES	HER	CP	NIC	CYZ	ANT
DN FL CL IVLIANVS PF AVG	—	—	X	—	—	—	—	—	—	—	—	—	—

c. *Reverse type:* Emperor in mil. dress stg. facing, head r., hldg. globe and sceptre, to r. Victory crowns him, both standing under arch.

Reverse legend:

	TR	LVG	AR	R	AQ	SIS	SIR	THES	HER	CP	NIC	CYZ	ANT
VICTORIA ROMANORVM	—	—	—	—	—	—	X	—	—	—	—	—	—

Obverse legend:

	TR	LVG	AR	R	AQ	SIS	SIR	THES	HER	CP	NIC	CYZ	ANT
FL CL IVLIANVS PF AVG	—	—	—	—	—	—	X	—	—	—	—	—	—

d. *Reverse type:* Emperor in mil. dress stg. facing, head r., hldg. spear and globe: Victory moves towards him hldg. wreath and palm.

Reverse legend:

	TR	LVG	ARL	R	AQ	SIS	SIR	THES	HER	CP	NIC	CYZ	ANT
VICTORIA ROMANORVM	—	—	—	—	—	—	—	—	—	—	—	—	X

Obverse legend:

	TR	LVG	ARL	R	AQ	SIS	SIR	THES	HER	CP	NIC	CYZ	ANT
FL CL IVLIANVS PF AVG	—	—	—	—	—	—	—	—	—	—	—	—	X

3 Siliquae

Reverse type: Victory walking l. hldg. wreath and palm.

Reverse legends:

	TR	LVG	AR	R	AQ	SIS	SIR	THES	HER	CP	NIC	CYZ	ANT
VICTORIA DD NN AVG	—	X	—	—	—	—	—	—	—	—	—	—	—
VICTORIA AVGVSTI N	—	—	—	X	—	—	—	—	—	—	—	—	—

Obverse legends:

	TR	LVG	AR	R	AQ	SIS	SIR	THES	HER	CP	NIC	CYZ	ANT
DN CONSTANTIVS PF AVG	—	X	—	—	—	—	—	—	—	—	—	—	—
FL CL IVLIANVS PP AVG	—	X	—	X	—	—	—	—	—	—	—	—	—

4 Half siliquae

Reverse type: Victory walking l. hldg. wreath and palm.

Reverse legend:

	TR	LVG	AR	R	AQ	SIS	SIR	THES	HER	CP	NIC	CYZ	ANT
VICTORIA PERPETV	X	—	—	—	—	—	—	—	—	—	—	—	—

Obverse legend:

	TR	LVG	AR	R	AQ	SIS	SIR	THES	HER	CP	NIC	CYZ	ANT
FL CL IVLIANVS AVG	X	—	—	—	—	—	—	—	—	—	—	—	—

Vota Coinage

5. Siliquae

Reverse type: Wreath.

Reverse legend:

	TR	LVG	AR	R	AQ	SIS	SIR	THES	HER	CP	NIC	CYZ	ANT
VOTIS V MVLTIS X	X	X	X	—	—	—	X	X	—	—	—	—	—
VOT V MVLT X	—	X	—	—	—	—	—	—	—	—	—	—	—
VOT X MVLT XX	—	X	X	—	—	—	—	—	—	X	—	—	X
VOTIS X MVLTIS XX	—	—	—	—	—	—	—	—	—	—	—	—	X
VOTIS XXX MVLTS XXXX	—	X	X	X	—	—	—	—	—	—	—	—	—

Obverse legends:

	TR	LVG	AR	R	AQ	SIS	SIR	THES	HER	CP	NIC	CYZ	ANT
FL CL IVLIANVS AVG	X	—	—	—	—	—	—	—	—	—	—	—	—
DN CL IVLIANVS AVG	X	—	X	—	—	—	—	—	—	—	—	—	—
FL CL IVLAINVS PP AVG	—	X	—	—	—	—	X	X	—	—	—	—	—
DN IVLIANVS PF AVG	—	—	X	—	—	—	—	—	—	—	—	—	—
FL CL IVLIANVS PF AVG	—	—	—	—	—	X	—	—	—	—	—	—	X
DN FL CL IVLIANVS PF AVG	—	X	X	—	—	—	—	—	—	X	—	—	—
DN CONSTANTIVS PF AVG	—	X	X	X	—	—	—	—	—	—	—	—	—

Table 8: Jovian—*Regular Coinage*

1 Light miliarenses

a. *Reverse type:* Emperor stg. l. in mil. dress, head r., hldg. labarvm in r. hand: Victory on globe in l.

Reverse legend:	ARL	R	AQ	SIS	SIR	CP	NIC	CYZ	ANT
RESTITVTOR REIP	X	—	—	—	—	—	—	—	—
Obverse legend:									
DN IOVIANVS PF AVG	X	—	—	—	—	—	—	—	—

b. *Reverse type:* Emperor in mil. dress stg. facing beneath arch, head r., hldg. spear and globe.

Reverse legend:	ARL	R	AQ	SIS	SIR	CP	NIC	CYZ	ANT
GLORIA ROMANORVM	—	—	—	—	—	—	—	—	X
Obverse legend:									
DN IOVIANVS PEP AVG	—	—	—	—	—	—	—	—	X

Vota Coinage

2 Heavy miliarenses

Reverse type: Wreath.

Reverse legend:	ARL	R	AQ	SIS	SIR	CP	NIC	CYZ	ANT
VOTIS V MVLTIS X	—	—	—	—	—	—	—	—	X
Obverse legend:									
DN IOVIANVS PEP AVG	—	—	—	—	—	—	—	—	X

3 Siliquae

Reverse type: Wreath.

Reverse legends:	ARL	R	AQ	SIS	SIR	CP	NIC	CYZ	ANT
VOT V MVLT X	X	—	—	—	X	X	X	—	X
VOT X MVLT XX	X	—	—	—	—	—	—	—	—
VOT V MVL X	—	—	—	—	—	X	—	—	—
Obverse legend:									
DN IOVIANVS PF AVG	X	—	—	—	X	X	X	—	X

Jovian Table 8.

During the course of Jovian's brief reign he minted light miliarenses with different reverses at Arles and Antioch as his regular coinage. A group of heavy miliarenses with vota reverses and vota siliquae were issued at Arles, Sirmium, Constantinople, Nicomedia, and Antioch. He introduced no new types and his mint practice seems to have copied that of the later years of Constantius and Julian in which the commonest issues with the widest geographical distribution consisted of vota siliquae.

Silver Issues of 364–395

The acession of Valentinian I and Valens whom he co-opted as Augustus initially resulted in little change in the pattern of silver output. The Gallic mints were predominant in the Western half of the empire throughout most of this period. Under the usurpers Magnus Maximus and Eugenius, both of whom invaded Northern Italy, Aquileia and Milan began producing moderately sized silver issues. There was also a reduction in the weight of the siliqua under Magnus Maximus in 387–388 when it dropped from *c.* 1.9g. to 1.6g.

The coinage has been subdivided chronologically according to Pierce's divisions in RIC IX and geographically into Western and Eastern issues, while typologically regular and vota issues have again been distinguished. As the century progressed differences in minting practice between the Eastern and Western halves of the empire began to emerge. In the East silver issues tended to become fewer, smaller in size and, after 375, entirely restricted to Constantinople. In the West the size of silver issues increased after 367 and Trier regained its position as the major silver-producing mint in Gaul minting very large issues of siliquae.

The major reverse types are those representing the emperor in military dress and a Victory in a number of variants. Representations of Roma and Constantinopolis were introduced on Western siliquae, as was the rare phoenix standing on a globe. In the East the anepigraphic chi-rho in wreath made its first appearance in this period and was later to become a major type in the fifth century.

364–367 Tables 8A, 8B, 8C.
In this period only Valentinian I and Valens were represented on the coinage. In the West Valentinian I minted multiples, heavy miliarenses, light miliarenses, and siliquae in his regular coinage. The heavier pieces tended to be restricted to one or two mints. At times they were issued in conjunction with a lighter denomination which had the same type and legend. Only the RESTITVTOR REIP siliquae was issued at a large number of mints with a broad geographical distribution: Trier, Lugdunum, Arles, Aquileia, and Thessalonica.

In the East regular silver issues were produced at Constantinople, Nicomedia, and Antioch. The denominations comprised heavy miliarenses, light miliarenses, and siliquae. Only RESTITVTOR REIP siliquae were produced at all three Eastern mints with a variant of the type used in the West.

The types of the vota coins in both East and West consisted of the legend within wreath and two variants of a Victory reverse. The commoner types are those with the wreath reverse and were produced as heavy miliarenses and siliquae in the West; argentei (unreduced or heavy siliquae) at Constantinople, and reduced at Constantinople, Nicomedia, Cyzicus and Antioch.

367–375 Tables 9A, 9B.
During this period Valentinian elevated his son Gratian as emperor. In the West the issues of regular coinage included multiples, light miliarenses, siliquae and half-siliquae; in the East light miliarenses and argentei (unreduced or heavy siliquae). The heavier denominations employed variants of the type with the emperor in military dress. The argentei re-used the three standards reverse while in the West the output of siliquae was restricted to Trier which produced large issues with the VRBS ROMA legend with Roma seated left on a throne. The half-siliquae with the VICTORIA AVGVSTORVM legend was also restricted to Trier.

The vota coinages employed both the wreath and Victory types on the heavier denominations in East and West, but the wreath type was found at more mints in both areas than the Victory type.

375–378 Tables 10A, 10B.
Valentinian I died in 375 and his young son Valentinian II was proclaimed Augustus. In the East no regular coinage was produced in this period and the only vota coin was a siliqua from Constantinople with the reverse VOT XX MVLT XXX. In the West, light miliarensis were minted at Trier and siliquae at Trier, Aquileia and Siscia. The other Gallic mints had temporarily ceased minting silver, as had Rome.

The common reverse type on the siliquae was VRBS ROMA with Roma initially sitting left on a throne and later on a cuirass and, as in the preceding period, its issue was restricted to Trier. Vota coins included heavy miliarenses and siliquae but only with the wreath type; they were minted at Trier, Aquileia, Siscia and Thessalonica, but only Trier and Siscia produced both denominations.

378–383 Tables 11A, 11B.

Valens died in 378 at the battle of Adrianople and Gratian co-opted Theodosius I as Eastern emperor. Siliqua issues in the East were restricted to vota reverses minted only at Constantinople. In the West the vota coinage consisted of a heavy miliarensis produced at Trier with the VOTIS XV MVLTIS XX legend for Gratian; siliquae with VOT V, VOT X, and VOT XV reverses at Trier and Siscia, and VOT XV only at Thessalonica.

The regular coinage in the West was much more adventurous. Multiples, heavy miliarenses, light miliarenses, siliquae and half-siliquae were minted in a variety of reverses whose types tended to copy those of preceding periods. The emperor in military dress holding a standard or labarum is found on multiples and heavy miliarenses; Victory advancing right in a number of variants is found on light miliarenses, argentei (unreduced or heavy siliquae) and siliquae. VRBS ROMA siliquae with Roma seated left on a cuirass were produced at Trier and Lugdunum, then the type was altered to Roma seated facing on a throne and the legend to VIRTVS ROMANORVM at Trier, Rome, Aquileia and Siscia with GLORIA ROMANORVM at Lugdunum. CONCORDIA AVGGG with a turreted Constantinopolis seated facing was minted at Trier, Lugdunum, and Aquileia; VICTORIA AVGGG at Trier, Lugdunum, and Aquileia (also VICTORIA AVGG at Aquileia only) with the Victory advancing left reverse type. Half-siliquae were minted only at Rome.

383–388 Tables 12A, 12B.

Silver production in the East once again was very limited. The only regular type to be minted was the siliqua with the chi-rho in wreath reverse for Flaccilla at Constantinople. The Eastern vota coinage consisted solely of siliquae from Constantinople with the reverse VOT X MVLT XX in wreath for Valentinian, Theodosius, and Arcadius.

In the West the range of denominations is much more varied consisting of multiples, light miliarenses, and siliquae with types and legends which echo the preceding period. The picture is complicated by usurpation of Magnus Maximus who was elevated by British troops in 383 and crossed to Gaul. Gratian was deserted by his troops and killed in August 383 leaving Maximus a clear field. However, he was not recognized by Valentinian II or Theodosius I. From 383 to 387 Maximus was content with controlling Gaul but in 387 he moved to Italy and began minting there.

Valentinian II issued regular coins in the following denominations: multiples at Rome and Thessalonica in his own name and light miliarenses at Thessalonica in his name and those of Theodosius I and Arcadius. His siliquae minted at Milan, Rome, and Aquileia were again in his name and those of Theodosius I and Arcadius and repeated the types and legends of the preceding period. His vota coinage consisted of siliquae at Milan and Thessalonica in his own name and those of Theodosius I and Arcadius.

The only heavy denomination minted by Magnus Maximus was a group of light miliarenses in his name at Trier, where he also continued to produce CONCORDIA AVGGG siliquae. The only other Gallic mint in operation, Lugdunum, minted the light miliarenses with the VIRTVS EXERCITVS reverse in the name of Maximus. Siliquae with the VIRTVS ROMANORVM reverse were not only produced in large quantities at Trier but in 387 and 388 at Milan, again in large quantities, and Aquileia. At the time Maximus moved into Italy he lowered the weight standard of the siliqua from *c.* 1.9g. to 1.6g. The only vota coinage minted by Maximus was a group of heavy miliarenses at Trier with VOTIS V MVLTIS X or VOTIS V MLTIS X (*sic*) at Trier.

388–392 Tables 13A, 13B.

Once the West had been restored to the empire light miliarenses and siliquae were minted at Trier and Lugdunum in the names of Valentinian II, Theodosius I and Arcadius in the regular coinage. The types continued those of the preceding period. The only regular coinage produced at the central mints was a rare issue of light miliarenses for Arcadius and Theodosius I at Aquileia and for Arcadius at Milan. At the Eastern mints the regular coinage consisted solely of miliarenses (heavy and light) with the GLORIA ROMANORVM legend whose military types echo those of preceding periods while at the same time foreshadowing the interrelationship of type and denomination which was to characterize the fifth century. The emperor in military dress leaning on his shield was associated with the heavy miliarensis, the emperor in military dress, raising his right hand and holding a globe in his left with the light miliarensis. Output was restricted to Constantinople and there was no vota coinage.

In the West in the regular coinage light miliarenses were issued with VIRTVS EXERCITVS and GLORIA ROMANORVM reverses which repeated the types in the East. The type with the emperor resting his hands on a shield was restricted to Trier and Lugdunum, that with him holding a globe to Milan and Aquileia. VIRTVS ROMA-NORVM and VRBS ROMA with Roma seated left on a cuirass were minted at Trier and Lugdunum only. The Central mints of Milan and Rome were the only ones except Lugdunum to produce vota coinage. Heavy miliarenses were minted at Milan, argentei (unreduced or heavy siliquae) at Lugdunum and siliquae at Rome.

392–395 Tables 14A, 14B.

Regular coinage in this period was restricted to the Western and Central mints, the East produced none. Light miliarenses were minted at Trier and Milan which continued the types and legends of the preceding period. Siliquae with the Roma seated on cuirass type were produced at Trier and Roma with the VIRTVS ROMANORVM legend and at Lugdunum with the VRBS ROMA reverse. Half-siliquae were minted at Milan and Aquileia with the VICTORIA AVGGG reverse.

The usurpation of Eugenius, 392–394, had little effect on the development of the coinage apart from the fact that he chose to use Lugdunum as one of his silver mints. Like Magnus Maximus he moved into Italy (in 393) where he minted coins in his name at Milan and Aquileia. His vota coinage consisted exclusively of heavy miliarenses from Milan.

An issue of siliquae with the VOT V MVLT X legend in the names of Arcadius and Honorius was issued at Milan, the only other Western vota coinage. In the East Constantinople produced an issue of siliquae in the names of Theodosius I, Arcadius and Honorius.

Silver issues in the fifth century

By the early years of the fifth century the Roman empire had undergone significant changes. The empire had been divided in half upon the death of Theodosius I in

395 and was ruled in the West by Honorius and in the East by Arcadius. Neither was ever more than a figurehead and real power in the West lay with the barbarian generals who controlled the army and in the East by court officials. Both halves of the empire were under attack by the barbarians and, as the century progressed, the West lost significant amounts of territory. The Eastern emperors in this period never lost the hope of re-uniting the empire under their domination but did not have sufficient strength to do so. For large parts of the century East and West were at odds with one another, frequently over religious issues or questions of legitimacy; consequently they did not recognize each other's emperors. In the circumstances it is hardly surprising that the coinage lost the uniformity it had in the earlier fourth century and that its evolution in the East began to be quite different from that of the West. Issues of silver in both halves of the empire tended to be small and sporadic, as were those of copper coins, and the main emphasis was on the production of gold.

Although it is usual in the fifth century to group the Western and Eastern emperors and their coinage separately, they have been intermingled in this catalogue. However, given the disjointed nature of the coinage in this period, it is easier to see how it developed in the two halves of the empire by treating them as separate entities.

The East

Silver issues in the East in the fifth century were confined almost exclusively to Constantinople, the exception being a group of miliarenses with blundered legends for Marcian, Leo, and Zeno with a Thessalonica mintmark. Production was restricted to ceremonial occasions like celebrations of the emperors' vota. In the earlier part of the century the traditional denominations continued to be struck: heavy and light miliarenses and siliquae were minted under Arcadius and Theodosius II. By the time of Marcian, the literacy of the legends and the regularity of the coinage had begun to deteriorate. Although the division of the coinage into regular and vota series is again observable under Honorius and Theodosius II, the latter was the last Eastern emperor until Anastasius for whom 'proper' vota coins were minted since the VOT MVLT xxxx piece for Marcian was overstruck on a coin of Theodosius II. A group of lightweight vota siliquae in the names of Marcian, Pulcheria and Leo, which will be discussed below, was also minted but their badly blundered legends give rise to the speculation that they may not have been official issues.

The weight standards of the heavier silver denominations remained the same as those of the fourth century until about 450. Heavy miliarenses were still struck at 1/60th of the Roman pound (c 5.4g.) and light miliarenses at 1/72nd (c. 4.5g.). Siliquae were presumably struck on a theoretical standard of 144th of the pound (c. 2.26g.) but in fact the weight of the few coins recorded averages 1.8g. It is unclear on the basis of such a small sample whether coins were issued on two separate standards or simply at a lower weight than has previously been thought. The last multiple that seems to have been produced in this period was a vota type for Leo.

The types repeat those of the fourth century. The vota pieces consist of a wreath inscribed with the relevant vows. The heavy and light miliarenses can be distinguished by their obverse busts and reverse types. On heavy miliarenses, the bust of the emperor faces right, on the light miliarenses it faces left. While the reverses of both have the same legend, GLORIA ROMANORVM, and the emperor is represented in military dress, on the heavy miliarenses he is shown with a sceptre in his right hand and resting his left on a shield while on the light miliarenses he is raising his right hand and holding a globe in his left. No siliquae in the regular coinage were issued for Arcadius, Honorius, or Theodosius II. There were, however, issues for the empresses Aelia Eudocia, the wife of Theodosius II, and for Aelia Pulcheria, his sister, who later married Marcian. The usual type is a cross within a wreath. The only miliarenses to be issued for an empress was for Aelia Eudoxia, the wife of Arcadius, and it is the only known silver coin minted in her name.

After the death of Theodosius in 455 the quality of the Eastern silver coinage deteriorated somewhat in style and more dramatically in terms of its literarcy. Although the heavy miliarenses with the GLORIA ROMANORVM reverse minted for Marcian, Leo, and Basiliscus (possibly for Zeno, although this piece needs confirmation) and light miliarenses for Marcian and Leo were still of good quality, the miliarenses with the Thessalonica mintmark had blundered legends and seem to have been struck at 1/72nd of the Roman pound (i.e. light miliarenses). Iconographically, however, they should be heavy miliarenses. The legend which should be GLOR ORBIS TERRAR is misspelt as: GLOR ORVS TARRAR; GLOR ORVS TERRAHL; GLOR ORVS TERRHL, and GLOR ORVS TERRRHL.

Siliquae minted for Marcian, Pulcheria and Leo which should read SAL REI PVB are rendered as SAL REI PVI or SAL REI PPI. By the reign of Zeno the transcription of reverse legends has become even more garbled: SAL REI PVB has become SRI REI RVL and VOT V MVLT X has become TOV VIM V MTI or VOT V M I ITIS. The SAL REI PVI pieces appear to have been minted on a lower weight standard (c. 1.06g.) than the siliquae produced by Theodosius II and may even have been intended to be half-siliquae. The range of weights is large enough to admit the possibility that these pieces were minted in two denominations (half- and quarter-siliquae) if it is accepted that the theoretical weight of the siliquae remained above 2g. It is certainly possible that these lightweight siliquae and miliarenses and siliquae with blundered legends are not official pieces but local barbarian copies.

The West

Silver emissions in the Western empire fall into two groups; the issues produced in Italy by the legitimate rulers and the occasional usurper, and the coins minted in Gaul by the Western usurpers Constantine III, Constans, Jovinus, Maximus, and Sebastian. The latest issues from Gaul, commonly believed to be in the names of Valentinian III and Theodosius II, may in fact be a proto-barbarian coinage for reasons which will be discussed below. Other possible and probable proto-barbarian pieces have been listed under the emperor in whose name they were minted and references to literature which identifies and discusses them have been included in the bibliography.

The Central Mints

Rome, Milan, Aquileia briefly, and later Ravenna were the chief mints in operation under Honorius. Aquileia closed early in the fifth century and Ravenna opened in about 402. Multiples, heavy miliarenses, light miliarenses, siliquae, and half-siliquae were produced for Honorius at his Western mints in his own name and in that of Arcardius. The basic type used on the heavier denominations in the regular issues features the emperor in military dress. On the multiple TRIVMFATOR GENT BARB he is holding a globe and labarum and there is a kneeling captive to his right. On the light miliarenses (VIRTVS EXERCITVS; VIRTVS EXERCITVM; VIRTVS ROMANORVM) the type is the same as that employed on the light miliarenses at Constantinople, the emperor standing facing, holding a reversed spear in his right hand and leaning on a shield with his left hand. Heavy miliarenses were issued with vota reverses (VOT X MVLT XX; VOT XV MVLT XX), as were light ones (VOT V MVLT).

The very common siliquae from Milan with the VIRTVS ROMANORVM reverse in the name of Honorius were largely minted after 395 and almost certainly before the opening of Ravenna. They were the last really large Western silver issues. The common reverse type is Roma seated left on a cuirass and this type was also used with a number of other reverse legends and is found at Ravenna. The half-siliqua usually has a Victory walking left for its reverse type. Vota siliquae were minted at Milan and Rome. The half-siliqua with the legend SALVS REIPVBLICAE with a Victory reverse type has no mintmark and is difficult to attribute to a mint, given the oddity of its style.

The weight standard of the heavy and light miliarensis continued without change, as did that of the siliqua which had been reduced under Magnus Maximus to c. 1.6g. Siliquae of Galla Placidia with the anepigraphic cross within wreath reverse from Aquileia are forgeries while pieces with the chi-rho in wreath reverse are half-siliquae.

Priscus Attalus minted a large multiple, what was probably a heavy miliarensis, siliquae and what may have been a half-siliqua. He did not use the emperor in military dress types although Roma sitting left on a cuirass did appear on his INVICTA ROMA AETERNA and VICTORIA AVGG siliquae. On the miliarensis a victory type and legend were coupled, as they were on his half-siliqua. His only vota coin was a siliqua with the VOT V reverse. The weight of his siliquae seems to be c. 1.8g., but this is only a tentative estimate since there are far too available specimens with recorded weights to be able to establish a standard.

Silver coins of John are extremely rare. Of the known specimens, one seems to have been struck from gold dies (the VICTORIA AVGGG reverse with the mintmark $\frac{R|V}{COMOB}$); one may be a siliqua on the 1/144th of the Roman pound weight standard, and the third, a half-siliqua. The siliqua type is Roma seated left and that of the half-siliqua a Victory walking left.

By the reign of Valentinian III the heavier denominations have disappeared and only siliquae and half-siliquae were minted for him and his successors. The range of types narrowed as the century progressed. Under Valentinian III siliquae with the reverses VRBS ROMA and VRBIS ROMA were minted which represent Roma seated left holding a Victory on a globe; half-siliquae with the VICTORIA AVGG reverse with Victory walking left with a wreath and palm, and the legendless pieces with the chi-rho or cross in wreath. The only known silver coin attested for Avitus is an VRBIS ROMA siliqua which was also said to have been produced for Libius Severus. Confirmation of both is required. Half-siliquae with the chi-rho in wreath reverse were minted for Libius Severus and Anthemius. The sole silver coin for Aelia Marcia, the wife of Anthemius, was an VRBIS ROMA siliqua and the type continued to be issued in the reign of Julius Nepos. Under Majorian half-siliquae were minted with the VOTIS MVLTIS reverse coupled with a reverse featuring the emperor in military dress, but these can only be forgeries. The half-siliquae with the Victory standing left reverse tends either to have a blundered obverse or badly blundered reverse legend (CC TIV) and are barbarian pieces. A half-siliqua with the legend VICTORIA AVG, Victory advancing left holding a wreath and palm, is known for Romulus from Ravenna.

The final group of coins to be discussed were those minted by the Ostrogoths in the names of Julius Nepos, Romulus, and the Eastern emperors Zeno, Basiliscus, and possibly Leo. They seem to have been half-siliquae weighing about 1g. and have legendless reverses with a new range of types whose significance is unclear. There is a short-skirted turreted figure standing left on a prow holding a sceptre and cornucopiae (who may represent Constantonopolis) and two variants of an eagle.

From the reign of Valentinian III the weight of the siliquae seems to have averaged c. 2g., although the coin itself was largely superseded by the half-siliquae. These weighed about 1g. and became the dominant silver denomination.

There was a deterioration in iconography and spelling in the West as the century progressed which paralleled that in the Eastern half of the empire. Some of the more barbarous pieces may in fact be ancient copies, but in the absence of a sufficiently large corpus of material to enable us to distinguish the genuine from the contemporary copy, doubtful pieces have on the whole been included in the catalogue.

The Gallic and Spanish mints

Virtually all of the fifth-century silver coinage minted in Gaul was produced by a succession of usurpers in the early years of the century, A.D. 407–413. The first of them was Constantine III who was elevated by troops in Britain in 407 and quickly established a power base in Gaul. There he minted siliquae in a single mintmark at Trier, two at Lugdunum and five at Arles. He also minted the rare half siliqua from Lugdunum which has been included in the catalogue, although almost certainly a modern forgery. The reverse type employed was Roma seated left on a cuirass or on a throne which repeated the late fourth-century types. The reverse legends VICTORIA AAVGGG and VICTORIA AAAVGGGG refer to Constantine III and his son Constans (for whom he also minted siliquae) and the legitimate emperors Arcadius and Honorius, with whom he was asserting his equality. the weight standard of his siliquae at 1.5g. continued that of the last issues of the house of Theodosius, 1.6g.

Jovinus also minted siliquae with the reverse legends RESTITVTOR REIP and VICTORIA AVGG with Roma seated left on a throne or cuirass at Trier, Lugdunum and Arles in a variety of mint marks and, again, the very rare half-siliqua supposedly issued at Lugdunum is a modern forgery. If the unique specimen in the British Musem is genuine, and its style is conspicuously different from the other pieces minted by Jovinus, then he also minted an argenteus (unreduced siliqua) at Arles. Jovinus' weight standard seems to have been the same as that employed by Constantine III. Jovinus also issued very rare siliquae in the name of Sebastian at Arles with the VICTORIA AVGG reverse and the seated Roma.

The usurper Maximus was proclaimed emperor by Gallic troops in Spain in a rebellion against Jovinus. He minted siliquae at Barcelona with the mark SMBA. Coins with the unambiguous SMB mark are Cigoi forgeries. His coins were on a lighter weight standard (c. 1.12g.) than those of the Gallic usurpers.

The coinage of the Western usurpers was characterized by conservatism in the choice of legend and type. The seated Roma had figured prominently on the late fourth-century siliquae and was obviously regarded as the type appropriate to the siliqua and in consequence its use served to identify the denomination. The representation of the design soon began to show a deterioration in the manner in which certain details were rendered which suggests that the die cutters did not fully understand the image they were intended to engrave. It is often unclear from the design of the seat whether Roma is seated on a cuirass or a throne and the rendering of her drapery tends to become increasingly schematic.

Finally there is a group of coins apparently minted in the names of Valentinian

III and Theodosius II at Trier, again with the seated Roma type and the reverse legend VIRTVS ROMANORVM or, more commonly, the blundered VRTVS ROMANORVM with the mintmark $\frac{*}{\text{TRPS}}$. A rare variant with the emperor standing facing holding a standard and globe is also known. These pieces have been included in the catalogue although there are good reasons to believe that some at least represent a proto-barbarian coinage rather than official issues. The style of the suspect coins is distinctly barbarous by comparison with that of the contemporary 'official' pieces and the weight standard is significantly lower. Even taking into account the small number of pieces for which figures are available, none weighs more than 1g. The range of the official specimens is 0.96–0.46g., while that of the unofficial ones declines to 0.3 and even 0.2g. The reverse legend VIRTVS (or VRTVS) ROMANORVM was not a fifth-century type, nor was the form of the mintmark TRPS current, although both had been common in the fourth century. The distribution of this group of coins, both official and unofficial, is restricted to Northern France and Belgium. Although it is tempting to believe that these coins were fifth-century imitations of fourth-century siliquae, the fact that they were issued in the names of living emperors (and not, for example, in the names of Valens or Gratian) suggests that they were intended to be accepted as Roman and official. The relationship between the very barbarous illiterate pieces and the more obviously official pieces is, however, less clear, but the former may have been local copies of the latter.

Taken as a whole fifth-century silver issues present a sharp contrast with those of the fourth century. Issues were much fewer and smaller. The separation between the Eastern and Western empires resulted in differences of mint practice, in the range of denominations struck and in the choice of types. As the century progressed large denominations virtually ceased to be struck and in the West the half-siliquae superseded the siliqua as the major silver denomination. Vota issues also became increasingly rare. It seems clear that fifth-century silver issues had a predominantly ceremonial character.

Table 8A: Regular Coinage 364–367
Western Mints

1   Heavy miliarenses

a.   *Reverse type:* Four standards.

Reverse legend:	TR	LVG	AR	R	AQ	SIS	SIR	TH
SALVS REIPVBLICAE	—	X	X	—	—	—	—	—

   Obverse legends:

	TR	LVG	AR	R	AQ	SIS	SIR	TH
DN VALENTINIANVS PF AVG	—	X	X	—	—	—	—	—
DN VALENS PF AVG	—	X	X	—	—	—	—	—

b.   *Reverse type:* Victory advg. r., head l., dragging captive in r. hand, hldg. trophy in l.

Reverse legend:	TR	LVG	AR	R	AQ	SIS	SIR	TH
VICTORIA AVGSTORVM	—	—	—	X	—	—	—	—

   Obverse legend:

	TR	LVG	AR	R	AQ	SIS	SIR	TH
DN VALENTINIANVS PF AVG	—	—	—	X	—	—	—	—

2 Light miliarenses

Reverse type: Two emperors stg. facing, heads turned towards each other, hldg. labarum and globe.

	TR	LVG	AR	R	AQ	SIS	SIR	TH
Reverse legend:								
GLORIA ROMANORVM	—	—	—	—	—	X	—	—
Obverse legends:								
DN VALENTINIANVS PF AVG	—	—	—	—	—	X	—	—
DN VALENS PF AVG	—	—	—	—	—	X	—	—

3 Multiples and light muliarenses

Reverse type: Emperor stg. facing, head r., resting l. hand on shield and (a) hldg. reversed spear in r. or (b) hldg. labarum in r.

	TR	LVG	ARL M (a)	ARL LM (a)	R	AQ	SIS	SIR	TH M (ab)	TH LM (a)	TH LM (b)
Reverse legends:											
VIRTVS EXERCITVS	—	—	X	X	—	—	—	—	X	X	X
VIRTVS ROMANI EXERCITVS	—	—	—	—	—	—	—	—	X	—	—
Obverse legends:											
DN VALENTINIANVS PF AVG	—	—	X	X	—	—	—	—	X	X	X
DN VALENS PF AVG	—	—	—	—	—	—	—	—	—	X	X

4 Light miliarenses and siliquae

Reverse type: Emperor stg. facing, head r., hldg. labarum and Victory on globe.

	TR LM	TR S	LVG LM	LVG S	ARL LM	ARL S	R LM	R S	AQ LM	AQ S	SIS LM	SIS S	SIR LM	SIR S	TH LM	TH S
Reverse legends:																
RESTIVITVTOR REIPVBLICAE	—	—	X	—	—	—	—	—	—	—	—	—	—	—	—	—
RESTITVTOR REIP	—	X	—	X	X	X	X	—	—	X	—	—	—	—	—	X
Obverse legends:																
DN VALENTINIANVS PF AVG	—	X	X	X	—	X	X	—	—	X	—	—	—	—	—	X
DN VALENS PF AVG	—	—	—	X	X	X	X	—	—	X	—	—	—	—	—	X

5 Siliquae

a. *Reverse type:* Victory advg. hldg. wreath and palm.

	TR	LVG	ARL	R	AQ	SIS	SIR	TH
Reverse legend:								
VICTORIA DD NN AVGG	—	X	—	—	—	—	—	—
Obverse legend:								
DN VALENS PF AVG	—	X	—	—	—	—	—	—

b. *Reverse type:* Emperor stg. facing, head l., hldg. globe and spear.

	TR	LVG	ARL	R	AQ	SIS	SIR	TH
Reverse legend:								
VIRTVS EXERCITVS	—	—	—	—	—	—	—	X
Obverse legend:								
DN VALENTINIANVS PF AVG	—	—	—	—	—	—	—	X

Table 8B: *Eastern Mints*

1 Heavy miliarenses

Reverse type: Two emperors stg. facing, each hldg. labarum and Victory on globe who crowns them.

	CP	NIC	CYZ	ANT
Reverse legend:				
SECVRITAS REIP	X	—	—	—
Obverse legend:				
DN VALENTINIANVS PF AVG	X	—	—	—

2 Light miliarenses

a. *Reverse type:* Two emperors stg. facing under arch, heads turned towards one another, hldg. globe and sceptre.

	CP	NIC	CYZ	ANT
Reverse legend:				
GLORIA ROMANORVM	X	—	—	X
Obverse legend:				
DN VALENTINIANVS PF AVG	X	—	—	X

b. *Reverse type:* Victory stg. l. hldg. wreath and trophy and spurning fallen enemy.

	CP	NIC	CYZ	ANT
Reverse legend:				
SECVRITAS REIPVBLICAE	—	X	—	—
Obverse legends:				
DN VALENTINIANVS PF AVG	—	X	—	—
DN VALENS PF AVG	—	X	—	—

c. *Reverse type:* Emperor stg. facing under arch, head r., hldg. transverse sceptre and globe.

	CP	NIC	CYZ	ANT
Reverse legend:				
GLORIA ROMANORVM	—	—	—	X
Obverse legends:				
DN VALENTINIANVS PF AVG	—	—	—	X
DN VALENS PERF AVG	—	—	—	X
DN VALENS PER AVG	—	—	—	X

3 Light miliarenses and siliquae

Reverse type: Emperor stg. facing, head r., hldg. Victory on globe and standard with + on banner.

	CP		NIC		CYZ		ANT	
	LM	S	LM	S	LM	S	LM	S
Reverse legends:								
RESTITVTOR REIPVBLICAE	—	—	—	—	—	—	X	—
RESTITVTOR REIP	—	X	X	X	—	—	—	X
Obverse legends:								
DN VALENTINIANVS PF AVG	—	X	X	X	—	—	X	X
DN VALENS PF AVG	—	—	X	X	—	—	—	X

Table 8C: Vota Coinage
Western Mints

1 Light miliarenses

Reverse type: Victory stg. r., l. foot on globe, inscribing shield on cippus.

	TR	LVG	ARL	R	AQ	SIS	SIR	TH
Reverse legend:								
VICTORIA AVGVSTORVM								
VOT V MVLT X	—	—	X	—	—	—	—	—

Obverse legends:

	TR	LVG	ARL	R	AQ	SIS	SIR	TH
DN VALENTINIANVS PF AVG	—	—	X	—	—	—	—	—
DN VALENS PF AVG	—	—	X	—	—	—	—	—

2 Argentei

Reverse type: Two Victories hldg. inscribed shield.

Reverse legend:

	TR	LVG	ARL	R	AQ	SIS	SIR	TH
VICT DD NN AVGG VOT V	—	—	—	X	—	—	—	—

Obverse legend:

	TR	LVG	ARL	R	AQ	SIS	SIR	TH
DN VALENS PF AVG	—	—	—	X	—	—	—	—

3 Heavy miliarenses and siliquae

Reverse type: Wreath.

Reverse legends:

	TR		LVG		ARL		R		AQ		SIS		SIR		TH	
	HM	S	HM	S	HM	S	HM	S	HM	S	HM	S	HM	S	HM	S
VOT V MVLT X	—	X	—	X	—	—	—	X	X	X	—	—	—	—	—	X
VOTIS V MVLTIS X	—	—	—	—	—	—	—	—	—	—	—	—	—	X	—	—
VOT V MVL X	—	—	—	—	—	—	—	—	—	—	—	—	—	—	X	—

Obverse legends:

	TR		LVG		ARL		R		AQ		SIS		SIR		TH	
	HM	S	HM	S	HM	S	HM	S	HM	S	HM	S	HM	S	HM	S
DN VALEN-TINIANVS PF AVG	—	X	X	—	—	—	—	X	X	X	—	—	—	X	X	—
DN VALENS PF AVG	—	X	—	X	—	—	—	X	X	—	—	—	—	—	—	X

Eastern Mints

1 Light miliarenses

Reverse type: Two Victories hldg. inscribed shield.

Reverse legend:

	CP	NIC	CYZ	ANT
VICTORIA AVGSTORVM VOT V	X	—	—	—

Obverse legend:

	CP	NIC	CYZ	ANT
DN VALENTINIANVS PF AVG	X	—	—	—

2 Argentei and siliquae

Reverse type: Wreath.

Reverse legend:

	CP		NIC		CYZ		ANT	
	A	S	A	S	A	S	A	S
VOT V	X	X	—	X	—	X	—	X

Obverse legends:

	CP		NIC		CYZ		ANT	
	A	S	A	S	A	S	A	S
DN VALENTINIANVS PF AVG	X	X	—	—	—	—	—	—
DN VALENS PF AVG	X	X	—	—	—	—	—	X
DN PROCOPIVS PF AVG	—	X	—	X	—	X	—	—

Table 9A: Regular Coinage 367–375
Western Mints

1 Multiples

Reverse type: Emperor stg. facing, head l., hldg. labarum and globe, kneeling captive to his l.

Reverse legend:

	TR	LVG	ARL	R	AQ	SIS
TRIVMFATOR GENT BARB	X	—	—	—	—	X

Obverse legend:

	TR	LVG	ARL	R	AQ	SIS
DN VALENTINIANVS PF AVG	—	—	—	—	—	X
DN VALENS PF AVG	X	—	—	—	—	—

2   Light miliarenses

Reverse type: Emperor stg. facing, head l., resting l. hand on shield and hldg. (a) standard in r. hand, or (b) labarum in r. hand.

	TR	LVG	ARL	R	AQ	SIS
Reverse legend:	a				b	b
VIRTVS EXERCITVS	X	—	—	—	X	X
Obverse legends:						
DN VALENTINIANVS PF AVG	X	—	—	—	—	X
DN VALENS PF AVG	X	—	—	—	—	X
DN GRATIANVS PF AVG	X	—	—	—	X	X

3   Siliquae

Reverse type: Roma seated l. on throne hldg. Victory on globe and spear or sceptre.

	TR	LVG	ARL	R	AQ	SIS
Reverse legend:						
VRBS ROMA	X	—	—	—	—	—
Obverse legends:						
DN VALENTINIANVS PF AVG	X	—	—	—	—	—
DN VALENS PF AVG	X	—	—	—	—	—
DN GRATIANVS PF AVG	X	—	—	—	—	—

4   Half siliquae

Reverse type: Victory advg. l. hldg. wreath and palm.

	TR	LVG	ARL	R	AQ	SIS
Reverse legend:						
VICTORIA AVGVSTORVM	X	—	—	—	—	—
Obverse legend:						
DN GRATIANVS PF AVG	X	—	—	—	—	—

Eastern Mints

1   Light miliarenses

a. *Reverse type:* Emperor stg. l. hldg. Victory on globe and standard, r. foot on crouching captive, seated captive behind.

	CP	NIC	ANT
Reverse legend:			
VICTORIA DN AVG	X	—	—
Obverse legend:			
DN VALENTINIANVS PF AVG	X	—	—

b. *Reverse type:* Emperor stg. r. hldg. spear and globe.

	CP	NIC	ANT
Reverse legend:			
VIRTVS EXERCITI	X	—	—
Obverse legend:			
DN VALENTINIANVS PF AVG	X	—	—

c. *Reverse type:* (a) Emperor stg. facing, head r., under arch, hldg. transverse spear and globe; (b) Two emps. stg. facing, heads turned towards one another, under arch, each hldg. sceptre and globe.

	CP		NIC		ANT	
Reverse legend:	a	b	a	b	a	b
GLORIA ROMANORVM	—	—	—	—	X	X

Obverse legends:

DN VALENTINIANVS PF AVG	—	—	—	—	—	X
DN VALENS PF AVG	—	—	—	—	X	X
DN GRATIANVS PF AVG	—	—	—	—	X	—

Table 9B: Vota Coinage
Western Mints

1 Heavy and light miliarenses
Reverse type: Wreath.

	TR		LVG		ARL		R		AQ		SIS	
Reverse legends:	HM	LM	HM	LM	HM	LM	HM	LM	HM	LM	HM	LM
VOT V MVLT X	—	—	—	—	X	—	—	—	—	—	—	—
VOTIS V MVLTIS X	X	—	X	—	X	—	—	—	—	—	—	—
VOTIS X MVLTIS XV	—	—	X	—	X	—	—	—	—	—	—	—
VOTIS XV MVLTIS XX	—	—	—	—	—	—	—	—	—	—	X	—
Obverse legends:												
DN VALENTINIANVS PF AVG	X	—	X	—	X	—	—	—	—	—	X	—
DN VALENS PF AVG	X	—	X	—	X	—	—	—	—	—	X	—
DN GRATIANVS PF AVG	X	—	X	—	—	X	—	—	—	—	—	—

2 Light miliarenses
Reverse type: Victory stg. r., l. foot on globe, inscribing shield on cippus.

Reverse legends:	TR	LVG	ARL
VICTORIA AVGVSTORVM VOT V MVLT X	X	X	—
VICTORIA AVGVSTORVM VOT V MVLTIS X	X	—	—
VICTORIA AVGVSTORVM VOT X MVLT XV	—	—	X
Obverse legends:			
DN VALENTINIANVS PF AVG	X	—	X
DN VALENS PF AVG	X	X	X
DN GRATIANVS PF AVG	X	X	—

3 Siliquae
Reverse type: Wreath.

Reverse legends:	TR	LVG	ARL	R	AQ	SIS	SIR	TH
VOT V MVLT X	—	—	—	—	—	X	—	—
VOT X MVLT XX	—	X	—	—	—	X	—	X
VOT XV MVLT XX	—	—	—	—	—	X	—	—
Obverse legends:								
DN VALENTINIANVS PF AVG	—	—	—	—	—	X	—	—
DN VALENS PF AVG	—	X	—	—	—	X	—	X
DN GRATIENVS PF AVG	—	—	—	—	—	X	—	—

Eastern Mints

1 Heavy miliarenses
Reverse type: Victory stg. facing, head l., hldg. wreath and inscribed shield on staff, crouching captives to r. and l.

Reverse legend:	CP	NIC	ANT
VICTORIA DN AVG VOT X MVLT XX	X	—	—
Obverse legend:			
DN VALENTINIANVS PF AVG	X	—	—

2 Heavy miliarenses, argentei and siliquae

Reverse type: Wreath.

Reverse legends:	CP			NIC			ANT		
	HM	AR	S	HM	AR	S	HM	AR	S
VOT V MVLT X	—	—	X	—	—	X	X	—	X
VOT V MVLTIS X	—	—	—	—	X	X	—	—	—
VOTIS V	—	—	X	—	—	—	—	—	—
VOT X MVLT XX	—	X	X	—	—	X	X	—	X
VOT X MVL XX	—	—	—	—	—	—	—	—	X
VOT VX MVLT XX	—	X	X	—	—	—	—	—	—
Obverse legends:									
DN VALENTINIANVS PF AVG	—	X	X	—	X	X	—	—	X
DN VALENS PF AVG	—	X	X	—	X	X	X	—	X
DN GRATIANVS PF AVG	—	—	X	—	—	X	—	—	X

Table 10A: Regular Coinage 375–378
Western Mints

1 Light miliarenses

Reverse type: Emperor stg. facing, head l., hldg. standard in r. hand, resting l. on shield.

Reverse legend:	TR	AQ	SIS	TH
VIRTVS EXERCITVS	X	—	—	—
Obverse legends:				
DN VALENS PF AVG	X	—	—	—
DN GRATIANVS PF AVG	X	—	—	—
DN VALENTINIANVS IVN PF AVG	X	—	—	—

2 Siliquae

a. *Reverse type:* Victory advg. l., hldg. wreath and palm.

Reverse legend:	TR	AQ	SIS	TH
VICTORIA AVGGG	X	—	—	—
Obverse legend:				
DN VALENTINIANVS PF AVG	X	—	—	—

b. *Reverse type:* Victory advg. l. hldg. wreath in either hand.

Reverse legend:	TR	AQ	SIS	TH
VICTORIA AVGGG	—	X	—	—
Obverse legend:				
DN VALENTINIANVS PF AVG	—	X	—	—

c. *Reverse type:* Roma seated l. on throne hldg. Victory on globe and spear or sceptre.

Reverse legend:	TR	AQ	SIS	TH
VRBS ROMA	X	—	—	—
Obverse legends:				
DN VALENS PF AVG	X	—	—	—
DN GRATIANVS PF AVG	X	—	—	—
DN VALENTINIANVS IVN PF AVG	X	—	—	—

d. *Reverse type:* Roma seated l. on cuirass hldg. Victory on globe and reversed spear.

Reverse legend:	TR	AQ	SIS	TH
VRBS ROMA	X	X	X	—

Obverse legends:

DN VALENS PF AVG	X	X	X	—
DN GRATIANVS PF AVG	X	X	X	—
DN VALENTINIANVS IVN PF AVG	X	X	—	—
DN VALENTINIANVS PF AVG	—	—	X	—

Eastern Mints

None

Table 10B: Vota Coinage

Western Mints

1 Heavy miliarensis and siliquae

Reverse type: Wreath.

	TR		AQ		SIS		TH	
Reverse legends:	HM	S	HM	S	HM	S	HM	S
VOTIS X MVLTIS XX	X	—	—	X	—	—	—	—
VOTIS X MVLTIS XV	—	—	—	—	X	—	—	—
VOT X MVLT XV	—	X	—	—	—	—	—	—
VOTIS V MVLTIS XX	—	—	—	X	—	—	—	—
VOT X MVLT XX	—	—	—	—	—	X	—	—
VOT XV MVLT XX	—	—	—	—	—	X	—	—
VOT V MVLT X	—	—	—	—	—	—	—	X
VOT VX MVLT XX	—	—	—	—	—	—	—	X
Obverse legends:								
DN VALENS PF AVG	X	X	—	X	X	X	—	X
DN GRATIANVS PF AVG	X	X	—	X	X	X	—	X
DN VALENTINIANVS PF AVG	—	—	—	—	—	X	—	—
DN VALENTINIANVS IVN PF AVG	—	—	—	X	—	—	—	X

Eastern Mints

1 Siliquae

Reverse type: Wreath

Reverse legend:	CP	NIC	CYZ	ANT
VOT XX MVLT XXX	X	—	—	—
Obverse legend:				
DN VALENS PF AVG	X	—	—	—

Table 11A: Regular Coinage 378–383

Western Mints

1 Multiples

Reverse type: Emperor stg. facing, head l., hldg. labarum and globe, crouching captive at foot l.

Reverse legend:	TR	LVG	ARL	R	AQ	SIS	SIR	TH
TRIVMFATOR GENT BARB	—	—	—	X	—	—	—	—
Obverse legend:								
DN VALENTINIANVS PF AVG	—	—	—	X	—	—	—	—

2   Heavy miliarenses

Reverse type: Victory advg. r., head l., dragging captive with r. hand, hldg. trophy in l.

Reverse legend:	TR	LVG	ARL	R	AQ	SIS	SIR	TH
VICTORIA AVGVSTORVM	—	—	—	X	—	—	—	—
Obverse legends:								
DN GRATIANVS PF AVG	—	—	—	X	—	—	—	—
DN VALENTINIANVS								
IVN PF AVG	—	—	—	X	—	—	—	—
DN VALENTINIANVS								
PF AVG	—	—	—	X	—	—	—	—
DN THEODOSIVS PF AVG	—	—	—	X	—	—	—	—

3   Light miliarenses

Reverse type: Emperor stg. facing, head l., hldg. (a) standard, or (b) labarum in r. hand, resting l. on shield.

Reverse legend:	TR	LVG	ARL	R	AQ	SIS	SIR	TH
	a				a	a	b	
VIRTVS EXERCITVS	X	—	—	X	X	X	—	—
Obverse legends:								
DN GRATIANVS PF AVG	X	—	—	X	X	X	—	—
DN VALENTINIANVS								
IVN PF AVG	X	—	—	X	X	—	—	—
DN THEODOSIVS PF AVG	X	—	—	X	—	X	—	—

4   Argentei

a.   *Reverse type:* Victory advg. r., head l., hldg. wreath in either hand.

Reverse legend:	TR	LVG	ARL	R	AQ	SIS	SIR	TH
VICTORIA AVGG	X	—	—	—	—	—	—	—
Obverse legend:								
DN VALENTINIANVS IVN								
PF AVG	X	—	—	—	—	—	—	—

b.   *Reverse type:* Two emperors seated facing on throne, jointly hldg. globe, Victory between and behind them below a palm branch.

Reverse legend:	TR	LVG	ARL	R	AQ	SIS	SIR	TH
VICTORIA AVGVSTORVM	—	—	—	—	X	—	—	—
Obverse legend:								
DN GRATIANVS PF AVG	—	—	—	—	X	—	—	—

5   Siliquae

a.   *Reverse type:* Roma seated l. on cuirass, hldg. Victory on globe and reversed spear.

Reverse legend:	TR	LVG	ARL	R	AQ	SIS	SIR	TH
VRBS ROMA	X	X	—	—	—	—	—	—
Obverse legends:								
DN GRATIANVS PF AVG	X	X	—	—	—	—	—	—
DN VALENTINIANVS PF AVG	X	—	—	—	—	—	—	—
DN THEODOSIVS PF AVG	X	—	—	—	—	—	—	—

b. *Reverse type:* Roma seated facing, head l., on throne hldg. Victory on globe and reversed (a) spear, or (b) sceptre.

Reverse legends:	TR	LVG	ARL	R	AQ	SIS	SIR	TH
	a	b	—	a	a		a	
VIRTVS ROMANORVM	X	X	—	—	X	—	—	—
GLORIA ROMANORVM	—	—	—	—	—	—	X	—
VRBS ROMA	—	—	—	X	—	—	—	—
Obverse legends:								
DN GRATIANVS PF AVG	X	X	—	X	X	—	—	—
DN VALENTINIANVS PF AVG	—	—	—	X	X	—	—	—
DN THEODOSIVS PF AVG	X	—	—	X	X	—	X	—
DN VALENTINIANVS IVN PF AVG	—	—	—	—	X	—	—	—

c. *Reverse type:* Victory advg. l. hldg. wreath and palm.

Reverse legends:	TR	LVG	ARL	R	AQ	SIS	SIR	TH
VICTORIA AVGGG	X	X	—	—	X	—	—	—
VICTORIA AVGG	—	—	—	—	X	—	—	—
Obverse legends:								
DN GRATIANVS PF AVG	—	—	—	—	X	—	—	—
DN VALENTINIANVS IVN PF AVG	X	X	—	—	X	—	—	—
DN VALENTINIANVS PF AVG	X	—	—	—	X	—	—	—
DN THEODOSIVS PF AVG	—	—	—	—	X	—	—	—

d. *Reverse type:* Constantinopolis turreted, seated facing head r., r. foot on prow, hldg. sceptre and cornucopiae.

Reverse legend:	TR	LVG	ARL	R	AQ	SIS	SIR	TH
CONCORDIA AVGGG	X	X	—	—	X	—	—	—
Obverse legends:								
DN GRATIANVS PF AVG	X	X	—	—	—	—	—	—
DN THEODOSIVS PF AVG	X	X	—	—	X	—	—	—

e. *Reverse type:* Phoenix stg. l. on globe.

Reverse legend:	TR	LVG	ARL	R	AQ	SIS	SIR	TH
PERPETVETAS	X	—	—	—	—	—	—	—
Obverse legends:								
DN GRATIANVS PF AVG	X	—	—	—	—	—	—	—
DN VALENTINIANVS IVN PF AVG	X	—	—	—	—	—	—	—
DN THEODOSIVS PF AVG	X	—	—	—	—	—	—	—

6 Half siliquae

Reverse type: Victory walking l. hldg. wreath and palm.

Reverse legend:	TR	LVG	ARL	R	AQ	SIS	SIR	TH
VICTORIA AVGGG	—	—	—	X	—	—	—	—
Obverse legends:								
DN GRATIANVS PF AVG	—	—	—	X	—	—	—	—
DN VALENTINIANVS PF AVG	—	—	—	X	—	—	—	—
DN THEODOSIVS PF AVG	—	—	—	X	—	—	—	—

Eastern Mints

None

Table 11B: Vota Coinage

1 Heavy miliarenses
Reverse type: Wreath.

Reverse legend:	TR	LVG	ARL	R	AQ	SIS	SIR	TH
VOTIS XV MVLTIS XX	X	—	—	—	—	—	—	—
Obverse legend:								
DN GRATIANVS PF AVG	X	—	—	—	—	—	—	—

2 Siliquae
Reverse type: Wreath.

Reverse legend:	TR	LVG	ARL	R	AQ	SIS	SIR	TH
VOT V MVLT X	X	—	—	—	—	X	—	—
VOT V MVLTIS X	X	—	—	—	—	—	—	—
VOT X MVLTIS XV	X	—	—	—	—	—	—	—
VOT XV MVLT XX	X	—	—	—	—	X	—	—
VOT XV MVLTIS XX	X	—	—	—	—	—	—	—
VOT XV MVLT XXX	—	—	—	—	—	X	—	X
Obverse legends:								
DN GRATIANVS PF AVG	X	—	—	—	—	X	—	X
DN VALENTINIANVS IVN PF AVG	X	—	—	—	—	—	—	—
DN VALENTINIANVS PF AVG	—	—	—	—	—	X	—	—
DN THEODOSIVS PF AVG	X	—	—	—	—	X	—	—

Eastern Mints

1 Siliquae
Reverse type: Wreath.

Reverse legend:	CP	NIC	ANT
VOT V MVLT X	X	—	—
Obverse legends:			
DN VALENTINIANVS IVN PF AVG	X	—	—
DN THEODOSIVS PF AVG	X	—	—

Table 12A: Regular Coinage 383–388
Western Mints

1 Multiples
Reverse type: Emperor stg. facing, head l., hldg. labarum and globe, crouching captive at foot l.

Reverse legend:	TR	LVG	ARL	R	AQ	SIS	TH
TRIVMFATOR GENT BARB	—	—	—	X	—	—	—
Obverse legend:							
DN VALENTINIANVS PF AVG	—	—	—	X	—	—	—

2 Multiples, light miliarenses
Reverse type: Emperor stg. facing, head l. hldg. (a) labarum or (b) standard in r. hand, resting l. on shield.

	TR M	TR LM (b)	LVG M (a)	LVG LM	ARL M	ARL LM	R M	R LM	AQ M	AQ LM	SIS M	SIS LM	TH M (a)	TH LM
Reverse legends:														
RESTITVTOR REIPVBLICE	—	—	—	—	—	—	—	—	—	—	—	—	X	—
VIRTVS EXERCITVS	—	X	—	X	—	—	—	—	—	—	—	—	—	—
Obverse legends:														
DN MAG MAXIMVS PF AVG	—	X	—	X	—	—	—	—	—	—	—	—	—	—
DN VALENTINIANVS PF AVG	—	—	—	—	—	—	—	—	—	—	—	—	X	—

3 Light miliarenses

Reverse type: Emperor carrying trophy on shoulder, dragging captive r.

	TR	LVG	ARL	M	R	AQ	SIS	SIR	TH
Reverse legend:									
VICTORIA AVGVSTORVM	—	—	—	—	—	—	—	—	X
Obverse legends:									
DN VALENTINIANVS PF AVG	—	—	—	—	—	—	—	—	X
DN THEODOSIVS PF AVG	—	—	—	—	—	—	—	—	X
DN ARCADIVS PF AVG	—	—	—	—	—	—	—	—	X

4 Siliquae

a. *Reverse type:* Constantinopolis seated facing head (a) r., or (b) l., hldg. sceptre and cornucopiae, r. foot on prow.

	TR a	TR b	LVG a	LVG b	ARL a	ARL b	M a	M b	R a	R b	a
Reverse legend:											
CONCORDIA AVGGG	X	X	—	—	—	—	—	—	—	—	—
Obverse legends:											
DN THEODOSIVS PF AVG	X	—	—	—	—	—	—	—	—	—	—
DN MAG MAXIMVS PF AVG	X	X	—	—	—	—	—	—	—	—	—

b. *Reverse type:* Roma seated facing on throne, head l., hldg. globe and reversed spear.

	TR	LVG	ARL	M	R	AQ
Reverse legends:						
VIRTVS ROMANORVM	X	—	—	X	—	X
VRBS ROMA	—	—	—	—	X	—
Obverse legends:						
DN VALENTINIANVS PF AVG	—	—	—	X	X	X
DN THEODOSIVS PF AVG	X	—	—	X	X	X
DN ARCADIVS PF AVG	—	—	—	—	X	X
DN MAG MAXIMVS PF AVG	X	—	—	X	—	X
DN FL VICTOR PF AVG	X	—	—	X	—	X

c. *Reverse type:* Victory advg. l. hldg. wreath and palm.

	TR	LVG	ARL	M	R	AQ
Reverse legend:						
VICTORIA AVGVSTORVM	—	—	—	—	—	X
Obverse legends:						
DN MAG MAXIMVS PF AVG	—	—	—	—	—	X
DN FL VICTOR PF AVG	—	—	—	—	—	X

Eastern Mints

Siliquae
Reverse type: Chi-rho in wreath.

Reverse legend:	CP	NIC	ANT
No legend	X	—	—

Obverse legend:			
AEL FLACCILLA AVG	X	—	—

Table 12B: Vota Coinage
Western Mints

1 Heavy miliarenses
Reverse type: Wreath.

Reverse legends:	TR	LVG	ARL	M	R	AQ	SIS	TH
VOTIS V MVLTIS X	X	—	—	—	—	—	—	—
VOTIS V MLTIS X (sic)	X	—	—	—	—	—	—	—

Obverse legend:								
DN MAG MAXIMVS PF AVG	X	—	—	—	—	—	—	—

2 Siliquae
Reverse type: Wreath.

Reverse legends:	TR	LVG	ARL	M	R	AQ	SIS	TH
VOT V MVLT X	—	—	—	X	—	—	—	—
VOT X MVLT XX	—	—	—	X	—	—	—	X

Obverse legends:								
DN VALENTINIANVS PF AVG	—	—	—	X	—	—	—	X
DN THEODOSIVS PF AVG	—	—	—	X	—	—	—	X
DN ARCADIVS PF AVG	—	—	—	X	—	—	—	X

Eastern Mints

Siliquae
Reverse type: Wreath.

Reverse legend:	CP	NIC	ANT
VOT X MVLT XX	X	—	—

Obverse legends:			
DN VALENTINIANVS PF AVG	X	—	—
DN THEODOSIVS PF AVG	X	—	—
DN ARCADIVS PF AVG	X	—	—

Table 13A: Regular Coinage 388–392
Western Mints

1 Light miliarenses
a. *Reverse type:* Emperor stg. facing, head l., hldg. standard in r. hand, resting l. on shield.

Reverse legends:	TR	LVG	ARL	M	R	AQ
VIRTVS EXERCITVS	X	X	—	—	—	—
GLORIA ROMANORVM	—	X	—	—	—	—

Obverse legends:						
DN VALENTINIANVS PF AVG	X	X	—	—	—	—
DN THEODOSIVS PF AVG	X	—	—	—	—	—

b. *Reverse type:* Emperor, nimbate stg. facing, head l., raising r. hand, hldg. globe in l.

Reverse legend:	TR	LVG	ARL	M	R	AQ
GLORIA ROMANORVM	—	—	—	X	—	X
Obverse legends:						
DN VALENTINIANVS PF AVG	—	—	—	—	—	X
DN THEODOSIVS PF AVG	—	—	—	X	—	—
DN ARCADIVS PF AVG	—	—	—	X	—	X

2 Siliquae

a. *Reverse type:* Roma seated l. on cuirass, hldg. Victory on globe and reversed spear.

Reverse legends:	TR	LVG	ARL	M	R	AQ
VIRTVS ROMANORVM	X	—	—	—	—	—
VRBS ROMA	X	X	—	—	—	—
Obverse legends:						
DN VALENTINIANVS PF AVG	X	X	—	—	—	—
DN THEODOSIVS PF AVG	X	X	—	—	—	—
DN ARCADIVS PF AVG	X	X	—	—	—	—

b. *Reverse type:* Roma seated l. on cuirass, hldg. Victory on globe with cippus beneath and reversed spear.

Reverse legend:	TR	LVG	ARL	M	R	AQ
VRBS ROMA	—	X	—	—	—	—
Obverse legend:						
DN THEODOSIVS PF AVG	—	X	—	—	—	—

Eastern Mints

1 Heavy miliarenses

Reverse type: Emperor stg. facing, head l., hldg. sceptre in r. hand, resting l. on shield.

Reverse legend:	CP	NIC	ANT
GLORIA ROMANORVM	X	—	—
Obverse legend:			
DN VALENTINIANVS PF AVG	X	—	—

2 Light miliarenses

Reverse type: Emperor stg. facing, head l., raising r. hand, hldg. globe in l.

Reverse legend:	CP	NIC	ANT
GLORIA ROMANORVM	X	—	—
Obverse legends:			
DN THEODOSIVS PF AVG	X	—	—
DN ARCADIVS PF AVG	X	—	—

Table 13B: Vota Coinage
Western Mints

1 Heavy miliarenses

Reverse type: Wreath.

Reverse legend:	TR	LVG	ARL	M	R	AQ
VOT X MVLT XX	—	—	—	X	—	—
Obverse legend:						
DN ARCADIVS PF AVG	—	—	—	X	—	—

2 Argentei
Reverse type: Wreath.

Reverse legend:	TR	LVG	ARL	M	R	AQ
VOT XV MVLT XX	—	X	—	X	—	—
Obverse legend:						
DN VALENTINIANVS PF AVG	—	—	—	X	—	—

3 Siliquae
Reverse type: Wreath.

Reverse legend:	TR	LVG	ARL	M	R	AQ
VOT X MVLT XX	—	—	—	—	X	—
Obverse legend:						
DN VALENTINIANVS PF AVG	—	—	—	—	X	—
DN THEODOSIVS PF AVG	—	—	—	—	X	—
DN ARCADIVS PF AVG	—	—	—	—	X	—

Eastern Mints

None.

Table 14A: Regular Coinage 392–395
Western Mints

1 Light miliarenses
Reverse type: Emperor stg. facing, head l., hldg. standard in r. hand, resting l. on shield.

Reverse legends:	TR	LVG	ARL	M	R	AQ
GLORIA ROMANORVM	X	—	—	X	—	—
VIRTVS EXERCITVS	X	—	—	—	—	—
Obverse legends:						
DN EVGENIVS PF AVG	X	—	—	X	—	—
DN ARCADIVS PF AVG	—	—	—	X	—	—

2 Siliquae
a. *Reverse type:* Roma seated l. on cuirass, hldg. Victory on globe and reversed spear.

Reverse legends:	TR	LVG	ARL	M	R	AQ
VIRTVS ROMANORVM	X	—	—	X	—	—
VRBS ROMA	—	X	—	—	—	—
Obverse legends:						
DN THEODOSIVS PF AVG	X	—	—	X	—	—
DN ARCADIVS PF AVG	X	—	—	X	—	—
DN ARCAPIVS PF AVG	X	—	—	—	—	—
DN EVGENIVS PF AVG	X	X	—	X	—	—

3 Half-siliquae
Reverse type: Victory advg. l. hldg. wreath and palm.

Reverse legends:	TR	LVG	ARL	M	R	AQ
VICTORIA AVGGG	—	—	—	X	—	X
SPES ROMANORVM*	—	—	—	—	X	—
Obverse legends:						
DN THEODOSIVS PF AVG	—	—	—	X	X	X
DN ARCADIVS PF AVG	—	—	—	X	—	X

	TR	LVG	ARL	M	R	AQ
DN EVGENIVS PF AVG	—	—	—	X	—	—
DN HONORIVS PF AVG	—	—	—	X	—	—
*CIGOI FORGERY?						

Eastern Mints

None.

Table 14B: Vota Coinage
Western Mints

1 Heavy miliarenses

Reverse type: Wreath.

Reverse legend:

	TR	LVG	ARL	M	R	AQ
VOT V MVLT X	—	—	—	X	—	—

Obverse legend:

	TR	LVG	ARL	M	R	AQ
DN EVGENIVS PF AVG	—	—	—	X	—	—

2 Siliquae

Reverse type: Wreath.

Reverse legend:

	TR	LVG	ARL	M	R	AQ
VOT V MVLT X	—	—	—	X	—	—

Obverse legends:

	TR	LVG	ARL	M	R	AQ
DN ARCADIVS PF AVG	—	—	—	X	—	—
DN HONORIVS PF AVG	—	—	—	X	—	—

Eastern Mints

Siliquae

Reverse type: Wreath.

Reverse legend:

	CP	NIC	ANT
VOT X MVLT XX	X	—	—

Obverse legends:

	CP	NIC	ANT
DN THEODOSIVS PF AVG	X	—	—
DN ARCADIVS PF AVG	X	—	—
DN HONORIVS PF AVG	X	—	—

GENEALOGICAL TABLES

TABLE 15: Diocletian and Galerius

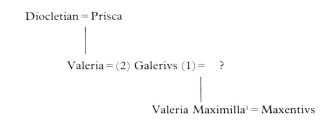

Diocletian = Prisca
|
Valeria = (2) Galerivs (1) =   ?
|
Valeria Maximilla[1] = Maxentivs

1. Valeria Maximilla may have been the daughter of Valeria and Galerius

TABLE 16: Maximian and Constantius I

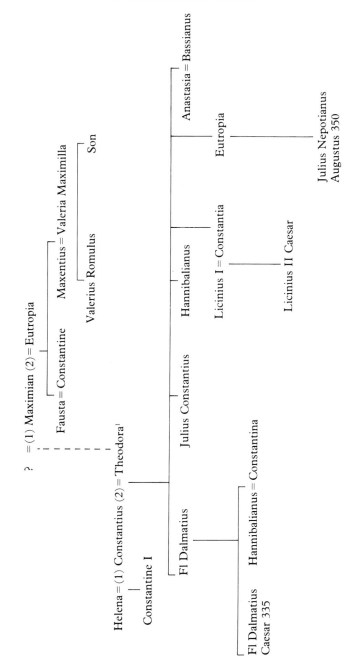

1. Theodora may have been the daughter of Eutropia by a previous marriage to Afranius Hannibalianus

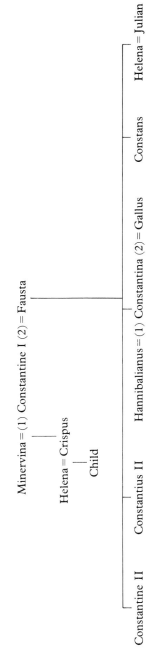

TABLE 17: The Family of Constantine

TABLE 18: House of Valentinian I

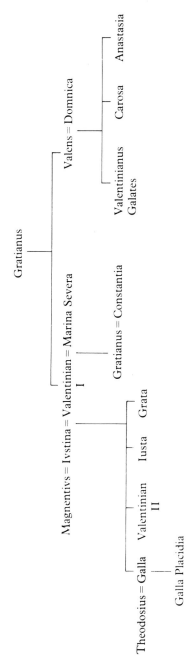

TABLE 19: The House of Theodosius

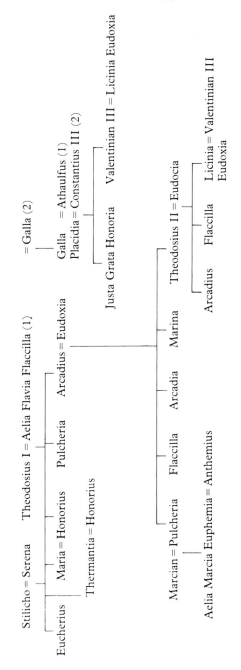

72

SELECT BIBLIOGRAPHY

Abbreviations

ANSMN   *American Numismatic Society Museum Notes*
BAR   *British Archaeological Reports*
BNJ   *British Numismatic Journal*
BSFN   *Bulletin de la Société Française de Numismatique*
CENB   *Cercle d'Études Numismatiques Bulletin*
NZ   *Numismatische Zeitschrift*
RN   *Revue Numismatique*
SNR   *Schweizerische Numismatische Rundschau*

BALAGUER, A. M., 'Descoberta d'un nou exemplar de les rares siliqües de Màxim Tirà, attribuïdes a la seca de Barcelona. Corpus de los emissions de Màxim', *Numisma* 30 (1980), 141–54.

BARNES, T. D., *The New Empire of Diocletian and Constantine* (Cambridge, Mass., 1982).

BASTIEN, P., *Le monnayage de l'atelier de Lyon (337–363)* (Wetteren, 1985).

— *Le monnayage de Magnence (350–353)*, 2nd ed. (Wetteren, 1983).

— and METZGER, C., *Le trésor de Beaurains (dit l'Arras)* (Wetteren, 1977).

BELLINGER, A. R., BRUUN, P., KENT, J. P. C. and SUTHERLAND, C. H. V., *Late Roman Gold and Silver Coins at Dumbarton Oaks: Diocletian to Eugenius. Dumbarton Oaks Papers* 18 (1964).

BRUNETTI, Lodovico, *Opus Monetale Cigoi* (1966).

BRUUN, P. M., *The Roman Imperial Coinage* vol. VII (London, 1966).

CAHN, H. A., 'Kleinhuningen', *SNR* 26 (1934–38), 425–430.

CALLU, J. P., 'Silver hoards and emissions from 324 to 392', *Imperial Revenue, Expenditure and Monetary Policy in the Fourth Century A.D.* (ed. C. E. King) *BAR International Series* 76 (Oxford, 1980) 213–54.

CARSON, R. A. G., *Principal Coins of the Romans. Vol. III: The Dominate A.D. 294–498* (London, 1981).

COHEN, H., *Description historique des monnaies frapées sous l'empire romain,* vol. VII (Paris, 1888), VIII (1892).

DHÉNIN, M., 'Monnaies des Vᵉ–VIᵉ siecles des nécropoles de Vron (Somme) et de Hordain (Nord)', *Mélanges de Numismatique, d'Archéologie et d'Histoire offerts à Jean Lafaurie* (ed. P. Bastien, F. Dumas, H. Huvelin and C. Morrisson) (Paris, 1980), 201–7.

GNECCHI, *I medaglioni Romani. Vol. I: Oro ed Argento* (Milan, 1912).

HAHN, W., 'Die östliche Gold– und Silberprägung unter Theodosius I', *Litterae Numismaticae Vindobonenses Roberto Goebl dedicatae* (Vienna, 1982), 103–28.

— 'Die letzten Jahre der Mediolanenser Münzprägung vor der Schliessung der Münzstätte durch Theoderich', *La Zecca Di Milano* (Milan, 1984), 229–39.

HENDY, M. F., *Studies in the Byzantine Monetary Economy c. 300–1450* (Cambridge, 1985).

JELOČNIK, A., *The Sisak hoard of Argentei of the Early Tetrarchy*, Situla 3 (Ljubljana, 1961).

JONES, A. H. M., *The Later Roman Empire, 289–602* (Oxford, 1973).

KENT, J. P. C., 'Julius Nepos and the fall of the Western Empire', *Corolla Memoriae Erich Swoboda Dedicata* (Graz, 1966), 146–50.

— *The Roman Imperial Coinage* vol. VIII (London, 1981).

— 'Un monnayage irrégulier au debut du Ve siècle de notre ère', *CENB* 11 (1974), 22–9.

KING, C. E., 'Late Roman silver hoards in Britain and the problem of clipped siliquae', *BNJ* 51 (1982) 5–32.

LAFAURIE, J., 'La chronologie des monnaies de Constantin III et de Constan II' *RN* (1953) 37–65.

— 'Une série de médaillons d'argent de Constantin I et Constantin II', *RN* (1949) 35–48.

— and Lafont, V., '*Argenteus* de l'usurpateur Maximus trouvé près d'Argelès-sur-Mer' (Pyrénées-Orientales, ar. Céret)', *BSFN* 34 (1979), 540–4.

MAZZINI, G., *Monete Imperiale Romane* vol. V (Milan, 1958).

MICKWITZ, G., *Die Systeme des römischen Silbergeldes im IV Jhdt. n. Chr.* (Helsinki, 1933).

MITARD, P. H., 'Monnaies de V^e/VIe et VIIe siècles découvertes à Genainville (Val d'Oise)', *RN* 19 (1977), 117–30.

MORRISSON, C. and SCHWARTZ, J. H., 'Vandal silver coinage in the name of Honorius', *ANSMN* 27 (1983), 149–79.

PEARCE, J. W. E., *The Roman Imperial Coinage* vol. IX (London, 1951).

PINK, K., 'Die Silberprägung des Diocletianischen Tetrarchie', *NZ* 63 (1930), 9–38.

RATTO sale (Monnaies Byzantines) Lugano, Switzerland, December 1950.

ROBERTSON, A. S., *Roman Imperial Coins in the Hunter Coin Cabinet, University of Glasgow* vol. V (Oxford, 1982).

SABATIER, J., *Description générale des monnaies Byzantine frappées sous les empereurs d'orient* vol. 1 (Paris, 1982).

SHIEL, N., *The Episode of Carausius and Allectus BAR* 40 (Oxford, 1977).

SUTHERLAND, C. H. V., *The Roman Imperial Coinage* vol. VI (London, 1967).

TOLSTOI, J., *Monnaies byzantines* (St Petersburg, 1913–14).

TOYNBEE, J. M. C., *Roman Medallions* ANS Numismatic Series 5 (New York, 1944).

ULRICH-BANSA, O., *Moneta Mediolanensis* (Vienna, 1949).

74

ACKNOWLEDGEMENTS

I should like to thank David Sear in particular for not only providing valuations but in emending and expanding the imperial biographies. These are to be regarded as a joint effort; the remainder of the introductory matter and catalogue entries are entirely my own responsibility. Special thanks are due also to Dr. Wolfgang Hahn of Vienna, who supplied me with a list of all the fifth-century Eastern types known to him. I am also indebted to the following who supplied me with casts or photographs of relevant material: J. P. C. Kent, A. Burnett, British Museum (London); N. Hampartumian, Barber Institute, Birmingham; D. Bateson, Hunter Coin Cabinet, Glasgow; D. Walker, Oxford; M. Amandry, Paris; Baron Chaurand, Lyon; J. Lallemand, Brussels; D. Klese, Munich; P. H. Martin, Karlsruhe; H. D. Schutz, Berlin; G. Dembski, Vienna; A. Arslan, R. Martini, Milan; S. de Caro Balbi, Rome; P. Grierson, Dumbarton Oaks, Washington; Dr. W. Metcalf, American Numismatic Society, New York.

CARAUSIUS
A.D. 286–293

Marcus Aurelius Maus (Mausaeus or Mausaius) Carausius was born in the Netherlands and is said to have been a helmsman in his youth. In about 286 Maximian put him in charge of the Channel Fleet and ordered him to clear the North Sea of pirates. He succeeded admirably in his mission but failed to turn over the booty to Maximian, who branded him a traitor and condemned him to death. Carausius fled to Britain with the booty, where his troops proclaimed him emperor. He minted a copious coinage and was the first emperor after the financial crisis of the mid-third century to produce silver coins with a fineness in excess of 90%. Maximian failed to overthrow Carausius in an abortive attempt to invade Britain in about 289. Carausius had gained a toehold in northern Gaul but received a severe setback when he lost Boulogne to Constantius in 293. Shortly afterwards he was murdered by Allectus, his alleged finance minister, who succeeded him.

Obverse legends.

A. CARAVSIVS PF AVG.
B. IMP CARAVSIVS AVG.
C. IMP CARAVSIVS PA.
D. IMP CARAVSIVS P AV.
E. IMP CARAVSIVS P AVG.
F. IMP CARAVSIVS PF.
G. IMP CARAVSIVS PF A.
H. IMP CARAVSIVS PF AV.
I. IMP CARAVSIVS PF AVG.
J. IMP CARAVSIVS PF AG.
K. IMP CARAVSIVS PF I.

L. IMP CARAVSIVS PF IN AVG.
M. IMP CARAVSIVS F AV.
N. IMP C CARAVSIVS PF AV.
O. VIRTVS CARAVSI.
P. IMP CARAVSIVS AV.
Q. IMP CARAVSIVS PI.
R. IMP CARAVSIVS PI AV.
S. IMP CARAVSIVS PI AVG.
T. IMP CARAVSIVS PE AVG.
U. IMP CARAVSIVS PE AV.
V. IMP CARAVSIVS PE AG.
W. IMP C CARAVSIVS PF AVG.

Obverse busts.

a. laureate, cuirassed, right.
b. laureate, draped, right.
c. laureate, draped, cuirassed, right.
d. laureate, draped, holding globe in right hand, right.
e. laureate, wearing consular robes, holding eagle-tiped sceptre in left hand, left.
f. laureate, wearing consular robes, holding globe, left.
g. laureate, helmeted, holding spear and shield, right.

All coins are denarii

		F	VF
1	Dc ℞ ADVE[ ], emperor riding left, captive before horse. ·XX>. C 3† RIC 1067† Shiel 3 – 4 .	900	2,300
2	Cc ℞ As last. ⊥. C — RIC 707 var. Shiel 5†	900	2,300

		F	VF
3	Bc ℞ ADEVENTVS AV (*sic*), as last. R̄S̄R̄. C — RIC — Shiel 1	900	2,300

		F	VF
4	Dc ℞ ADVENTVS AVG, as last. $\overline{\ni\in}$. *C 4† RIC 1068 Shiel 2 (mint 2)* .	900	2,300
5	Ic ℞ As last. $\overline{\text{RSR}}$. *C — RIC 535 Shiel 4–6*	750	2,000
6	Ec ℞ As last. $\overline{\text{RSR}}$. *C — RIC — Shiel 8A*	900	2,300
7	Ie ℞ As last. $\overline{\text{RSR}}$. *C 8† RIC 535 Shiel 7*	1,200	3,000
8	Ic ℞ As last. ⊥. *C 7† RIC 707 Shiel 1 (mint 2)*	900	2,300
9	Hc ℞ As last, but no captive. $\overline{\text{RSR}}$. *C — RIC 536 Shiel 8* . .	900	2,300
10	Ic ℞ As last. $\overline{\text{RSR}}$. *C — RIC 535 Shiel 2*	900	2,300
11	Ic ℞ ADVENTVS AVGG, emperor riding r., holding spear horizontally over head, captive beneath horse. $\overline{\text{RSR}}$. *Coh 11† RIC 541 Shiel 9*	950	2,400

		F	VF
12	Ge ℞ CLARIT CARAVSI AV, but of Sol, radiate draped, r. ⊥. *C — RIC 542 Shiel 6 (mint 2)*	2,500	5,000
13	Ic ℞ CONCORND [ ], emperor stg. r. clasping hand of Concordia stg. l. $\overline{\text{RSR}}$. *C — RIC 551 Shiel 27*	950	2,400

		F	VF
14	Ic ℞ CONCORDIA AVG, clasped hands. $\overline{\text{RSR}}$. *C — RIC 545 Shiel 10*	600	1,500
15	E? ℞ As last. $\overline{\text{RSR}}$. *C — RIC 546 Shiel 11*	600	1,500
16	Rb ℞ CONCORDIA COMMILI, as last. ⊥ *C — RIC — Shiel 7† (mint 2)*	600	1,500
17	Dc ℞ CONCORDIA MI, as last. $\overline{\text{RSR}}$. *C — RIC — Shiel 13*. . .	600	1,500
18	Ic ℞ As last. $\overline{\text{RSR}}$. *C — RIC 548 Shiel 12*	600	1,500
19	Bc ℞ CONCOR MI, as last. $\overline{\text{RSR}}$. *C — RIC 543 Shiel 26*	600	1,500
20	Wc ℞ CONCORDIA MILI, as last. $\overline{\text{RSR}}$. *C — RIC 548† Shiel —* . .	600	1,500
21	Ie ℞ CONCORD MILIT, Concordia stg. l. with two ensigns. $\overline{\text{RSR}}$. *C 33† RIC 544 Shiel 25*	1,200	3,000
22	Hc ℞ CONCORDIA MILIT, clasped hands. $\overline{\text{RSR}}$. *C 36 RIC 549 Shiel 15*	600	1,500
23	Ic ℞ As last. $\overline{\text{RSR}}$. *C 36† RIC 548 Shiel 14*	600	1,500
24	Ic ℞ CONCORDIA MILITVM, as last. $\overline{\text{RSR}}$. *C 41† RIC 548 Shiel 16–19*	500	1,350
25	As last. $\overline{\text{C}}$. *C 41† RIC 186 Shiel 1 (C mint)*	600	1,500

		F	VF
26	Ie ℞ As last. $\overline{\text{RSR}}$. *C 42 RIC 548 Shiel 20* .	1,100	2,500
27	Hc ℞ As last. $\overline{\text{RSR}}$. *C 42† RIC 549 Shiel 21*	600	1,500
28	Vc ℞ As last. $\overline{\text{X}}$. *C — RIC — Shiel —*	650	1,700
29	Gc ℞ [ ] A MILITVM AV [ ], as last. $\overline{\text{RSR}}$. *C — RIC — Shiel —*.	600	1,500
30	Ic ℞ CONCORDIA MILTVM (*sic*), as last. $\overline{\text{RSR}}$. *C — RIC — Shiel 22*.	600	1,500
31	Ic ℞ CONCORDIA MTLITVM (*sic*), as last. $\overline{\text{RSR}}$. *C — RIC 547 Shiel 23–4†*. .	600	1,500
32	Hc ℞ CONS[ER] A[V], Neptune seated l. with anchor and trident. $\overline{\text{RSR}}$. *C 45† RIC 553† Shiel 28*	950	2,250
33	Eb ℞ CONSER AVG, as last. ⊥. *C — RIC 709† Shiel 8 (Mint 2)* .	950	2,250

		F	VF
34	Ic ℞ As last. $\overline{\text{RSR}}$. *C — RIC 552 var. Shiel 29* .	900	2,250

		F	VF
35	Aa ℞ CONSERVAT AVG, Jupiter stg. l. hldg. thunderbolt and sceptre, eagle at feet. ML. *C 46 (gold) RIC — Shiel 1 (ML mint)*	1,250	2,500
36	Ic ℞ EXPE[ ], Britannia stg. r. with wreath, clasping hand of emperor stg. l., altar between them. ⊥. *C — RIC — Shiel 9 (Mint 2)* .	900	2,250

		F	VF
37	Hc ℞ EXPECTATE VENI, Britannia stg. r. with ensign, clasping hand of emperor stg. l. with sceptre. $\overline{\text{RSR}}$. *C 58† RIC 555 Shiel 33–39*	750	2,000

		F	VF
38	Ic ℞ As last. $\overline{\text{RSR}}$. *C 56† RIC 554 Shiel 31–2*	800	2,200
39	Ib ℞ EXPECTATE VENI, as last. $\overline{\text{RSR}}$. *C — RIC 554 var. Shiel 30* .	800	2,200
40	Fd ℞ EXPECTATE VENIES, as last. $\overline{\text{RSR}}$. *C 57† RIC 558(†?) Shiel 41–2*	1,000	2,250
41	Gc ℞ As last. ⊥. *C — RIC 715† Shiel 10 (Mint 2)*	800	1,950
42	Hc ℞ EXPECTATI, as last. $\overline{\text{RSR}}$. *C — RIC 557 Shiel 40*	800	1,950
43	Rc ℞ EXPECTATI VEN[I], as last. ⊥. *C59† RIC — Shiel 11 (mint 2)*	800	1,950

		F	VF
44	Ic ℞ FEDES (*sic*) MILITVM, Fides stg. l. with two ensigns. $\overline{\text{RSR}}$. *C — RIC 559 Shiel 43*	900	2,250
45	Hc ℞ FELICIT[ ], galley 1. $\overline{\text{RSR}}${℞}. *C — RIC 560 Shiel —* .	750	2,000
46	Vc ℞ FELICITA, as last. ⊥. *C — RIC — Shiel 13 (mint 2)* . .	750	2,000
47	Dc ℞ As last, galley r. $\overline{\text{RSR}}$. *C — RIC Shiel 44*	650	1,700
48	Ic ℞ FELICITA AV, as last. $\overline{\text{RSR}}$. *C 65 RIC 560 Shiel 45*	650	1,700
49	Hc ℞ As last. $\overline{\text{RSR}}$. *C 65† RIC — Shiel 46*	650	1,700
50	Ic ℞ FELICITA AVG, as last. $\overline{\text{RSR}}$. *C 65† RIC 560 Shiel 47–50, 52*	600	1,500
51	Sc ℞ As last. $\overline{\text{RSR}}$. *C — RIC 560 Shiel 51†*	650	1,700
52	Ie ℞ As last. $\overline{\text{RSR}}$. *C — RIC 560 Shiel 53–4*	100	2,400
53	Ic ℞ FELICITAS, as last. $\overline{\text{RSR}}$. *C 66† RIC 560 Shiel 55–7*	600	1,500
54	Hc ℞ FELICITAS AVG, galley 1. $\overline{\text{RSR}}$. *C — RIC 560† Shiel 59* . .	750	2,000

		F	VF
55	Ie ℞ As last. $\overline{\text{RSR}}$. *C — RIC 560† Shiel 58*	1,000	2,400
56	Qc ℞ FELICITI A [ ], galley r. $\overline{\text{RSR}}$. *C — RIC — Shiel —* . .	750	2,000
57	Kb ℞ FL IVI AV (*sic*) As last. $\overline{\text{XXX}}$. *C 105† RIC 1069–70† Shiel 15† (Mint 2) irreg.*	750	2,000
58	Ic ℞ FL IVI (*sic*) As last. $\overline{\text{XXX}}$. *C 105† RIC 1069–70† Shiel 14* (Mint 2) irreg.	750	2,000
59	Hc ℞ II I VTI IIV As last. ⊥. *C — RIC — Shiel 16† (Mint 2) irreg.* . .	750	2,000

		F	VF
60	Gc ℞ [FI] DE MI AV, Fides with one ensign clasping hand of emperor. ⊥. *C — RIC 562 Shiel 17 (Mint 2)*	950	2,250

		F	VF
61	Rc ℟ FIDEM MILITVM [NN], Aequitas stg. l. hldg. scales and cornucopiae. ⊥. *C 78† RIC 711† Shiel 18*	900	2,250
62	Bc ℟ FIDES EXERC, Fides seated l. hldg. cornucopiae and patera. ⊥. *C — RIC — Shiel —*	950	2,300
63	Ic ℟ FIDES MILIT, Fides stg. l. with two ensigns. R̄S̄R̄. *C — RIC 564 Shiel 60*	900	2,250
64	Ic ℟ FIDES MILITVM, as last. R̄S̄R̄. *C — RIC — Shiel —* . .	900	2,250
65	Ic ℟ [F]ORTVNA AVG, bust of Fortuna in wreath hldg. branch with flower behind. ⊥. *C 86† RIC 565† Shiel 19 (Mint 2)* . .	1,500	3,500
66	Nc ℟ FORTVNA AVG, Fortuna seated l. on wheel with rudder and cornucopiae. R̄S̄R̄. *C 87† RIC 567 Shiel 61* . . .	900	2,250
67	Ic ℟ IIDVCI IVS IP C (*sic*), emperor riding l. R̄S̄R̄. Blundered ADVENTVS reverse. *C 138† RIC — Shiel 1† (irreg. mint)*. .	750	2,000
68	Hc ℟ IXPICTATI VENIES (*sic*), Britannia stg. r. with wreath, clasping hand of emperor stg. l. with sceptre. [ ]XX. *C 114† RIC 715† Shiel 12 (Mint 2)*	800	2,250
69	Ic ℟ LEG IIII [FLAVIA], centaur l. hldg. club transversely with both hands. *C̄. C 143† RIC 187 Shiel 2 (C Mint)*	1,200	2,500
70	Ib ℟ LEG IIII FL, lion walking l., thunderbolt in mouth. R̄S̄R̄. *C 140† RIC 568 Shiel 62*	1,200	2,500
71	Ic ℟ MONETA AVG, Moneta stg. l. hldg. scales and cornucopiae. ⊥. *C 171 RIC 717 Shiel 20 and (?22) (Mint 2)* . .	900	2,250

		F	VF
72	Ic ℟ As last. X̄. *C 171† RIC 1073 Shiel 21 (Mint 2)*	900	2,250
73	Hc ℟ As last. ⊥. *C 171† RIC — Shiel (?23) 24 (Mint 2)*. . .	900	2,250

		F	VF
74	Ic ℟ ORIENS AVG, Sol stg. l., raising r. hand hldg. globe in l. hand. R̄S̄R̄. *C 183† RIC 570 Shiel 64*	900	2,250
75	Ic ℟ PAX AVG, Pax stg. l. with olive branch and vertical sceptre. ⊥. *C 190† RIC 719 Shiel 25–6 (Mint 2)*	800	2,100

		F	VF
76	Gc ℟ As last. ⊥. *C 190† RIC — Shiel 28 (Mint 2)*	800	2,100

		F	VF
77	Ie ℞ As last but cornucopiae not sceptre. ⊥. *C 221 RIC 720 Shiel 27 (Mint 2)*	1,100	2,500
78	Ic ℞ PRINCIPI IVVENT, soldier stg. l. hldg. olive branch and sceptre. ⊥. *C 249† RIC 721 Shiel 29 (Mint 2)*	1,100	2,400

		F	VF
79	Ic ℞ PRO[VI]D AVG, Providentia stg. l. with baton and cornucopiae, globe at feet. |C. *C — RIC — Shiel 1 (C Mint)*	900	2,250
80	Ic ℞ RENOVAT ROMA, Wolf r. with Twins R̄S̄R̄. *C 291 RIC 571 Shiel 66*	600	1,500
81	Ic ℞ RENOVAT ROMAN, as last. R̄S̄R̄. *C — RIC 571 Shiel 65, 67*. .	600	1,500

		F	VF
82	Ic ℞ RENOVAT ROMANO, as last. R̄S̄R̄. *C 293 RIC 571 Shiel 68–71*	550	1,350
83	Tc ℞ As last. R̄S̄R̄. *C — RIC — Shiel 72*	600	1,500
84	Hc ℞ ROMANO RENA, as last. R̄S̄R̄. *C — RIC 572† Shiel 73* . .	600	1,500
85	Jc ℞ ROMANO RENO, as last. R̄S̄R̄. *C — RIC 575 Shiel 82*	600	1,500
86	Vc ℞ ROMANO RENOV, as last. R̄S̄R̄. *C — RIC 572 var. Shiel 74–5.*	600	1,500
87	Uc ℞ As last. R̄S̄R̄. *C — RIC 572 var. Shiel 76*	600	1,500
88	Ic ℞ As last. R̄S̄R̄. *C 300 RIC 572 Shiel 77–8*	600	1,500
89	Og ℞ As last. R̄S̄R̄. *C 301 RIC 577 Shiel 79*	1,200	3,000

		F	VF
90	Ic ℞ ROMANO RENOVA, as last. R̄S̄R̄. *C — RIC 572 Shiel 80* . .	600	1,500
91	Hc ℞ As last. R̄S̄R̄. *C — RIC 573 Shiel 80a*	600	1,500

		F	VF
92	Db ℞ As last. A̅X̅A̅. *C — RIC 574 Shiel 81.*	750	1,850

		F	VF
93	Pc R [ ] NO RIVIVA, as last. ⊥. *C 303† RIC 594† Shiel 2 (Mint 2) irreg.*	750	1,850
94	Ic R ROME AET [ ], Rome seated l. in hexastyle temple. R̄S̄R̄. *C 303† RIC 579† Shiel 83*	1,200	3,000
95	Hc R [SALV]S AVG, Salus seated l. feeding serpent rising from altar. [ ]I. *C — RIC 723† Shiel 32 (Mint 2)*	800	2,100
96	Ic R As last. ⊥. *C — RIC 723 Shiel —*	800	2,100
97	Ic R As last, Salus stg. l. with a short and long ensign. ⊥. *C — RIC 722 Shiel 31 (Mint 2)*	800	2,100
98	Ic R TEMPORVM FELICT (sic), Felicitas stg. l. with globe and cornucopiae. ⊥. *C — RIC 724† Shiel 30† (Mint 2)* . .	800	2,100
99	Ic R TEMPORVM FELICITA, Felicitas stg. l. with vertical sceptre and cornucopiae. R̄S̄R̄. *C 350† RIC — Shiel —* .	800	2,100
100	Ic R TVMT [ ], Felicitas stg. l. with baton and cornucopiae. R[SR]. *C 364† RIC 580 var. Shiel 84†*	800	2,100
101	Ge R VBERITAS AVG, Uberitas stg. r. with standard, clasping hand of soldier stg. l. with spear. R̄S̄R̄. *C 368 RIC 589 Shiel 89* . .	1,100	2,250
102	Ff R As last. R̄S̄R̄. *C 367† RIC 590 Shiel 88* . . .	1,100	2,250
103	Bc R VBERTA AVG (sic), woman milking cow stg. r. R̄S̄R̄. *C 371 RIC 585 Shiel 90*	1,100	2,250

		F	VF
104	Ge R VBERVTA AV, woman milking cow stg. r. R̄S̄R̄. *C 364† RIC 583† Shiel 86*	1,200	3,000
105	Gf R As last. R̄S̄R̄. *C 365† RIC 586† Shiel 87*	1,200	3,000
106	Ic R VLTO PAX AVG, Pax stg. r. with wreath (or patera) clasping hand of emperor over altar. ⊥. *C 406† RIC 729 Shiel 33 (Mint 2)*	1,100	2,400
107	Ic R VICTORIA AVG, emperor stg. l. hldg. globe and spear, crowned by Victory stg. l. ⊥. *C 375† RIC 727 Shiel 34 (Mint 2)* . . .	1,100	2,400

		F	VF
108	Sc R As last. ⊥. *C — RIC — Shiel 35†*	1,100	2,400

		F	VF
109	Lc R VIRTVS INV AVG, emperor stg. r. hldg. globe and spear. L̄. *C 401† RIC 9 Shiel 2† (London Mint)*	1,100	2,250

CARAUSIUS

		F	VF

110 Ic VIRTVS AVG, lion walking l., thunderbolt in mouth. $\overline{RSR}$. C 390
RIC 591 Shiel 92–3   1,150   2,400

111 Mc R As last. $\overline{RSR}$. C 390† RIC 592 Shiel 91   1,150   2,400

112 Ib R VIRTVS AVGG, Jupiter stg. r. hldg. sceptre, presenting thunderbolt to Hercules stg. l. with club and lion skin. $+++$. C —
RIC 1074 Shiel 36 (Mint 2).   1,150   2,400

113 Ic R VOTO PVBLICO, MVLTIS XX IMP in wreath. $\overline{RSR}$. C 407† RIC
596 Shiel 102–3   600   2,000

114 Ic R As last, but altar not wreath. $\overline{RSR}$. C 408† RIC 595 Shiel 98–
100   600   2,000

115 Ic R VOTO [   ] NIII TIX IXX MP (sic) in altar. $\overline{RSR}$. C — RIC —
Shiel 101 irreg.   550   2,000

116 Ic R VOTVM PVBLIC, MVLTIS XX IMP in altar. $\overline{RSR}$. C 409† RIC 595/
597 Shiel 94–96   600   2,000

117 Ic R VOTVM PVBLICVM, MVLTIS XX IMP in altar. $\overline{RSR}$. C 410† RIC
597 Shiel 97   650   2,100

ALLECTUS
A.D. 293–296

Allectus had served under Carausius, most probably as his finance minister but possibly as his Praetorian Prefect. Little is known about his personality or the character of his reign which lasted for about three years after he succeeded Carausius. In 296 the newly appointed Caesar Constantius decided to mount a two-pronged attack on Britain. His subordinate Asclepiodotus arrived in Britain before him and, benefiting from a fog off the Isle of Wight, eluded the British fleet. He is then said to have sailed up Southampton Water to Clausentum where he burned his boats and marched on London. Allectus went out to meet him but his army was destroyed and he himself killed in the ensuing battle. Constantius arrived to receive the capitulation of London and restored Britain to the empire (the scene represented on the reverse of the famous Arras gold medallion). Allectus minted coins in gold and billon but produced no silver.

DIOCLETIAN
A.D. 284–305

Gaius Aurelius Valerius Diocletianus, Commander of the Imperial Guard, became emperor after Numerian was assassinated. He ruled for over twenty years, selecting Maximian as his co-Augustus in 286 and Constantius and Galerius as Caesars in 293, thereby establishing the Tetrarchy. This rule of four was designed to allow power and responsibility to be shared among two Augusti and two Caesars. However, power was to be exercised on the basis of seniority, thus allowing Diocletian final control in making decisions. In 305 Diocletian and Maximian voluntarily abdicated and their Caesars succeeded as Augusti. Two new Caesars (Maximinus and Severus) were chosen but the system soon broke down in the absence of its founder's guidance. Diocletian was also responsible for the introduction of a wide range of administrative reforms including that of the coinage. In the process of reorganizing the coinage in 294–5, Diocletian increased the number of mints and both restructured and attempted to stabilize the denominational system. He issued a silver coinage on a fineness standard in excess of 90% at a large number of mints. These coins are often referred to as 'argentei' but are more correctly termed 'siliquae'. These were struck at 96 to the Roman pound (c. 3.4g.).

Obverse legends
A.   DIOCLETIANVS PF AVG.
B.   DIOCLETIANVS AVG.
C.   DIOCLETIANVS P AVG.

Obverse busts
Unless otherwise stated all are:
a.   laureate, right.

Other varieties
b.   laureate, cuirassed, right.
c.   laureate, draped, right.
d.   laureate, drapery on left shoulder, right.

All coins are siliquae unless otherwise specified. For a discussion of fourth-century silver denominations and their names, see the Introduction.

		VF	EF
64	B R̦ F ADVENT AVGG NN, Africa stg. facing wearing elephant headdress, hldg. standard and tusk, lion at feet to l. Carthage P̄. *RIC 13a*	325	750
65a	B R̦ FEL ADVENT AVGG NN, as last. Carthage P̄. *RIC 11a* . . .	350	800
65b†	B R̦ FELIX ADVENT AVGG NN, as last. Carthage P̄. *RIC 10* . . .	350	800

411	B R̦ PROVIDENTIA AVGG, four princes sacrificing over tripod before camp gate with six turrets. Rome ⊥. *RIC 10a*	250	550

		VF	EF
412a	As last. Rome $\overline{\text{R}}$. *RIC 30a*	250	550
412b	As last. Rome $\overline{\text{A}}$. *RIC 34a*	225	500
412c	As last but camp gate has eight turrets. Siscia $\perp$. *RIC 33a* . .	250	550
427a	B ℞ PROVIDENTIAE AVGG, as last but camp gate has four turrets. Antioch $\frac{*|\text{B}}{\text{ANT}}$. *RIC 31*	300	675
427b	As last. Alexandria $\frac{|\text{B}}{\text{ALE}}$. *RIC 7a*	325	750
483†a	B ℞ VICTORIA AVGG, four princes sacrificing over tripod before camp gate with six turrets. Siscia $\overline{\text{SIS}}$. *RIC 49, 51*	250	550

		VF	EF
483†b	As last. Siscia $\overline{*\text{SIS}}$. *RIC 56*	250	550
485a	A ℞ As last, three-turreted camp gate, open, no doors. Siscia $*\overline{\text{SIS}}$. *RIC 64a*	275	625
485†b	B ℞ As last. Siscia $*\overline{\text{SIS}}$. *RIC 63a*	275	625
484a	A ℞ As last, four-turreted camp gate, open, doors thrown back. Siscia $\overline{\text{SIS}}$. *RIC 72*	275	625
484b	B ℞ As last. Siscia $*\overline{\text{SIS}}$. *RIC 68*	275	625
487a	B ℞ VICTORIA SARM, four princes sacrificing over tripod before camp gate with six turrets. Rome $\perp$. *RIC 14a*	275	625
487†b	Bd ℞ As last. Rome $\perp$. *RIC 16*	275	625
488a	B ℞ VICTORIA SARMAT, as last. Trier $\perp$. *RIC 100*	250	550
488b	As last. Trier $\overline{\text{C}}$. *RIC 104a*.	250	550
488c	As last. Trier [club]. *RIC 114a*	250	550

		VF	EF
488d	As last. Ticinum $\perp$. *RIC 12a, 16a*	225	500
488e	As last. Rome $\perp$. *RIC 19a*	250	550
488f	As last. Rome $\overline{\text{R}}$. *RIC 31a*	250	550
488g	As last. Rome $\overline{\text{A}}$. *RIC 37a*	225	500
488h	As last. Siscia $\perp$. *RIC 36*	250	550
488i	As last. Heraclea $\overline{\text{HE}}$. *RIC 2*	250	550
488j	As last. Heraclea $\overline{\text{HA}}$. *RIC 6*	250	550

		VF	EF
489a	Bb ℞ As last. Trier [club]. *RIC 119a*	300	675

		VF	EF
489†b	Bd ℞ As last. Rome ⊥. *RIC 23*	275	625
489†c	B ℞ As last, but camp gate has eight turrets. Siscia ⊥. *RIC 34a, 37a*	250	550
490†	B ℞ VICTORIA SARMATIC, as last. Siscia ⊥. *RIC 39*	275	625
490a	B ℞ VICTORIA SARMATICA, as last but camp gate has six turrets. Siscia ⊥. *RIC 41*	250	550
490b	As last. Cyzicus C̄M̄. *RIC 5a*	250	550
490c	As last but sometimes camp gate has eight turrets. Trier C̄. *RIC 108*	250	550
490d	As last but camp gate always has eight turrets. Siscia ⊥. *RIC 40*	250	550
491a	B ℞ VICTORIAE SARMATICAE, four emperors sacrificing over tripod before camp gate with six turrets. Nicomedia S̄M̄N̄Γ̄. *RIC 19a* .	250	550
491b	As last. Heraclea H̄Ā. *RIC 10a*	250	550
491c	As last. Antioch $\frac{*|B}{ANT}$. *RIC 32*	325	750
491d	As last. Alexandria $\frac{|B}{ALE}$. *RIC 8*	325	750
492a	B ℞ As last, four turreted camp gate arch open, doors thrown back. Nicomedia S̄M̄N̄Γ̄. *RIC 22a*	250	550

		VF	EF
492b	As last, but star above gate Nicomedia. S̄M̄N̄Γ̄. *RIC 25a* . .	225	500
516†a	B ℞ VIRTVS MILITVM, four princes sacrificing over tripod before camp gate with six turrets. Trier ⊥. *RIC 102a*	225	500

		VF	EF
516†b	As last. Trier C̄. *RIC 109a*.	200	450
516†c	As last. Trier [club]. *RIC 116a, 128*	225	500
516†d	As last. Ticinum ⊥. *RIC 14a, 18a*	225	500

		VF	EF
516†e	As last. Rome ⊥. *RIC 27a*	200	450
516†f	As last. Rome R̄. *RIC 32a*	200	450
516†g	As last. Rome Ā. *RIC 40a*	200	450
516†h	As last. Siscia S̄ĪS̄. *RIC 52a*	250	550

	VF	EF
516†i As last. Siscia $\overline{\text{*SIS}}$. *RIC 60a*	250	550
516†j Bb Ɍ As last. Trier $\boxed{\text{club}}$. *RIC 123*.	300	675
516†k Bc Ɍ As last. Trier $\boxed{\text{club}}$. *RIC 122*.	300	675
516†l B Ɍ As last but camp gate has seven turrets. Siscia $\overline{\text{*SIS}}$. *RIC 59*	250	550
516†mB Ɍ As last but camp gate has eight turrets. Siscia ⊥. *RIC 32a, 43a, 46a*	200	450
520a B Ɍ As last, three-turreted camp gate, arch open, no doors. SIS $\overline{\text{*SIS}}$. *RIC 66a*	275	625
520b As last. Serdica $\overline{\text{·SM·SDA·}}$. *RIC 1a*	300	675
520c As last. Thessalonica $\overline{\text{TS·A·}}$. *RIC 13a*	275	625
520d As last. Thessalonica $\overline{\text{·T·S·A·}}$. *RIC 15a*	275	625
520e As last. Thessalonica $\overline{\text{TS·A·}}$. *RIC 17a*	275	625
520f As last. Antioch $\frac{\text{H}}{\text{ANT}}$. *RIC 35a*	275	625
520g As last. Antioch $\overline{\text{*ANTH}}$. *RIC 37a*	275	625
520h As last. Antioch $\overline{\text{ANT·H}}$. *RIC 39a*	275	625
520i As last. Antioch $\overline{\text{*ANTH*}}$. *RIC 42a*	275	625
520j As last. Alexandria $\frac{|\text{Γ}}{\text{ALE}}$. *RIC 9a*	300	675
521a B Ɍ As last, four-turreted camp gate, open, doors thrown back, star above arch. Thessalonica $\overline{\text{TSA}}$. *RIC 6*.	300	675
521b As last. Thessalonica $\overline{\text{TS·A·}}$. *RIC 11a*	300	675
545†a A Ɍ VOT XX SIC XXX in four lines in laurel wreath. Trier ⊥. *RIC 135* **half siliqua**.	450	1,000
545†b C Ɍ As last. Trier ⊥. *RIC 136* **half siliqua**	450	1,000
548a B Ɍ XCVI in wreath. Ticinum $\underline{\text{T}}$. *RIC 20a*	275	625
548b As last. Aquileia AQ. *RIC 16a*	275	625

| **548c** As last. Rome ⊥. $\overline{RIC}$ *15a (Carthage)* | 275 | 625 |

MAXIMIAN
A.D. 286–305

Maximian (Marcus Aurelius Valerius Maximianus Herculius) was probably born in about A.D. 250 in the Balkans, although neither the exact date nor place of his birth is known. His earlier career is also obscure but Diocletian raised him to the rank of Caesar in 284 and Augustus in 286 with responsibility for the Western half of the empire. Although technically equal to Diocletian in power Maximian was in fact a junior colleague. The relative status of the two rulers is reflected in their added names. Diocletian was Jovius and Maximian Herculius. Maximian made his headquarters in Gaul where he successfully restored order within the province and waged war against the Franks on the frontier. He failed in his attempt to quell the usurpation of Carausius in Britain since the fleet he had specially built to attack the rebel emperor was destroyed in 289 as the result of severe storms. He had two children by his wife Eutropia: Fausta, who became the wife of Constantine I, and Maxentius who proclaimed himself emperor in Rome in 306. His official reign came to an end in 305 when he voluntarily abdicated together with Diocletian. Maximian emerged from retirement in 307 after Maxentius made his bid for power and was instrumental in forging a short-lived alliance between Maxentius and Constantine. Returning to Rome, Maximian subsequently quarrelled with Maxentius and fled to Constantine in Gaul. Unable to refrain from politics, he tried to organize a rebellion against Constantine in 310 which the latter immediately quelled and forced Maximian to commit suicide.

Obverse legends
A. MAXIMIANVS AVG.
B. MAXIMIANVS PF AVG.
C. IMP MAXIMIANVS AVG.
D. IMP MAXIMIANVS PF AVG.
E. MAXIMIANVS SEN PF AVG.
F. IMP MAXIMIANVS PFS AVG.

Obverse busts
Unless otherwise stated all are:
a. laureate, right.
Other varieties
b. laureate, cuirassed, right.
c. laureate, cuirassed, left.

92 A R F ADVENT AVGG NN, Africa stg. facing wearing elephant-skin headdress, hldg. standard, bull at feet to l. Carthage S̄. *RIC 13b.*	325	750
91 A R FEL ADVENT AVGG NN, as last. Carthage S̄. *RIC 11b* . .	350	800
486a A R PROVIDENTIA AVGG, four princes sacrificing over tripod before camp gate with six turrets. Rome ⊥. *RIC 10b*	250	550

486b As last. Rome R̄. *RIC 30b*	250	550
486c As last. Rome Ā. *RIC 34b*	250	550

		VF	EF
486d	As last. Siscia ⊥. *RIC 33b* . .	250	550
486†e	B ℞ As last. Rome ⊥. *RIC 12*	250	550

		VF	EF
486†f	A ℞ PROVIDENTIAE AVGG, as last but camp gate often has four turrets. Alexandria $\frac{\triangle|}{ALE}$. *RIC 7b* . .	325	750
547	A ℞ VICTORIA AVGG, four turreted camp gate open, doors thrown back. Siscia *SIS. *RIC —* . .	275	625
547†a	A ℞ As last, four princes sacrificing before camp gate with six turrets. Siscia $\overline{SIS}$. *RIC 50* .	250	550
547†b	As last. Siscia *SIS. *RIC 55* .	250	550
547†c	A ℞ As last, three-turreted camp gate, arch open, no doors. Siscia *SIS. *RIC 63b*.	275	625
547†d	B ℞ As last. Siscia *SIS. *RIC 64b* .	275	625
548A	A ℞ VICTORIA SARM, four princes sacrificing before camp gate with six turrets — Rome ⊥. *RIC 14b*	275	625
548B	A ℞ VICTORIA SARMA, as last. Rome ⊥. *RIC 17* . .	275	625
548a	A ℞ VICTORIA SARMAT, as last. Trier $\overline{C}$. *RIC 104b* .	250	550
548b	As last. Trier ⊥. *RIC —*	250	550

		VF	EF
548c	As last. Trier [club]. *RIC 114b*	250	550
548d	As last. Ticinum ⊥. *RIC 12b, 16b*. .	225	550
548e	As last. Rome ⊥. *RIC 19b* . .	250	550
548f	As last. Rome $\overline{R}$. *RIC 31b* . .	250	550
548g	As last. Rome $\overline{A}$. *RIC 37b* . .	225	500

		VF	EF
549	Ab ℞ As last. Trier [club]. *RIC 119b*	300	675
550a	B ℞ As last. Rome ⊥. *RIC 20*	250	550
550b	A ℞ As last but gate has eight turrets. Siscia ⊥. *RIC 34b, 37b*. .	250	550
551a	A ℞ VICTORIA SARMATICA, four princes sacrificing over tripod before camp gate with six or seven turrets. Heraclea $\overline{HE}$. *RIC 3*	250	550
551b	As last. Heraclea $\overline{HA}$. *RIC 7*. .	250	550

		VF	EF
551c	As last. Cyzicus $\overline{\text{CM}}$. *RIC 5b*	250	550
552a	A Ŗ VICTORIAE SARMATICAE, as last. Heraclea $\overline{\text{HA}}$. *RIC 10b*	250	550
552b	As last, but gate has six turrets. Nicomedia $\overline{\text{SMNΓ}}$. *RIC 19b*	275	625
553a	A Ŗ As last, four-turreted camp gate, open, doors thrown back. Nicomedia $\overline{\text{SMNΓ}}$. *RIC 22b*.	275	625
553b	As last, but star above gate. Thessalonica $\overline{\text{TS·A·}}$. *RIC —*.	275	625

		VF	EF
553c	As last. Nicomedia $\overline{\text{SMNΓ}}$. *RIC 25b*	250	550
622a	A Ŗ VIRTVS MILITVM, four princes sacrificing before camp gate with six turrets. Trier ⊥. *RIC 102b*.	225	500
622b	As last. Trier $\overline{\text{C}}$. *RIC 109b*.	200	450
622c	As last. Trier [club]. *RIC 116b*	225	500
622d	As last. Ticinum ⊥. *RIC 14b, 18b*.	225	500
622e	As last. Rome ⊥. *RIC 27b*	225	500
622f	As last. Rome $\overline{\text{R}}$. *RIC 32b*	225	500

		VF	EF
622g	As last. Rome $\overline{\text{A}}$. *RIC 40b*	200	450
622h	As last. Siscia $\overline{\text{SIS}}$. *RIC 52b*.	225	500
623	Ab Ŗ As last. Trier [club]. *RIC 123b*	300	675
624	Ac Ŗ As last. Trier [club]. *RIC 125*.	325	750
625a	C Ŗ As last. Trier ⊥. *RIC 129*	225	500
625b	As last. Trier $\overline{\text{C}}$. *RIC 130*	225	500
625†c	B Ŗ As last. Trier ⊥. *RIC 131*	225	500
625†d	As last. Rome ⊥. *RIC 28*	225	500
625†e	As last. Rome $\overline{\text{A}}$. *RIC 41*	225	500

		VF	EF
625†f	As last but gate has eight turrets. Siscia ⊥. *RIC 32b, 43b, 46b*.	200	450
627a	A Ŗ As last, three-turreted camp gate, arch open, no doors. Serdica ·SM·SDA·. *RIC 16*.	300	675
627b	As last. Aquileia $\overline{\text{AQP}}$. *RIC 75*	450	1,000
627c	As last. Rome RS. *RIC 193*.	400	900
627d	As last. Siscia *$\overline{\text{SIS}}$. *RIC 66b*	275	625

		VF	EF
627e	As last. Thessalonica $\overline{TS\cdot A\cdot}$. *RIC 13b*	275	625
627f	As last. Thessalonica $\cdot T\cdot S\cdot A\cdot$. *RIC 15b*	275	625
627g	As last. Thessalonica. $\cdot TS\cdot A\cdot$. *RIC 17b*	275	625
627h	As last. Antioch $\frac{\|H}{ANT}$. *RIC 35b*	275	625
627i	As last. Antioch *$\overline{ANTH}$. *RIC 37b*	275	625
627j	As last. Antioch $\overline{ANT\cdot H}$. *RIC 39b*	275	625
627k	As last. Antioch *ANTH*. *RIC 42b*	275	625
627l	As last. Alexandria $\frac{\|B}{ALE}$. *RIC 9b*	300	675
627m	As last. Alexandria $\frac{\|A}{ALE}$. *RIC 10b*	300	675
629	D Ʀ As last. Rome $\overline{RS}$. *RIC 192*	300	675

		VF	EF
631	B Ʀ As last but gate open, doors thrown back. Trier $\overline{PTR}$. *RIC 635*	400	900
631†a	A Ʀ As last. Siscia *$\overline{SIS}$. *RIC 70*	275	625
631†b	E Ʀ As last. Rome $\overline{RS}$. *RIC 157*	400	900
631†c	A Ʀ As last, but star above gate. Thessalonica $\overline{TS\cdot A\cdot}$. *RIC 11b* .	300	675
632	B Ʀ As last, but four-turreted camp gate. Trier $\overline{PTR}$. *RIC 637* .	400	900
633	Bb Ʀ As last. Trier $\overline{TR}$. *RIC 762* **half siliqua**	325	750
634	Fb Ʀ As last. Trier $\overline{TR}$. *RIC 761* **half siliqua**	325	750
636	E Ʀ As last. Rome $\overline{RS}$. *RIC 156*	400	900
689A	B Ʀ VOT XX SIC XXX in four lines in laurel wreath. Trier $\perp$. *RIC 13b* **half siliqua** . .		
697	A Ʀ XCVI in wreath. Aquileia $\underline{AQ}$. *RIC 16b*	275	625
698	As last. Ticinum $\underline{\quad T\quad}$. *RIC 20b*	275	625
698†a	As last. Rome $\perp$. $\overline{RIC\ 15b}$ *(Carthage)*	275	625
698†b	D As last. Rome $\underline{PR}$. *RIC* —.	325	750

ACHILLEUS
A.D. 297

Aurelius Achilleus, a corrector *in Egypt under the regime of Domitianus is credited by all of the literary sources as the leader of the revolt in 297 against the Tetrarchy. In fact the rebellion was engineered by Domitianus, as is attested by both documentary evidence and the coinage which he minted in his own name. No coins are known to have been minted for Achilleus who may have taken over the leadership of the revolt in its final stages following the death of Domitius.*

DOMITIUS DOMITIANUS
A.D. 297

Lucius Domitius Domitianus organized a rebellion against the Tetrarchy in Egypt in 297 which was suppressed by Diocletian after a siege lasting several months. He issued coinage in his name on both the new imperial denominational system and Alexandrian tetradrachms, but he produced no silver.

CONSTANTIUS I
CAESAR A.D. 293–305
AUGUSTUS A.D. 305–306

Constantius (M. Flavius Valerius Constantius), like the other members of the Tetrarchy, was born in the Balkans probably about A.D. *250. He pursued a military career and later served as governor of Dalmatia. By 288 he was Maximian's Praetorian Prefect in Gaul. He married twice and Constantine I was the issue of his first marriage with Helena. His second wife was Theodora, Maximian's daughter, and they had six children. One of Constantius' first acts as Caesar was the overthrow of Carausius, whom he defeated in a campaign at Boulogne which resulted in the latter's murder. In 296 Constantius organized the successful invasion of Britain during which Allectus was defeated and killed in battle and Britain was restored to the empire. In 305 he became Augustus after the voluntary abdications of Diocletian and Maximian, but his reign was a brief one. Whilst campaigning against the Picts in the north of Britain he became seriously ill and died at York in July 306, having previously summoned his son Constantine to his side. Receptive to his father's wishes the troops acclaimed Constantine emperor immediately following Constantius' death.*

Obverse legends
As Caesar
A. CONSTANTIVS CAES.
B. CONSTANTIVS CAESAR.
C. CONSTANTIVS NC.
D. CONSTANTIVS NOB C.
E. DN CONSTANTIO NOB C.

As Augustus
F. CONSTANTIVS AVG.

Obverse busts
Unless otherwise stated all are:
a. laureate right.
Other varieties:
b. laureate, left.
c. laureate, cuirassed, right.
d. laureate, cuirassed, left.

All coins are siliquae unless otherwise specified. For a discussion of fourth-century silver denominations and their names, see the Introduction.

CAESAR

		VF	EF
33	A Ŗ ꜰ ᴀᴅᴠᴇɴᴛ ᴀᴠɢɢ ɴɴ, Africa stg. facing wearing elephant headdress, hldg. standard and tusk, lion at feet to l. Carthage T̄. *RIC 14a*	350	800
34	A Ŗ ꜰᴇʟ ᴀᴅᴠᴇɴᴛ ᴀᴠɢɢ ɴɴ, as last Carthage. T̄ *RIC 12a*. . . .	375	850

240†a	B Ŗ ᴘʀᴏᴠɪᴅᴇɴᴛɪᴀᴇ ᴀᴠɢɢ, four-turreted camp gate surmounted by eagles, arch open, doors thrown back. Nicomedia S̄M̄N̄Γ̄. *RIC 21*.	300	675

240†b	As last, but no eagles. Nicomedia S̄M̄N̄Γ̄. *RIC 24*	300	675
241a	A Ŗ ᴘʀᴏᴠɪᴅᴇɴᴛɪᴀ ᴀᴠɢɢ four princes sacrificing over tripod before camp gate with six turrets. Rome ⊥. *RIC 11a*. . . .	275	625
241b	As last. Rome Ā. *RIC 35a*	275	625
241†c	E Ŗ As last. Rome ⊥. *RIC 13*	275	625
242a	B Ŗ As last but camp gate may have seven turrets. Heraclea H̄Ē. *RIC 1*.	275	625

242b	As last. Heraclea H̄Ā. *RIC 5*.	275	625

242c	As last but gate always has six turrets. Cyzicus C̄M̄. *RIC 4* . .	275	625
243	D Ŗ As last. Siscia *S̄ĪS̄. *RIC 54a*	275	625
245Aa	B Ŗ ᴘʀᴏᴠɪᴅᴇɴᴛɪᴀᴇ ᴀᴠɢɢ, as last. Nicomedia S̄M̄N̄Γ̄. *RIC 18*. .	275	625
245Ab	As last but camp gate may have seven turrets. Heraclea H̄Ā. *RIC 9*	275	625
283†	D Ŗ ᴠɪᴄᴛᴏʀɪᴀ ᴀᴠɢɢ, four princes sacrificing before camp gate with six turrets. Siscia *S̄ĪS̄. *RIC 57a*	275	625
284†a	D Ŗ As last, four-turreted camp gate, open, doors thrown back. Siscia S̄ĪS̄. *RIC 73*	300	675
284†b	D Ŗ As last, three-turreted camp gate, arch open, no doors. Siscia *S̄ĪS̄. *RIC 65a*	300	675

		VF	EF
286Aa	A ℞ VICTORIA SARM, four princes sacrificing over tripod before camp gate with six turrets. Rome ⊥. *RIC 15*	300	675
286Ab	As last. Rome Ā. *RIC 36a*	300	675
286B	A ℞ VICTORIA SARMA, as last. Rome ⊥. *RIC 18*	300	675
286a	B ℞ VICTORIA SARMAT, as last. Ticinum ⊥. *RIC 13a, 17a*	250	550
286b	As last. Rome ⊥. *RIC 21.*	275	625

		VF	EF
286†c	A ℞ As last. Rome ⊥. *RIC 22a*	275	625
286†d	As last. Rome Ā. *RIC 38a*	250	550
287a	Cc ℞ As last. Trier C̄. *RIC 107*	325	750
287b	As last. Trier [club]. *RIC 120a*	325	750
287†c	C ℞ As last. Trier C̄. *RIC 106a*	250	550
287†d	As last. Trier [club]. *RIC 115a, 127*	275	625
288	D ℞ As last. Trier C̄. *RIC 105a*	250	550
289a	As last Trier. ⊥. *RIC 101*	275	625
289†b	B ℞ As last, but camp gate has eight turrets. Siscia ⊥. *RIC 35a, 38a*	275	625
289†c	A ℞ As last, three-turreted gateway, arch open, no doors. Rome $\frac{R\|F}{\Gamma}$. *RIC 43*	300	675
291†a	E ℞ VICTORIA SARMATI, four princes sacrificing over tripod before camp gate with six turrets. Rome ⊥. *RIC 25*	275	625
291†b	A ℞ As last. Rome ⊥. *RIC 24*	275	625
291A	B ℞ VICTORIA SARMATICA, as last. Siscia ⊥. *RIC 42*	275	625
291B	B ℞ VICTORIAE SARMATICAE, as last but camp gate has four turrets. Antioch $\frac{*\|B}{\text{ANT}}$. *RIC 33a*	300	675

		VF	EF
308	Cc ℞ VIRTVS MILITVM, four princes sacrificing over tripod before camp gate with six turrets. Trier [club]. *RIC 124a*	275	625
309a	C ℞ As last. Trier ⊥. *RIC 132*	250	550
309b	As last. Trier C̄. *RIC 112*	250	550

		VF	EF
309c	As last. Trier [club]. *RIC 117a*	250	550

		VF	EF
310	Cd ℞ As last. Trier [club]. *RIC 126.*	300	675
311a	Cb ℞ As last. Trier C̄. *RIC 113*	300	675
311b	As last. Trier [club]. *RIC 118*	300	675
312a	D ℞ As last. Trier ⊥. *RIC 103a*	250	550
312b	As last. Trier C̄. *RIC 110a.*	225	500
313	Db ℞ As last. Trier C̄. *RIC 111a*	300	675
314†a	A ℞ As last. Rome ⊥. *RIC 29a*	225	500
314†b	As last. Rome Ā. *RIC 42a*	225	500

		VF	EF
315†a	B ℞ As last. Ticinum ⊥. *RIC 15a, 19a.*	250	550
315†b	As last. Rome R̄. *RIC 33.*	250	550

		VF	EF
315†c	B ℞ As last but gate has eight turrets. Siscia ⊥. *44a, 47a.*	225	500
318a	B ℞ As last, three turreted camp gate, arch open, no doors. Antioch $\frac{*|A}{ANT}$. *RIC 34a*	300	675
318b	As last. Antioch $\frac{|H}{ANT}$. *RIC 36*	300	675

		VF	EF
318c	As last. Antioch *ANTH̄. *RIC 38a*	300	675
318d	As last. Antioch ĀN̄T·H. *RIC 40a*	300	675
318e	As last. Antioch *ANT·. *RIC 41a.*	300	675
318f	As last. Antioch *ANTH*. *RICH 43a*	300	675
318g	As last. Alexandria $\frac{|B}{ALE}$. *RIC 71*	325	750
319a	A ℞ As last. Rome $\frac{R|F}{\Gamma}$. *RIC 44a*	300	675
319b	As last. Alexandria $\frac{A|}{ALE}$. *RIC 12*	325	750
319c	As last. Alexandria ĀLE. *RIC 13a*	325	750
320a	D ℞ As last. Siscia *S̄IS. *RIC 67a*	300	675
320b	As last. Serdica ·SM·SDA·. *RIC 2a*	325	750
320c	As last. Thessalonica T̄S·Ā. *RIC 14a*	300	675
320d	As last. Thessalonica ·T·S·A·. *RIC 16a.*	300	675

	VF	EF
321a D Ŗ As last, four-turreted camp gate, open, doors thrown back.		
Siscia *SIS. *RIC 71a*.	300	675
321†b D Ŗ As last but star above arch. Thessalonica T̄S̄Ā. *RIC 7*	300	675
321†c As last. Thessalonica T̄S·Ā·. *RIC 12a*	300	675
334 C Ŗ VOT· X SIC XX in wreath. Trier ⊥. *RIC 134* **half siliqua**	450	1,000

| **345** A Ŗ XCVI in wreath. Rome ⊥. *RIC 16a (Carthage)* | 300 | 675 |

| **346a** B Ŗ As last. Ticinum T. *RIC 21a* | 300 | 675 |
| **346b** As last. Aquileia AQ. *RIC 17a* | 300 | 675 |

AUGUSTUS
304A F Ŗ VIRTVS AVGG, three-turreted camp gate, arch open, no doors.
Serdica ·SM·SDA· *RIC 11a*   650 | 1,500

GALERIUS
CAESAR A.D. 293–305
AUGUSTUS A.D. 305–311

Little is known of the early career of Galerius (C Galerius Valerius Maximianus) apart from the facts that he was born in the Balkans and pursued a military career. He was of humble origin and it is related that he had been a shepherd. In 293 he was made Caesar together with Constantius and became Diocletian's junior colleague. He married Diocletian's daughter Galeria Valeria, and their only recorded child was a daughter. In 298 he waged a successful campaign against the Persians and then returned to the Balkans where he commanded the frontier. He became Augustus in 305 after the abdications of Diocletian and Maximian. Despite heroic efforts he was unable to maintain the tetrarchic system in the face of Constantine's bid for power in Britain and Gaul and the usurpation of Maxentius in Rome. He was a vigorous persecutor of the Christians from 303, when Diocletian issued his edict, until 311 when, on his death bed, he abandoned this policy. During his reign as Augustus he minted very little silver in his own territory and very little was produced elsewhere in his name.

Obverse legends
As Caesar
A. MAXIMIANVS CAES.
B. MAXIMIANVS CAESAR.
C. MAXIMIANVS NC.
D. MAXIMIANVS NOB C.

As Augustus
E. MAXIMIANVS AVG.
F. MAXIMIANVS PF AVG.
G. IMP MAXIMIANVS PF AVG.

Obverse busts
Unless otherwise stated all are:
a. laureate, right.
Other varieties:
b. laureate, left.
c. laureate, cuirassed, right.
d. laureate, drapery on left shoulder, right.

All coins are siliquae unless otherwise stated. For a discussion of fourth-century silver denominations and their names, see the Introduction.

CAESAR

		VF	EF
22A	D R CONCORDIA MILITVM, four turreted camp gate, arch open, doors thrown back, star above arch. Thessalonica ·TS·A·. *RIC 8*	325	750

| 26 | A R F ADVENT AVGG NN, Africa stg. facing wearing elephant skin headdress, hldg. standard and tusk, lion at feet to l. Carthage T̅. *RIC 14b* . . . . | 350 | 800 |

27	A R FEL ADVENT AVGG NN, as last. Carthage T̅. *RIC 12b* . . .	350	800
183a	A R PROVIDENTIA AVGG, four princes sacrificing over tripod before camp gate with six turrets. Rome ⊥. *RIC 11b*	275	625
183b	As last. Rome A̅. *RIC 35b*	275	625

	VF	EF
183†c D R As last. Siscia *SIS. *RIC 54b* .	275	625

183†d D R As last, four-turreted camp gate, arch open, star above, doors
thrown back. Thessalonica ·TS·A·. *RIC 9* . . . . 300 / 675

203A D R VICTORIA AVGG, four princes sacrificing over tripod before
camp gate with six turrets. Siscia *SIS. *RIC 57b* . . . . 275 / 625

203†a D R As last, four-turreted camp gate, open, doors thrown back.
Siscia *SIS. *RIC 69* . . . . 300 / 675

203†b As last. Siscia SIS. *RIC* — . . . . 300 / 675

203†c D R As last but three-turreted camp gate arch open, no doors.
Siscia *SIS. *RIC 65b* . . . . 300 / 675

206A A R VICTORIA SARM, four princes sacrificing over tripod before
camp gate with six turrets. Rome A. *RIC 36b* . . . . 300 / 675

206a C R VICTORIA SARMAT, as last. Trier C. *RIC 106b* . . . 275 / 625

206b As last. Trier [club]. *Ric 115b* . . . . 275 / 625

206†c Cc R As last. Trier [club]. *RIC 120b* . . . . . . 325 / 750

207 D R As last. Trier C. *RIC 105b* . . . . 275 / 625

208a A R As last. Rome ⊥. *RIC 38b* . . . . 250 / 550

208b As last. Rome A. *RIC 38b* . . . . 250 / 550

208c B R As last. Ticinum ⊥. *RIC 13b, 17b* . . . . . 250 / 550

208†d Ad R As last. Rome ⊥. *RIC 39* . . . . 300 / 675

208†e B R As last but gate has eight turrets. Siscia ⊥. *RIC 35b, 38b*. . 275 / 625

208†f D R As last. Siscia *SIS. *RIC 58* . . . . 275 / 625

		VF	EF
208†g	A R VICTORIA SARMATICA, as last but gate has six turrets. Rome ⊥. *RIC 26*	275	625
209	B R VICTORIAE SARMATICAE, as last but gate has four turrets. Antioch $\frac{*\|B}{ANT}$. *RIC 33b*	300	675
209†	D R As last, four-turreted camp gate, open, star above, doors thrown back. Thessalonica T̄S·Ā·. *RIC 10*	300	675

		VF	EF
216a	D R VIRTVS MILITVM, four princes sacrificing before camp gate with six turrets. Trier ⊥. *RIC 103b*	250	550
216b	As last. Trier C̄. *RIC 110b*	225	500
216c	As last. Siscia *S̄ĪS̄. *RIC 61, 62*	275	625
216†d	Db R As last. Trier ⊥. *RIC 111b*	300	675
217	C R As last. Trier [club]. *RIC 117b*	225	500
218	Cc R As last. Trier [club]. *RIC 124b*	275	625
218†	Cd R As last. Trier [club]. *RIC 121, 133*	275	625
219a	A R As last. Rome ⊥. *RIC 29b*	225	500
219b	As last. Rome Ā. *RIC 42b*	225	500
220a	B R As last. Ticinum ⊥. *RIC 15b, 19b*	250	550
220b	As last. Siscia ⊥. *RIC 45*	250	550
220c	As last. Siscia S̄ĪS̄. *RIC 53*	275	625
220d	As last. Heraclea H̄Ē. *RIC 4*	275	625
220e	As last. Heraclea H̄Ā. *RIC 8*	275	625
220f	As last. Cyzicus C̄M̄. *RIC 6*	275	625
220†g	As last, but gate has eight turrets. Siscia ⊥. *RIC 44b, 47b, 48* . .	225	500
223a	D R As last, three-turreted camp gate, arch open, no doors. Siscia *S̄ĪS̄. *RIC 67b*	300	675
223b	As last. Serdica ·S̄M̄·S̄D̄Ā·. *RIC 2b*	325	750
223c	As last. Thessalonica T̄S·Ā·. *RIC 14b*	300	675
223d	As last. Thessalonica ·T̄·S̄·Ā·. *RIC 16b*	300	675
223e	As last. Thessalonica ·T̄S·Ā·. *RIC 18*	300	675
224a	A R As last. Rome $\frac{R\|F}{I}$. *RIC 44b*	300	675
224b	As last. Alexandria ĀL̄Ē. *RIC 13b*	325	750

		VF	EF
224c	As last. Alexandria $\frac{\|Γ}{ALE}$. *RIC 13b*	325	750
225a	B R As last. Antioch $\frac{*\|H}{ANT}$. *RIC 34b*	300	675
225b	As last. Antioch *ĀN̄T̄H̄. *RIC 38b*	300	675
225c	As last. Antioch ĀN̄T̄·H̄. *RIC 40b*	300	675

		VF	EF
225d	As last. Antioch $\overline{\text{*ANT}}$. *RIC 41b*	300	675
225e	As last. Antioch $\overline{\text{*ANT*}}$. *RIC 43b*	300	675
227	D ℞ As last, four-turreted ca<u>mp gat</u>e, open, doors thrown back, star above arch. Thessalonica $\overline{\text{TS·A·}}$. *RIC 12b*	300	675
227†a	D ℞ As last, but no star above arch. Siscia $\overline{\text{*SIS}}$. *RIC 71b* . .	300	675
234Aa	B ℞ VIRTVTI MILITVM, four princes sacrificing before camp gate with six (or seven) turrets. Heraclea $\overline{\text{HA}}$. *RIC 11*	275	625
234Ab	As last but gate has six turrets. Nicomedia $\overline{\text{SMN}\Gamma}$. *RIC 20* . .	275	625

234a	B ℞ As last, four-turreted camp gate <u>with ea</u>gles on the turrets, open, doors thrown back. Nicomedia $\overline{\text{SMN}\Gamma}$. *RIC 23*	300	675
234b	As last but no eagles, star above gate. Nicomedia $\overline{\text{SMN}\Gamma}$. *RIC 26*	300	675

249a	A ℞ XCVI in wreath. Rome $\perp$. *RIC 16b (Carthage)*	275	625
249b	As last. Ticinum $\underline{\text{T}}$, *RIC 22*	300	675
250a	B ℞ As last. $\underline{\text{T}}$. *RIC 21b*	300	675
250b	As last. $\underline{\text{AQ}}$. *RIC 17b*	300	675

AUGUSTUS

228†a	E ℞ VIRTVS MILITVM, three-turreted camp gate arch open, no doors. Serdica $\overline{\text{·SM·SDA·}}$. *RIC 11b*.	550	1,250
228†b	As last Antioch. $\overline{\text{*ANTH*}}$. *RIC —, c.f. p. 623, n.1* . .	550	1,250

228†c	G ℞ As last, four-turreted camp gate, arch open, no doors. Trier $\overline{\text{TR}}$. *RIC 757* **half siliqua**.	325	750

GALERIA VALERIA

Galeria Valeria was the daughter of Diocletian and became the wife of Galerius when he was made Caesar in 293. After the death of Galerius in 311 she fled from his successor, Licinius I, to Maximinus II, who seized her property when she refused to marry him. After Maximinus' defeat by Licinius and his subsequent death. Valeria was also condemned to die. She eluded capture for fifteen months but was finally arrested and executed in 315. No silver coins were minted in her name.

SEVERUS II
CAESAR A.D. 305–306
AUGUSTUS A.D. 306–307

Severus (Flavius Valerius Severus) was born in the Balkans but almost nothing is known of his life before 305 other than that he had pursued a military career and was a friend of Galerius. He was created Caesar upon the abdications of Diocletian and Maximian, and Galerius made him Augustus after the death of Constantius I in 306. Constantius' son, Constantine, was made Caesar in Severus' place, thereby disposing temporarily of his claim to be recognized as Augustus. In 307 Severus attempted to deal with the usurpation of Maxentius in Rome. Severus, however, was unsuccessful, falling victim to the machinations of Maxentius who bribed many of his troops into deserting during his siege of Rome. Forced to retreat, he was cut off by Maximian who drove him into Ravenna where he surrendered. He was taken to Rome where he was either executed or compelled to commit suicide. He minted no silver in his own name and the only known pieces were produced at Serdica, which was under the control of Galerius.

Obverse legend
A.   SEVERVS AVG.

Obverse bust
a.   laureate, right.

		VF	EF
77A Aa ℞ VIRTVS MILITVM, three-turreted camp gate, arch open, no doors. Serdica ·SM·SDA·. *RIC 21*		2,000	4,500

MAXIMINUS II
CAESAR A.D. 305–308
AUGUSTUS A.D. 310–313

C. Galerius Valerius Maximinus was the son of Galerius' sister and, although called Daia in the ancient sources, this name never formed part of his official title. He was probably born about 270 although a later date has been argued by some scholars. He followed a military career rising through the ranks to become a 'protector' and later a 'tribunus'. He was made Caesar by Diocletian on his abdication in 305 and was the junior colleague of Galerius. After the Conference at Carnuntum in 308 he was given the title of filius augustorum, together with Constantine I, while Licinius I was elevated to the rank of Augustus. Incensed at this slight he made no objection to being acclaimed Augustus by his troops and this 'fait accompli' was recognized by Galerius. He was a vigorous persecutor of the Christians. Maximinus met his end in 313 when he attempted to move against Licinius, who was allied with Constantine; he was defeated near Adrianople and fled to Asia Minor where he killed himself.

Obverse legends

As Caesar
A. MAXIMINVS NOB C.
B. MAXIMINVS NOB CAES.

As Augustus
C. IMP MAXIMINVS AVG.

Obverse busts
a. laureate, right.
b. laureate, cuirassed right.
c. radiate, draped, cuirassed, right hand raised, left hand holding globe, left.

All coins are siliquae unless otherwise specified. For a discussion of fourth-century silver denominations and their names, see the Introduction.

CAESAR

		VF	EF
206	A ℞ VIRTVS MILITVM, three-turreted camp gate, arch open, no doors. Serdica ·SM·SDA·. *RIC 22*	1,500	3,500
208	Bb ℞ VIRTVS MILITVM, as last but gate has four turrets. Trier T̄R. *RIC 763* **half siliqua**	550	1,250

AUGUSTUS

174	Cc SOLI INVICTO COMITI, Sol stg. facing in quadriga hldg. globe and whip. Trier P̄TR. *RIC 826 billon*	150	350

MAXENTIUS
A.D. 306–312

M. Valerius Maxentius, the son of Maximian, was born about 283. He married a daughter of Galerius (Valeria Maximilla) and had a son, Valerius Romulus, who is attested posthumously on the coinage. Maxentius came to power in Rome late in 306 when he was acclaimed emperor. Initially he used the title princeps invictus *on his coins rather than Augustus. In 307 he formed a brief alliance with Constantine I, who married his sister Fausta. He recognized his father Maximian (who had emerged from retirement), as Augustus on his coinage and with his help defeated Severus who had invaded Italy to put down the rebellion. Maxentius never received official recognition of his status and after the Conference at Carnuntum in 308, his days were clearly numbered. In 312 Constantine I, who had formed an alliance with Licinius, decided to move on Italy and within a few months he had reached Rome. On 28 October 312 Maxentius was decisively defeated at the Battle of the Milvian Bridge and was killed, his body later being recovered from the Tiber. He minted some silver, most of it in the earlier part of his reign.*

Obverse legends
A. MAXENTIVS PF AVG.
B. MAXENTIVS PRINC INVICT.
C. IMP MAXENTIVS PF AVG.

Obverse busts
Unless otherwise stated all are:
a. laureate right.
Other variety:
b. facing bare head, draped.

All coins are siliquae

		VF	EF
49	A R CONSERVATOR VRBIS SVAE, Rome seated facing in hexastyle temple, hldg. globe and sceptre, shield at side. Rome R̄S̄. *RIC 187*	1,250	2,800
65	C R FELIX PROCESS CONSVLAT AVG N, emperor stg. facing, hldg. globe and baton. Rome R̄S̄. *RIC 188*	2,000	4,500
92a	A R MARTI PROPAG IMP AVG N, Mars stg. r. hldg. spear, extending hand to stg. woman, between them Wolf and Twins r. Rome R̄S̄. *RIC 189*	1,500	3,500

92b	As last but Wolf l. Ostia M̄OSTB. *RIC 11*	1,500	3,500
92c	As last. Ostia P̄OSTΔ. *RIC 11*	1,500	3,500
92A	A R MARTI PROPAGATORI AVG N, Mars stg. r. handing Victory on globe to emperor in military dress stg. l. Ostia P̄OSTΔ RIC 12 .	1,750	4,000

	VF	EF
106†a A ℞ TEMPORVM FELICITAS AVG N, Wolf and Twins right. Rome $\overline{RS}$.		
RIC 190	1,500	3,500
106†b Ab ℞ As last. Rome $\overline{RS}$. *RIC 191.*	2,500	5,500

	VF	EF
107† A ℞ As last, but Wolf left. Ostia $\overline{MOSTA}$. *RIC 13*	1,500	3,500
134 B ℞ VIRTVS MILITVM, three-turreted gateway, arch open, no doors.		
Rome $\overline{RS}$. *RIC 153.*	1,500	3,500

ROMULUS

*Valerius Romulus was the son of Maxentius and Valeria Maximilla (the daughter of Galerius).
His only title was 'nobilissimus vir' and he was consul twice with his father in 308 and 309. He died
during 309 and Maxentius issued bronze coins in his memory. No silver coins were minted in his
name.*

DOMITIUS ALEXANDER
A.D. 308–309

*L. Domitius Alexander was Vicar of Africa during the early years of the fourth century. He staged
a revolt against the emperor Maxentius in 308, which was suppressed by the end of the following
year. He issued coinage in gold and bronze but not silver.*

104

LICINIUS I
A.D. 308–324

Valerius Licinianus Licinius, a native of Dacia, was born about 265. He had been a fellow soldier under Galerius and served with him in the Persian campaign in 298. In 308 he was elevated to the rank of Augustus at the Conference at Carnuntum to replace Severus who had perished following his abortive attempt to recover Italy in 307. Constantine and Licinius formed an alliance in 313 after the defeat and death of Maxentius. Licinius married Constantia the sister of Constantine I and together the two rulers promulgated the Edict of Tolerance in 313, after which Licinius returned to Illyricum. Maximinus, having learned of the alliance, mounted a campaign against Licinius but was defeated in April 313 and fled. The alliance with Constantine was an uneasy one and by 314 a brief civil war had occurred after which Licinius was forced to yield all of his European territories except Thrace. In 317 the two emperors nominated their three sons as Caesars. In the 320s the situation between the joint Augusti worsened and in July 324 Licinius was decisively defeated by Constantine. He surrendered at Nicomedia and was sent into retirement at Thessalonica, but was executed the following year.

Obverse legends
A.   IMP LICINIVS AVG.
B.   IMP LICINIVS PF AVG.

Obverse busts
a.   laureate, cuirassed, hldg. thunderbolt in r.h. sceptre over l. shldr., left.
b.   helmeted, cuirassed, spear over r. shldr., shield on l., left.

		VF	EF
99	Aa R IOVI CONSERVATORI AVG, Jupiter seated l. on eagle with spread wings, r. Trier $\overline{\text{PTR}}$. *RIC 825* **siliqua** (*billon*) . .	100	250
202†	Bb R VOTA ORBIS ET VRBIS SEN ET PR with XX XXX MVL FEL inscribed on altar with square base. Aquileia $\frac{\text{L}\vert}{\text{AQ}}$. *RIC 80* **multiple** . .	4,000	8,000

LICINIUS II
CAESAR A.D. 317–324

Valerius Licinianus Licinius was the son of Licinius I and Constantia (the daughter of Constantius I and Theodora). While still a young child he was proclaimed Caesar in 317 at the same time that Constantine elevated his sons Crispus and Constantine II. In 324, after the final defeat of Licinius I, his son's life was spared but he was later put to death by Constantine, probably in 326. No silver coins were minted in his name.

CONSTANTIA

Constantia, the half-sister of Constantine I, was married to Licinius I at Milan in 313. She bore him a son, Licinius II. No silver coins were minted in her name.

VALENS
A.D. 316

Aurelius Valerius Valens was dux limitis *in Dacia when Licinius made him emperor after his defeat at Cabalae, but he was deposed and executed before Licinius negotiated a peace treaty with Constantine. No silver was minted in his name and of his bronze coinage (which gives him the title Augustus) only two pieces (one in Berlin and one in Paris) have been accepted as genuine.*

MARTINIAN
A.D. 324

Sextus Marcius (?) Martinianus, magister officiarum *under Licinius, was created emperor by the latter shortly before his final defeat by Constantine. Constantine deposed him and shortly thereafter ordered his execution. Although the sources state that Licinius made Martinianus his Caesar, the very rare coins issued in his name (none in silver) give him the title Augustus.*

CONSTANTINE I, THE GREAT
CAESAR A.D. 306–307
AUGUSTUS A.D. 307–337

The son of Constantius I and his first wife Helena, Constantine was born in about 272 at Naissus. He followed a military career and served under Diocletian and Galerius in the East. In 305, or possibly 306, he received permission from Galerius to visit his father who was campaigning in northern Britain. He successfully eluded Galerius' messengers carrying a revocation of the permission and moved with great speed across Europe. On his father's death at York in July 306 he was proclaimed by his troops and received official recognition as Caesar by Galerius. From 306 to 312 he played a waiting game, allying himself first with Maxentius and Maximian in 307 and marrying the latter's daughter, Fausta, to cement the bargain. He adopted the title of Augustus in 307 but was not recognized as Augustus by Galerius and Maximinus until about 310, although he and Maximinus had been officially termed filii augustorum *after the Conference at Carnuntum late in 308. By 308 the alliance with Maxentius had collapsed and Constantine concentrated on campaigns on the frontier. After the death of Galerius in 311 Constantine allied himself with Licinius and in 312 moved against Maxentius in Italy and successfully overthrew him at the Battle of the Milvian Bridge in 312.*

From 312 to 324 he concentrated on winning sole control of the empire which he achieved in stages, culminating in Licinius' final defeat and political downfall. He was fervently pro-Christian and published an Edict of Toleration in 313 together with Licinius. He attributed his victory over Maxentius to a vision in which he was told he would conquer if his soldiers inscribed their shields with a Christian symbol. He founded the city of Constantinople on the site of ancient Byzantium, in 330, and was instrumental in introducing a variety of military and administrative reforms. He issued silver at the beginning of his reign but from about 310 to 324 issues were very sparse. After 324 they became commoner.

Obverse legends

As Caesar
A. CONSTANTINVS NOB C.
B. FL VAL CONSTANTINVS NC.
C. FL VAL CONSTANTINVS NOB C.

As Augustus
D. NO LEGEND.
E. AVGVSTVS.
F. CONSTANTINVS MAX AVG.
G. CONSTANTINVS MAX PF AVG.
H. CONSTANTINVS AVG.
I. IMP CONSTANTINVS AVG.
J. IMP CONSTANTINVS PF AVG.
K. IMP CONSTANTINVS MAX AVG.

Obverse busts
a. laureate, right.
b. laureate, draped, right.
c. laureate, draped, seen from rear, right.
d. head, right.
e. laureate, cuirassed right.
f. laureate, draped, cuirassed, right.
g. rosette diadem, right.
h. rosette diadem, cuirassed, right.
i. rosette diadem, draped, cuirassed, right.
j. rosette diadem, draped, cuirassed, left.
k. rosette diadem, looking upwards, right.
l. plain diadem, looking upwards, right.
m. diadem, draped, cuirassed, holding Victory on globe, left.
n. helmeted, cuirassed, spear across right shoulder, left.
o. helmeted, cuirassed, spear across right shoulder, shield on left, left.
p. helmeted, three-quarters facing, cuirassed, holding horse by bridle in right hand, reversed spear in left hand.
q. radiate, trabea, raising right hand, holding globe in left hand, right.
r. radiate, trabea, holding Victory on globe in right hand, left.
s. radiate, cuirassed, holding spear in right hand, left.

All coins are siliquae unless otherwise stated. For a discussion of fourth-century denominations and their names, see the Introduction.

CAESAR

		VF	EF
72	Aa ℞ CONSERVATOR KART SVAE, Carthage stg. facing in hexastyle temple with plain pediment. Carthage XCVI. *RIC 49* .	1,250	2,800
271†	Cb ℞ HAEC VOTA MVLT ANN in four lines in wreath. Trier ⊥. *RIC 639* **half siliqua** .	600	1,350
394	Cb ℞ PLVR NATAL FEL in three lines in wreath. Trier ⊥. *RIC 640.*	600	1,350

705	Aa ℞ VIRTVS MILITVM, three-turreted gateway, arch open, no doors. Rome RS. *RIC 154* .	650	1,500

706a	Aa ℞ As last, but four-turreted gateway. Trier PTR. *RIC 638*	650	1,500
706b	As last. Rome RS. *RIC 155*	650	1,500

706c	As last but gateway has doors thrown open. Trier PTR. *RIC 636* .	650	1,500
731A	Bb ℞ VOT X FELICITER, in four lines in wreath. Trier ⊥. *RIC 641* **half siliqua** .	600	1,350

AUGUSTUS

32Aa	Eg ℞ CAESAR in laurel wreath. Lugdunum LVG. *RIC 283* **multiple** .	8,000	16,000
32Ab	As last. Siscia SIS. *RIC 259* **multiple** .	8,000	16,000
32Ac	As last. Thessalonica TSE. *RIC 221* **multiple** .	8,000	16,000
32Ad	As last. Constantinople ⊥. *RIC 132* **multiple** .	8,000	16,000
32Ae	As last ℞ CAE·SAR in laurel wreath. Nicomedia ⊥. *RIC 197* **multiple**	8,000	16,000

		VF	EF
90	Fi ℞ CONSTANTINIANA DAFNE, Victory seated l. on cippus, hldg. palm branch in each hand, trophy in front, kneeling captive before her feet. Constantinople $\frac{A|}{CONS*}$. *RIC 37*	650	1,500
97a	Di ℞ CONSTANTINVS AVG, Victory walking l. hldg. wreath and palm. Constantinople $\overline{CONSA}$. *RIC 126*	375	850
97b	Dl ℞ As last. Siscia $\overline{SIS}$. *RIC 210*	350	800
97c	As last. Thessalonica $\overline{SMTS}$. *RIC 152*	350	800
97d	As last. Heraclea $\overline{SMH}$. *RIC 145*	350	800
97e	As last. Constantinople $\overline{CONS}$. *RIC*	350	800
97f	Dk ℞ As last. Rome $\overline{R}$. $\overline{R}$. *RIC 377*	350	800
97g	As last. Aquileia $\overline{SMAQ}$. *RIC 130A*	350	800
97h	As last. Siscia $\overline{SIS}$. *RIC 229*	350	800
97i	As last. Siscia $\overline{\cdot SIS\cdot}$. *RIC 230*	350	800
97j	As last. Thessalonica $\overline{TSE}$. *RIC 214*	325	750

		VF	EF
97k	As last. Constantinople $\overline{CONS}$. *RIC 5*	325	750
97l	As last. Constantinople $\overline{\cdot CONSA\cdot}$. *RIC 54*	325	750
97m	As last. Constantinople $\frac{M|}{CONSA}$. *RIC 131A*	350	800
97n	As last. Nicomedia $\overline{SMN}$. *RIC 140, 186A*	350	800
97o	As last. Nicomedia $\overline{SMN\cdot}$. *RIC 141*	350	800
97p	As last. Antioch $\overline{SMAN}$. *RIC 105.*	350	800
104a	Dl ℞ As last, Emperor in military dress stg. l. hldg. vexillum with wreath on drapery, sceptre in l. Trier $\overline{SMTR}$. *RIC 579* .	650	1,500
104†b	Dg ℞ As last. Rome $\overline{RT}$. *RIC 399* **multiple**	1,750	4,000
106a	Dl ℞ As last, four standards. Ticinum $\overline{SMT}$. *RIC 185* **multiple**	2,000	4,500
106b	As last. Thessalonica $\overline{SMTS}$. *RIC 151* **multiple** . .	1,500	3,500
106c	As last. Nicomedia $\overline{SMN}$. *RIC 86* **multiple**	1,500	3,500
106†d	Dk ℞ As last. Thessalonica $\overline{TSE}$. *RIC 218* **multiple**	1,500	3,500
106†e	As last. Heraclea $\overline{SMH}$. *RIC 103* **multiple**	1,500	3,500
106†f	As last. Constantinople $\overline{CONS}$. *RIC 99* **multiple**	1,500	3,500

		VF	EF
108†a	Fi ℟ As last. Trier $\overline{\text{SMTR}}$. *RIC 580* **multiple** . . .	1,250	2,800
108†b	As last. Constantinople $\overline{\text{CONSA}}$. *RIC* **multiple** . .	1,250	2,800
109	Fe ℟ As last. Siscia $\overline{\text{SIS}}$. *RIC 198* **multiple**	1,250	2,800
109†	Fh ℟ As last. Constantinople $\overline{\text{CONS}}$. *RIC 99A* **multiple** . .	1,250	2,800
114	Dl ℟ CONSTANTINVS MAX AVG, four standards. Thessalonica $\overline{\text{SMTS}}$. *RIC 150* **multiple**	1,500	3,500
135	Dg ℟ DN CONSTANTINVS MAX TRIVMF AVG, Tyche seated facing on throne hldg. cornucopiae, resting feet on prow. Constantinople $\overline{\text{MCONSA}}$. *RIC 53* **multiple**	10,000	20,000
3	Fd ℟ CRISPVS ET CONSTANTINVS CC bare-headed busts of the two Caesars facing one another. Sirmium $\overline{\text{SIRM}}$. *RIC 14* **multiple** (*debased metal*) . .	650	1,500
149†a	Fi ℟ FELICITAS ROMANORVM, emperor in military dress stg. l. under arch with two sons. Heraclea $\overline{\text{SMH}}$. *RIC 105* **multiple**	1,500	3,500
149†b	Fe ℟ As last. Sirmium $\overline{\text{SIRM}}$. *RIC 15* **multiple**	1,500	3,500
149†c	Ge ℟ As last. Thessalonica $\overline{\text{THES}}$. *RIC 140A* **multiple** . .	1,500	3,500
150	Fe ℟ As last, but three sons. Nicomedia $\overline{\text{SMN}}$. *RIC 88* **multiple**	1,500	3,500
235A	Hl ℟ GENIVM PR, Genius with modius on head stg. l., chlamys across l. shldr., globe in r., cornucopiae in l. Rome $\overline{\text{SMR}}$. *RIC 278* **multiple**	3,500	7,500
4a	Fm ℟ NOB CAESS, busts of the two Caesars facing one another, jointly hldg. Victory on globe. Thessalonica $\overline{\text{MTS}}$. *RIC 180* **multiple** (debased metal)	1,250	2,800
4b	As last. Constantinople $\overline{\text{CONS}}$. *RIC 6* **multiple** (debased metal).	1,250	2,800
484†	Jp ℟ SALVS REIPVBLICAE, emperor in military dress hldg. trophy, stg. l. on platform being crowned by Victory with nine soldiers standing about him. Ticinum $\perp$. *RIC 36* **multiple**	12,500	25,000
603A	Fi ℟ VICTORIA CONSTANTINI AVG, Victory walking l. hldg. wreath and palm. Thessalonica $\overline{\text{MTS}}$. *RIC 181*	450	1,000

643	In ℟ VICTORIAE LAETAE PRINC PERP VOT PR, two Victories stg. facing hldg. inscribed shield on altar. Trier $\overline{\text{PTR}}$. *RIC 208A* (billon)	80	200

		VF	EF
676A	Ia ℞ VIRTVS AVG ET CAES, trophy with two spears and four shields at base. Sirmium ⊥. *RIC 17*	900	2,000
700†a	Fi ℞ VIRTVS EXERCITVS, soldier stg. l. hldg. reversed vertical spear, l.h. resting on shield. Thessalonica T̅S̅. *RIC 197* **multiple**	1,250	2,800

700†b	As last. Constantinople ·C̅O̅N̅S̅A̅·. *RIC 58* **multiple**	1,250	2,800
700†c	As last. Constantinople ·C̅O̅N̅S̅A̅. *RIC 58A* **multiple** . . .	1,250	2,800
700†d	As last. Constantinople C̅O̅N̅S̅A̅. *RIC 131* **multiple** . . .	1,250	2,800
700†e	As last. Constantinople C̅·A̅·. *RIC 135* **multiple**	1,250	2,800
707a	Ie ℞ VIRTVS MILITVM, four-turreted gateway, no doors. Trier T̅R̅. *RIC 760* **half siliqua**	325	750

707b	As last. Trier P̅T̅R̅. *RIC 828* **half siliqua**	325	750
707†c	Ic ℞ As last. Trier T̅R̅. *RIC 759* **half siliqua**	325	750
707†d	As last. Trier P̅T̅R̅. *RIC 827* **half siliqua**	325	750

707†e	Je ℞ As last. Trier T̅R̅. *RIC 758* **half siliqua**	325	750
708†a	As last ℞ As last but gate has doors thrown back. Trier T̅R̅. *RIC 764* **half siliqua**	325	750

708†b	Ie ℞ As last. Trier T̅R̅. *RIC 765* **half siliqua**	325	750
717a	Ko ℞ VOTA ORBIS ET VRBIS SEN ET PR with XX XXX AVG inscribed on column with square base. Aquileia $\frac{*|*}{AQS}$. *RIC 82* **multiple** . .	3,000	6,500

		VF	EF
717†b	Kr ℞ As last. Ticinum $\frac{L|}{SMT}$. *RIC* **multiple**	3,500	7,500
717†c	Js ℞ As last. Aquileia $\frac{*|*}{AQS}$. *RIC 83†* **multiple**	3,000	6,500
718A	Fm ℞ VOTA POPVLI ROMANI with XXX FEL inscribed on column with square base. Rome $\frac{*|*}{PR}$. *RIC 224A* **multiple**	3,500	7,500

HELENA

Flavia Julia Helena was of lowly origin but married Constantius I and bore him a son, Constantine I. In November 324 she was given the title Augusta and coins were issued in her name in gold and bronze. She was converted to Christianity and made a pilgrimage to Palestine where she built the Churchs of the Holy Sepulchre, of the Ascension, and of the Nativity. Her alleged discovery of the True Cross was first recorded by Ambrose. She died in 329. No silver coins were minted in her name.

THEODORA

Theodora was either the full daughter or, as is more generally agreed, the step-daughter of Maximian. In 293 she married Constantius I and bore him six children: Flavius Dalmatius, Julius Constantius, Hannibalianus, Constantina, Eutropia, and Anastasia. She was honoured post-humously on the coinage of Constantine I's sons, after 337, when pieces were minted for her in bronze.

FAUSTA

Flavia Maxima Fausta was the daughter of Maximian and Eutropia and was probably born in Rome about 290. In 307 she was married to Constantine I in Trier. She later bore him three sons. Constantine II, Constantius II, and Constans and was stepmother to Crispus. She is blamed by some ancient sources for the death of Crispus, who was executed at Pola in 326. It is alleged that she sought to seduce him and, failing, accused him of an attempt on her. She was suffocated in a hot bath shortly thereafter, apparently on the orders of Constantine. At the time of his marriage Constantine issued some fractional silver pieces at Trier honouring Fausta and designating her nobilissima femina.

Obverse legend
A. FAVSTAE NOBILISSIMAE FEMINAE.
Obverse bust
a. draped, left.

		VF	EF
22	As ℞ VENVS FELIX, Venus seated l. hldg. globe in r. hand, palm in l. Trier $\overline{TR}$. *RIC 756* **half siliqua**	1,100	2,500

CRISPUS
CAESAR A.D. 317–326

Flavius Julius Crispus was the oldest son of Constantine I and was probably born about 305 to Minervina, who may not have been formally married to Constantine. Crispus was appointed Caesar by his father in March 317, together with Constantine II and Licinius II. He was placed in charge of Gaul, with a Praetorian Prefect to aid him, and undertook a number of successful military campaigns against the Franks and Alamanni in 320 and 323. In 322 Crispus married a woman named Helena who bore him a child, but nothing is known of their subsequent fate. Crispus held the consulship three times, in 318, 321, and 324. He was executed at Pola in 326, apparently on the orders of his father who mistakenly believed he had been involved with his stepmother Fausta.

Obverse legends
A. FL IVL CRISPVS NOB C.
B. FL IVL CRISPVS NOB CAES.
C. DN CRISPVS NOB CAESAR.

Busts
a. laureate, cuirassed, right
b. laureate, draped, cuirassed, holding Victory on globe in left hand, spear pointing forward in right hand, right
c. laureate, draped, cuirassed, holding Victory on globe in right hand, mappa in left hand, left
d. radiate, draped, cuirassed, raising right hand, holding globe in left hand, left

		VF	EF
70Aa	Ca ℞ FELICITAS ROMANORVM, emperor in military dress, stg. l. under arch with two sons. Nicomedia SMN. *RIC 89* **multiple**	3,500	7,500
70Ab	Ba ℞ As last. Thessalonica THES. *RIC 140B* **multiple**	3,500	7,500
84†a	Bb ℞ MONETAE AVGG ET CAESS NN, three Monetae stg. l. Aquileia MAQ. *RIC 32* **multiple**	5,000	10,000

183Aa	Ad ℞ VOTA ORBIS ET VRBIS SEN ET PR, XX XXX MVL FEL inscribed on column with square base. Aquileia $\frac{L}{AQ}$. *RIC 81†* **multiple**	5,000	10,000
183Ab	Ac ℞ As last. Siscia $\frac{*|*}{S|S}$. *RIC 158A* **multiple**	5,000	10,000

DALMATIVS
CAESAR A.D. 335–337

Dalmatius was the son of Julius Constantius and the brother of Hannibalianus. He was created Caesar in 335 and it was Constantine I's intention that after his death Dalmatius should rule over the dioceses of Thrace, Dacia and Macedonia. Dalmatius, however, perished in the massacre of the male descendants of Theodora (second wife of Constantius I) in 337, some months after the death of Constantine I.

Obverse legends
A. No legend
B. FL DELMATIVS NOB CAES.

Obverse busts
a. plain diadem, looking upwards, r.
b. laureate, draped, cuirassed, r.

All coins are siliquae

		VF	EF
3a	As ℞ DELMATIVS CAESAR, Victory walking l. hldg. wreath in r. hand palm branch in l. Nicomedia $\overline{\text{SMN}}$. *RIC 186*	2,000	4,500
3b	As last. Heraclea. $\overline{\text{SMH}}$. *RIC 147*.	2,000	4,500
3†c	Aa ℞ DELMATIVS NOB CAESAR, as last. Thessalonica $\overline{\text{TSE}}$. *RIC 217*	2,000	4,500
3†d	As last. Constantinople $\overline{\text{C·A}}$. *RIC 136A*	2,000	4,500
15†	Bb ℞ PRINCIPI IVVENTVTIS, prince in military dress, stg. l. hldg. vexillum and sceptre, two standards to r. Trier $\overline{\text{TR}}$. *RIC —* . . (*NB. This may be a Becker forgery.*)		

HANNIBALIANUS
REX A.D. 335–337

Little is known of the life of Flavius Hannibalianus, the son of Flavius Delmatius and the brother of the Caesar Dalmatius, other than the fact that he married Constantina, Constantine I's elder daughter. In 335 he received the title rex regum et Ponticarum gentium *and was put in charge of the diocese of Pontica. In 337, a few months after the death of Constantine I, Hannibalianus perished in the massacre of the male descendants of Theodora (second wife of Constantius I).*

Obverse legend
A. FL ANNIBALIANO REGI

Obverse bust
a. draped, cuirassed, right

		VF	EF
1	Aa ℞ FELICITAS PVBLICA, Euphrates reclining l., fish in r. hand, rudder in l. hand, l. elbow resting on water jug. Constantinople CONS. *RIC 100* **siliqua**	4,500	10,000

CONSTANTINE II
CAESAR A.D. 317–337
AUGUSTUS A.D. 337–340

Constantine II (Flavius Claudius Constantinus), the second son of Constantine I, was born in 316. In 317 he was made Caesar together with Crispus and Licinius II. In 328 he was sent to administer Gaul in the charge of a Praetorian Prefect. His share of the empire after Constantine I's death in 337 included Britain, Gaul, and Spain, the ancient sources suggest that he was anxious to add Italy and Africa (assigned to Constans) to his territory. Between 337 and 339 he tried with some success to dominate his younger brother Constans and, when the latter attempted to shake off this control, Constantine II decided to invade Italy in 340. However, the invasion was a fiasco, failing in its intention to catch Constans by surprise; Constantine II's army was ambushed and he himself killed near Aquileia.

Obverse legends

As Caesar

A. NO LEGEND.
B. CONSTANTINVS IVN NOB C.
C. CONSTANTINVS IVN NOB CAES.
D. DN CONSTANTINVS IVN NOB CAES.
E. CAESAR.

As Augustus

F. NO LEGEND.
G. IMP CONSTANTINVS AVG.
H. CONSTANTINVS MAX AVG.
I. FL CL CONSTANTINVS PF AVG.
J. CONSTANTINVS PF AVG.
K. CONSTANTINVS AVG.

Obverse busts

a. head, right.
b. laureate, cuirassed, right.
c. laureate, draped, cuirassed, right.
d. plain diadem, looking upwards, right.
e. plain diadem, draped, cuirassed, right.
f. radiate, draped, cuirassed, raising right hand, holding globe in left hand, left.
g. radiate, draped, holding Victory on globe in right hand, mappa in left hand, left.
h. head, bare, upward looking, right.
i. head, laureate, upward looking, right.
j. head, pearl diadem, upward looking, right.
k. head, rosette diadem, upward looking, right.
l. head, laurel and rosette diadem, upward looking, right.
m. draped, cuirassed, pearl diadem, right.
n. draped, cuirassed, rosette diadem, right.
o. draped, cuirassed, laurel and rosette diadem, right.
p. cuirassed, laurel and rosette diadem, right.

All coins are siliquae unless otherwise stated. For a discussion of fourth-century silver denominations and their names, see the Introduction.

CAESAR

		VF	EF
72	Ad ℞ CONSTANTINVS CAES, Victory, walking l. hldg wreath and palm. Constantinople CONSA. *RIC 127*	350	800
76a	Ad ℞ CONSTANTINVS CAESAR, as last. Rome ℞. *RIC 378* . . .	350	800
76b	As last. Thessalonica T̄S̄. *RIC 194*	350	800
76c	As last. Thessalonica T̄Sє. *RIC 215*	350	800

76d	As last. Constantinople C̄·Ā. *RIC 135A*	350	800

		VF	EF
76e	As last. Nicomedia $\overline{\text{N}}$. *RIC 117*	350	800
76f	Ai ℞ As last. Antioch $\overline{\text{SMAN}}$. *RIC 106*	375	850
80a	Bb ℞ As last, four standards. Trier $\overline{\text{SMTR}}$. *RIC 581* **multiple**	1,400	3,200
80b	As last. Constantinople $\overline{\text{CONSA}}$. *RIC 123* **multiple**	1,400	3,200
81a	Ad ℞ As last. Arles $\overline{\text{CONST}}$. *RIC 409* **multiple**	1,500	3,500
81b	As last. Heraclea $\overline{\text{SMH}}$. *RIC 104* **multiple**	1,500	3,500
81c	As last. Constantinople $\cdot\overline{\text{CONSA}}\cdot$. *RIC 55* **multiple**	1,500	3,500

81d	As last. Constantinople $\overline{\text{CONSA}}$. *RIC 124* **multiple**	1,500	3,500
81Aa	Bb ℞ CONSTANTINVS IVN NOB C, as last. Heraclea $\overline{\text{SMH}}$. *RIC 148* **multiple**	1,400	3,200
81Ab	Ad ℞ As last. Heraclea $\overline{\text{SMH}}$. *RIC 149* **multiple**	1,500	3,500
81B	Bb ℞ CONSTANTIVS CAESAR, as last. Arles $\overline{\text{CONST}}$. *RIC 409 note hybrid* **multiple**	—	—
82†a	Ad ℞ CONSTANTINVS CAESAR, three palm branches, star above. Ticinum $\overline{\text{MT}}$. *RIC 184*	450	1,000
82b	As last. Rome $\overline{\text{R}}$. *RIC 380*	450	1,000
82c	As last. Thessalonica $\overline{\text{TS}}$. *RIC 195*	450	1,000
105Aa	Bb ℞ FELICITAS ROMANORVM, emperor stg l. under arch with three sons. Rome $\overline{\text{SMR}}$. *RIC 275* **multiple**	1,500	3,500
105Ab	As last. Cyzicus $\overline{\text{SMK}}$. *RIC 42* **multiple**	1,500	3,500
105Ac	Bb ℞ As last, but only two sons. Thessalonica $\overline{\text{THES}}$. *RIC 140C* **multiple**	1,500	3,500
105Ad	Db ℞ As last. Nicomedia $\overline{\text{SMN}}$. *RIC 142* **multiple**	1,500	3,500
107A	Bc ℞ FIDIS MILITVM (*sic*), three standards. Rome $\overline{\text{PR}}$. *RIC 376* **multiple**	2,000	4,500
112a	Bb ℞ GLORIA EXERCITVS, female figure stg l. hldg. laurel branch and sceptre, leaning on column. Thessalonica $\overline{\text{TS}}$. *RIC 196* **multiple**	1,250	2,800
112b	As last. Constantinople. $\cdot\overline{\text{CONSΓ}}\cdot$ *RIC 57A* **multiple**	1,250	2,800
112c	As last. Constantinople $\overline{\text{CONSA}}$. *RIC 129* **multiple** . .	1,250	2,800
112d	As last. Constantinople $\overline{\text{C·A}}$. *RIC 133* **multiple**	1,250	2,800
112†e	Bc ℞ As last. Thessalonica $\overline{\text{TSE}}$. *RIC 219* **multiple** . .	1,250	2,800
203A	Ce ℞ VICTORIA CAESAR NN, Victory walking l. hldg wreath and palm. Thessalonica $\overline{\text{MTS}}$. *RIC 182*	450	1,000
204A	Bb ℞ VICTORIA CAESARVM, as last. Siscia $\overline{\text{SIS}}$. *RIC 212* . . .	450	1,000
265Aa	Bg ℞ VOTA ORBIS ET VRBIS SEN ET PR, XX XXX MVL FEL inscribed on column with square base. Siscia $\overset{*|*}{\overline{\text{SIS}}}$. *RIC 158B* **multiple** . .	4,000	8,000
265Ab	Bf ℞ As last. Aquileia $\overset{*|*}{\overline{\text{AQS}}}$. *RIC 84* **multiple**	4,000	8,000
280Aa	Ea ℞ x·x in laurel wreath. Lugdunum $\overline{\text{LVG}}$. *RIC 284* **multiple**	8,000	16,000
280Ab	As last. Siscia $\overline{\text{SIS}}$. *RIC 260* **multiple**	8,000	16,000
280Ac	As last. Nicomedia $\perp$. *RIC 198* **multiple**	8,000	16,000

		VF	EF
280Ad	As last but xx. Arles $\overline{\text{CONST}}$. *RIC 411* **multiple**	8,000	16,000
280Ae	As last. Aquileia $\overline{\text{AQ}}$. *RIC 138* **multiple**.	8,000	16,000

AUGUSTUS

		VF	EF
68A	Ko Ṛ CONSTANTINVS AVG, four standards. Trier $\overline{\text{SMTR}}$. *RIC 20–1* **light miliarensis**	1,250	2,800
69†a	Fi Ṛ As last, legend in wreath. Antioch $\overline{\text{ANT}}$. *RIC 33* . . .	450	1,000
69†b	Fj Ṛ As last. Antioch ANT. *RIC 32*	450	1,000

		VF	EF
69†c	As last. Alexandria $\overline{\text{ALE}}$. *RIC 1*.	450	1,000
69Aa	Fi Ṛ As last, Victory walking l. holdg. wreath and palm. Siscia $\overline{\text{SIS}}$. *RIC 53*	350	800
69Ab	Fj Ṛ As last. Siscia $\overline{\text{SIS}}$. *RIC 54*	350	800
69Ac	Fk Ṛ As last. Siscia $\overline{\text{SIS}}$. *RIC 55*	350	800
69Ad	As last. Siscia $\overline{\text{·SIS·}}$. *RIC 56*	350	800

		VF	EF
69Ae	Fl Ṛ As last. Rome $\overline{\text{R}}$. *RIC 1*	375	850
69Af	As last. Cyzicus $\overline{\text{SMK*}}$. *RIC 1*	375	850
69Ag	Ho Ṛ As last. Siscia $\overline{\text{SIS}}$. *RIC 57*	350	800
69Ah	Jo Ṛ As last. Siscia $\overline{\text{SIS}}$. *RIC 58*	350	800
69Ai	As last. Siscia $\overline{\text{·SIS·}}$. *RIC 59*	350	800
70a	Fk Ṛ CONSTANTINVS AVGVSTVS, as last. Constantinople $\overline{\text{C·A}}$. *RIC 15*	325	750
70b	Fl Ṛ As last. Constantinople $\overline{\text{C·A}}$. *RIC 16*	325	750
87A	Io Ṛ CONSTANTINVS PF AVG, three standards. Thessalonica $\overline{\text{TES}}$. *RIC 49* **light miliarensis**	1,250	2,800
108Aa	Jo Ṛ GAVDIVM POPVLI ROMANI; SIC XX SIC XXX, in wreath. Siscia $\overline{\text{SIS}∪}$. *RIC 47* **heavy miliarensis**	1,250	2,800
108Ab	As last. Siscia $\overline{\text{SIS}∪}$. *RIC 70*	450	1,000
138A	Jo Ṛ PAX AETERNA AVG, Pax stg. facing hldg. branch and sceptre, leaning l. elbow on column. Siscia $\overline{\text{·SIS·}}$. *RIC 46A* **heavy miliarensis**	1,500	3,500
138B	Go Ṛ PAX AVGVSTORVM, emperor in mil. dress stg. l. hldg. standard with Chi-rho on banner. Trier $\overline{\text{TRP}}$ *RIC 30* . . .	400	900
142A	Go Ṛ PRINCIPI IVVENTVTIS, emperor in mil. dress stg. r., hldg. spear and globe, spurning captive with foot. Trier $\overline{\text{TR}}$. *RIC 33*	375	850

		VF	EF
197Aa	Go ℞ VICTORIA AVGG NN, Victory walking l. hldg. wreath and palm. Trier TRP. *RIC 29* .	400	900
197Ab	Gm ℞ As last. Trier TRP. *RIC 28*	400	900
199Aa	Gn ℞ VICTORIA AVGVSTI, as last. Trier TRP. *RIC 25*	400	900
199Ab	Go ℞ As last. Trier TRP. *RIC 26*.	400	900
212†a	Jp ℞ VICTORIA DD NN AVGG, as last. Aquileia SMAQ. *RIC 9*	400	900
212†b	Jn ℞ As last. Thessalonica TS∈. *RIC 39* .	425	950

262A	Io ℞ VIRTVS EXERCITVS, helmeted soldier in mil. dress, stg. facing, hldg. spear and resting l. hand on shield. Thessalonica TES. *RIC 46* **heavy miliarensis.**	1,250	2,800

CONSTANS
CAESAR A.D. 333–337
AUGUSTUS A.D. 337–350

Flavius Julius Constans, the fourth son of Constantine, was born in 320 (or possibly 323) and proclaimed Caesar in December 333. After his father's death in 337 Constans controlled Italy, Africa and Illyricum, but was initially dominated by his elder brother Constantine II. In 340 the latter invaded Italy where he was promptly defeated by Constans and killed. Constans then took possession of Constantine II's territory which he ruled until his own death in 350. During the earlier part of his reign he successfully undertook a number of military campaigns. He crossed to Britain in 343 for a brief visit, the precise purpose of which is obscure. Later in his reign he became immensely unpopular and had a reputation for greed, cruelty, and homosexuality. He was the first of Constantine's sons to be baptized and was a devout, if fanatical, Christian, actively persecuting sects opposed to the doctrines of Athanasius. He was overthrown in a conspiracy which led to the usurpation of Magnentius. Constans tried to flee but was pursued and killed by rebel troops.

Obverse legends

As Caesar
A. No legend.
B. FL IVL CONSTANS NOB CAES.
C. FL CONSTANS NOB CAES.
D. FL CONSTANTIS BEA C.

As Augustus
E. No legend.
F. FL IVL CONSTANS PERP AVG.
G. FL IVL CONSTANS PIVS FELIX AVG.
H. FL IVL CONSTANS PF AVG.
I. FL IVL CONSTANS AVG.
J. DN CONSTANS PF AVG.
K. CONSTANS PF AVG.

Obverse busts
a. laureate, draped, cuirassed, right.
b. plain diadem, looking upwards, right.
c. head, laureate, right.
d. head, pearl diadem, right.
e. head, rosette diadem, right.
f. head, laurel and rosette diadem, right.
g. head, pearl diadem, upward looking, right.
h. head, rosette diadem, upward looking, right.
i. head, laurel and rosette diadem, upward looking, right.
j. draped, cuirassed, pearl diadem, right.
k. draped, cuirassed, rosette diadem, right.
l. draped, cuirassed, laurel and rosette diadem, right.

All coins are siliquae unless otherwise specified. For a discussion of fourth-century silver denominations and their names, see the Introduction.

CAESAR

		VF	EF
4	Ab ℞ CONSTANS CAESAR, Victory walking l. hldg. wreath and palm. Antioch SMAN. *RIC 107.*	300	700
4†	As last ℞ CONSTANS NOB CAESAR, as last. Constantinople C·A. *RIC 136*	300	700
5	Ba ℞ CONSTANS CAESAR, four standards. Trier SMTR. *RIC 585* **multiple**	1,000	2,250
143†a	Ca ℞ VICTORIA CAESARVM, Victory walking l. hldg. wreath and palm. Siscia SIS. *RIC 233* .	250	550
143†b	Da ℞ As last. Siscia SIS. *RIC 234*	250	550

AUGUSTUS

		VF	EF
1†a	Hk ℞ CONSTANS AVG, three palm branches, star above. Siscia SIS◡. *RIC 67*	350	800

		VF	EF
1†b	Hl ℞ As last. Siscia $\overline{\text{SIS}}\cup$. *RIC 68*	350	800
1†c	As last. Siscia $\cdot\overline{\text{SIS}}\cup$. *RIC 69*	350	800
1†a	Kk ℞ As last. Siscia $\cdot\overline{\text{SIS}}\cdot$. *RIC 65*	350	800
1†e	Kl ℞ As last. Siscia $\cdot\overline{\text{SIS}}\cdot$. *RIC 66*	350	800
1†f	As last. Siscia $\overline{\text{SIS}}\cup$. *RIC 66A*	350	800
2a	Eg ℞ CONSTANS AVG, in wreath. Alexandria $\overline{\text{ALE}}$. *RIC 3* . .	400	900

		VF	EF
2†b	As last. Antioch $\overline{\text{ANT}}$. *RIC—*	450	1,000
2Aa	Ia ℞ CONSTANS AVG, four standards. Trier $\overline{\text{SMTR}}$. *Ric 24* **light miliarensis**	850	1,900
2Ab	Hl ℞ As last. Siscia $\cdot\overline{\text{SIS}}\cdot$. *RIC 50* **heavy miliarensis.** . .	850	1,900
2B	Ei ℞ CONSTANS AVG, Victory walking l. hldg. wreath and palm. Heraclea $\overline{\text{SMH}}$. *RIC 12*	250	550
2Ca	Eh ℞ CONSTANS AVGVSTVS, as last. Constantinople $\overline{\text{C·A}}$. *RIC 19*	250	550
2Cb	Ei ℞ As last. Constantinople $\overline{\text{C·A}}$. *RIC 20*	250	550
3†	Hl ℞ CONSTANS PF AVG, three standards. Thessalonica $\overline{\text{TES}}$. *RIC 51* **light miliarensis**	850	1,900
8†a	Hj ℞ FEL TEMP REPARATIO VOT XX, Victory stg. r. with foot on globe, inscribing shield supported by kneeling figure. Rome $\overline{\text{R}}$. *RIC 61, 62A, 63*	225	500
8†b	Hl ℞ As last. Rome $\overline{\text{R}}$. *RIC 62*	225	500
24†a	Jl ℞ FELICITAS PERPETVA, Victory walking l. hldg. wreath and trophy. Aquileia *$\overline{\text{AQ}}$. *RIC 68*	200	450
24†b	As last. Aquileia $\overline{\text{AQ}}$. *RIC 71*	200	450
25†	Hl ℞ As last but Victory hldg. wreath and palm. Aquileia $\overline{\text{AQ}}$. *RIC 65*	200	450
28†a	Hl ℞ FELICITAS PERPETVA VOT V, three emperors enthroned, facing, inscribed footstool. Siscia $\overline{\text{SIS}}\cup$. *RIC 41* **multiple** . .	10,000	20,000
28†b	As last. Thessalonica $\overline{\text{TES}}$. *RIC 52* **light miliarensis** . . .	2,500	5,500
30†	Hj ℞ FL IVL CONSTANS PF AVGG (*sic*), Victory walking l. hldg. wreath and palm, captive behind. Rome $\overline{\text{R}}$. *RIC 70* . .	250	550
33	Gl ℞ GAVDIVM POPVLI ROMANI SIC V SIC X in wreath. Thessalonica $\overline{\text{TES}}$. *RIC 45* **multiple**	6,500	13,000
34a	Hl ℞ As last. Siscia $\overline{\text{SIS}}\cup$. *RIC 45* **multiple**	6,500	13,000
34b	As last. Siscia $\cdot\overline{\text{SIS}}\cdot$. *RIC 46* **multiple**	6,500	13,000
35a	As last. Siscia $\overline{\text{SIS}}\cup$. *RIC 49* **heavy miliarensis** . . .	750	1,750
35b	As last. Siscia $\overline{\text{SIS}}\cup$. *RIC 52* **light miliarensis** . . .	750	1,750
35c	Hk ℞ As last. Siscia $\overline{\text{SIS}}\cup$. *RIC 51* **light miliarensis** . .	750	1,750

		VF	EF
35d	Hl ℞ As last. Thessalonica T̄S̄∈. *RIC 42* **light miliarensis** . .	750	1,750
38†a	Hk ℞ As last. Siscia S̄ĪS̄◡. *RIC 72*	275	625
38†b	As last. Thessalonica T̄S̄∈. *RIC 43*	275	625
38†c	Hl ℞ As last. Siscia S̄ĪS̄◡. *RIC 73*	275	625
40†a	Hl ℞ GAVDIVM POPVLI ROMANI, SIC X SIC XX in wreath. Siscia S̄ĪS̄Q. *RIC 149* **heavy miliarensis**	750	1,750
40†b	As last. Siscia S̄ĪS̄Q. *RIC 151* **heavy miliarensis**	750	1,750
40†c	As last. Siscia S̄ĪS̄. *RIC 153* **heavy miliarensis**	750	1,750
40†d	As last. Siscia S̄ĪS̄Q. *RIC 154* **light miliarensis**	750	1,750
40†e	Hj ℞ As last. Trier T̄R̄. *RIC 169* .	275	625
40A	Gl ℞ GAVDIVM POPVLI ROMANI, SIC XX SIC XXX in wreath. Thessalonica T̄Ē̄S. *RIC 77* **multiple** . .	6,500	13,000
41†	Gl ℞ GAVDIVM POPVLI ROMANI, VOT V MVLT X in wreath. Aquileia A̅Q̅. *RIC 47* **multiple**	6,500	13,000
44†	Hl ℞ GAVDIVM ROMANORVM, VOT X MVLT XV inscribed on banner of standard, seated captive either side. Trier T̄R̄. *RIC 152* **light miliarensis** .	750	1,750

		VF	EF
45†a	Hl ℞ As last but VOT X MVLT XX. Trier T̄R̄. *RIC 158* **light miliarensis** .	750	1,750
45†b	Hj ℞ As last. Trier T̄R̄. *RIC 159* **light miliarensis** . .	750	1,750
45†c	Hl ℞ As last but VOT V MVLT X. Trier T̄R̄. *RIC 160* . .	750	1,750
45A	Kl ℞ GLORIA EXERCITVS, four standards. Thessalonica T̄S̄∈. *RIC 38* **heavy miliarensis**	900	2,000
90A	Ic ℞ PAX AVGVSTORVM, emperor in mil. dress, stg. l. hldg. standard with Chi-rho on banner. Trier T̄R̄P. *RIC 32* . .	250	550
96	Ic ℞ PRINCIPI IVVENTVTIS, emperor in mil, dress stg. r., hldg. spear and globe, spurning captive with foot. Trier T̄R̄P. *RIC 35*	250	550

		VF	EF
112†a	Hl ℞ TRIVMFATOR GENTIVM BARBARARVM emp. in mil. dress stg. l. hldg. transverse spear and standard with Chi-rho on banner. Siscia ·S̄ĪS̄·. *RIC 148* **multiple** . .	7,000	14,000

		VF	EF
112†b	As last Aquileia $\overline{\text{*AQ}}$. *RIC* — **multiple**.	7,500	15,000
112c	Gl ℞ As last. Aquileia $\overline{\text{*AQ}}$. *RIC 49* **multiple**	7,500	15,000
113†a	Gl ℞ As last but no spear, standard has wreath on banner. Trier $\overline{\text{TR}}$. *RIC 145* **multiple**	7,000	14,000
113†b	Gj ℞ As last but emperor stg. r. Trier $\overline{\text{TR}}$. *RIC 149A* **multiple**	7,000	14,000
113†c	Gk ℞ As last. Trier $\overline{\text{TR}}$. *RIC 149* **multiple**	7,000	14,000
113†d	Gl ℞ As last. Trier $\overline{\text{TR}}$. *RIC 148* **multiple**	7,000	14,000
114†a	Gj ℞ As last, emperor in mil. dress stg. l. hldg. standard with wreath (?) on banner, resting l. hand on shield. Thessalonica $\overline{\text{TES}}$. *RIC 81* **multiple**	7,000	14,000
114†b	Gl ℞ As last. Thessalonica $\overline{\text{TES}}$. *RIC 80* **multiple** . . .	7,000	14,000
115a	Hj ℞ As last. Thessalonica $\overline{\text{TES}}$. *RIC 86* **heavy miliarensis** .	750	1,750
115b	Hk ℞ As last. Thessalonica $\overline{\text{TES}}$. *RIC 85* **heavy miliarensis** .	750	1,750
115c	Hj ℞ As last. Thessalonica $\overline{\text{TES}}$. *RIC 92* **light miliarensis**. .	750	1,750
115d	Hk ℞ As last. Thessalonica $\overline{\text{TES}}$. *RIC 91* **light miliarensis** .	750	1,750

		VF	EF
115e	Hl ℞ As last. Thessalonica. $\overline{\text{TES}}$. *RIC 90* **light miliarensis** . .	750	1,750
129†a	Kk ℞ VICTORIA AVGG NN, Victoria walking l. hldg. wreath and palm. Arelate $\overline{\text{PARL}}$. *RIC 67*	150	350
129†b	Kl ℞ As last. Arelate $\overline{\text{PARL}}$. *RIC 68*	150	350

		VF	EF
135†a	Hl ℞ VICTORIA AVGVSTORVM, Victory walking l. hldg. wreath and palm. Siscia $\frac{\text{≝∥}}{\text{SISQ}}$. *RIC 158* **light miliarensis**	650	1,500
135†b	As last. Siscia $\frac{\text{≝∥}}{\text{SISQ}}$. *RIC 159A* **light miliarensis**	650	1,500
135†c	As last. Siscia $\frac{}{\text{SIS•}}$. *RIC 161* **light miliarensis**.	650	1,500
135†d	Hj ℞ As last. Siscia $\frac{\text{≝∥}}{\text{SISQ}}$. *RIC 157* **light miliarensis**. . . .	650	1,500
136†	Hl ℞ As last. Siscia $\overline{\text{SIS •}}$. *RIC 163*	150	350
137a	Hj ℞ As last, Victory hldg. palm and trophy. Siscia $\overline{\text{SIS •}}$. *RIC 166*	150	350

	VF	EF
137b Hk ℞ As last. Siscia $\overline{\text{SIS}\cup}$. *RIC 167*	150	350
137c Hl ℞ As last. Siscia $\overline{\text{SIS}\cup}$. *RIC 168.*	150	350
138†a Hj ℞ As last but Victory hldg. wreath and trophy. Siscia $\overline{\text{SIS}\cup}$. *RIC 171*	150	350
138†b Hk ℞ As last. Siscia $\overline{\text{SIS}\cup}$. *RIC 172*	150	350

	VF	EF
138†c Hl ℞ As last. Siscia $\overline{\text{SIS}\cup}$. *RIC 173.*	150	350
151†a Jj ℞ VICTORIA DD NN ACGG, Victory walking l. hldg. wreath and palm. Trier $\overline{\text{SIS}\cup}$. *RIC 179* **half siliqua**	200	450
151†b As last. Arelate $\overline{\text{PARL}}$. *RIC 70*	150	350
151†c As last. Arelate $\overline{\text{ARL}}$. *RIC 71*	150	350

	VF	EF
152†a Hj ℞ As last. Trier $\overline{\text{TR}}$. *RIC 176*	150	350
152†b Hl ℞ As last. Trier $\overline{\text{TR}}$. *RIC 177*	150	350

	VF	EF
155†a Kk ℞ As last, Victory hldg. wreath and trophy. Lugdunum $\overline{\text{PLG}}$·. *RIC 35*	150	350
155†b Kj ℞ As last. Thessalonica $\overline{\text{TES}}$. *RIC 98.*	150	350
155†c Kk ℞ As last. Thessalonica $\overline{\text{TES}}$. *RIC 97*	150	350
155†d Kl ℞ As last. Thessalonica $\overline{\text{TES}}$. *RIC 96.*	150	350
156†a Kl ℞ As last, Victory hldg. wreath and palm. Thessalonica $\overline{\text{TS}\epsilon}$. *RIC 41*	150	350

		VF	EF
156†b	As last. Thessalonica T̄ĒS̄. *RIC 54*	150	350
158†a	Hj Ɍ As last but captive behind. Rome R̄. *RIC 67*	150	350
158†b	Hk Ɍ As last. Rome R̄. *RIC 68*	150	350
158†c	Hl Ɍ As last. Rome R̄. *RIC 69*	150	350
160†a	Hj Ɍ VICTORIAE DN AVG VOT X MVLT XV, two Victories stg. facing one another hldg. inscribed wreath. Trier T̄R̄. *RIC 167A†* . .	175	400
160†b	Hk Ɍ As last. Trier T̄R̄. *RIC 166*	175	400
160†c	Hl Ɍ As last. Trier T̄R̄. *RIC 167*	175	400
160†d	Hk Ɍ As last. Aquileia *ĀQ̄. *RIC 55*	175	400
160†e	Hl Ɍ As last. Aquileia ĀQ̄. *RIC 53*	175	400
160†f	As last. Aquileia *ĀQ̄. *RIC 54*	175	400
161†a	Hk Ɍ As last but VOT V MVLT X. Trier T̄R̄. *RIC 164*	175	400
161†b	Hl Ɍ As last. Trier T̄R̄. *RIC 165*	175	400
161†c	As last. Aquileia *ĀQ̄. *RIC 52A*	175	400
162†	Hj As last but VOT X MVLT XX. Trier T̄R̄. *RIC 168*	175	400
163†	Hl Ɍ VICTORIAE DD NN AVGG VOT X MVLT XV. Victory seated r. on cuirass and shield, inscribing shield held on l. knee. Aquileia *ĀQ̄. *RIC 50* **heavy miliarensis**.	750	1,750
163Aa	Hk Ɍ As last but VOT X MVLT XX. Aquileia *ĀQ̄. *RIC 51* **heavy miliarensis**	750	1,750
163Ab	As last. Aquileia ĀQ̄. *RIC 52* **heavy miliarensis**	750	1,750
164†a	Jl Ɍ As last. Aquileia L̄X̄ĀQ̄. *RIC 57* **heavy miliarensis** . .	750	1,750
164†b	As last. Aquileia ĀQ̄. *RIC 57A* **heavy miliarensis**	750	1,750
164†c	As last. Aquileia *ĀQ̄. *RIC 61* **light miliarensis**	750	1,750
164†d	As last. Aquileia ĀQ̄. *RIC 62* **light miliarensis**	750	1,750
164†e	As last. Aquileia ĀQ̄S̄. *RIC 63* **light miliarensis**	750	1,750
189†a	Hj Ɍ VIRTVS AVGG, emperor in mil. dress stg. l., hldg. standard with Chi-rho on banner. Trier T̄R̄. *RIC 172* **heavy miliarensis**	750	1,750
189†b	Hl Ɍ As last. Trier T̄R̄. *RIC 173* **heavy miliarensis** . . .	750	1,750
189†c	Hj Ɍ As last but emperor stg. facing. Trier T̄R̄. *RIC 174* **heavy miliarensis**	750	1,750

189†d	Hk Ɍ As last but emperor resting l. hand on shield. Lugdunum P̄L̄Ḡ. *RIC 33* **heavy miliarensis**	800	1,850
192†	Jl Ɍ VIRTVS EXERCITVM, four standards, the two central ones inscribed alpha and omega, between them Chi-rho. Rome R̄. *RIC 71* **light miliarensis**	1,000	2,250
193†	Hl Ɍ VIRTVS EXERCITVS, helmeted soldier stg. facing, hldg. vertical spear and resting l. hand on shield. Thessalonica T̄ĒS̄. *RIC 48* **heavy miliarensis**	800	1,850
193A	Fe Ɍ As last, three standards. Cyzicus S̄M̄K̄B̄. *RIC 39A* **heavy miliarensis**	900	2,000
199a	Jd Ɍ VOTIS XXV MVLTIS XXX in wreath. Nicomedia S̄M̄N̄. *RIC 42*	125	300
199b	Je Ɍ As last. Nicomedia S̄M̄N̄. *RIC 43*	125	300
199c	Jf Ɍ As last. Nicomedia S̄M̄N̄. *RIC 44*	125	300

CONSTANTIUS II
CAESAR A.D. 324–337
AUGUSTUS A.D. 337–361

Flavius Julius Constantius, the third son of Constantine I, was born in 317 and made Caesar in 324. By 333 he had been installed in Antioch and, at Constantine I's death in 337, the Eastern portion of the empire came under his control. He was by far the ablest of Constantine I's surviving sons and capable of incisive action although possessed of a deeply suspicious temperament. Throughout his reign he fought a series of campaigns against the Persians but the war was never resolved in his favour. His religious policy favoured the Arian Christians rather than the Athanasians. In 353 he was finally able to put down the rebellion of Magnentius and thereby gained control of the whole empire. After spending some time in Gaul Constantius returned to the East, leaving behind his cousin Julian who had been proclaimed Caesar at Milan in November, 355. Following an unsuccessful campaign against the Persians in 360, prior to which he had learned that Julian's troops had proclaimed him emperor, Constantius determined to march west against his cousin, and married for a third time in the hope of securing a male heir. On the journey he fell ill and died in Cilicia in 361, being baptized a Christian on his deathbed.

Obverse legends

As Caesar
A. NO LEGEND
B. CONSTANTIVS NOB C.
C. CONSTANTIVS NOB CAES.
D. FL IVL CONSTANTIVS NOB C.
E. FL IVL CONSTANTIVS NOB CAES.
F. DN CONSTANTIVS NOB CAES.

As Augustus
G. NO LEGEND
H. FL IVL CONSTANTIVS PERP AVG.
I. FL IVL CONSTANTIVS PIVS FELIX AVG.
J. FL IVL CONSTANTIVS PF AVG.
K. FL IVL CONSTANTIVS AVG.
L. DN CONSTANTI AVGVSTI.
M. DN CONSTANTIVS PERP AVG.
N. DN CONSTANTIVS MAX AVG.
O. DN CONSTANTIVS PF AVG.
P. DN CONSTANTIVS AVG.
Q. CONSTANTIVS PF AVG.

Obverse busts
a. bare, right.
b. laureate, cuirassed, right.
c. laureate, cuirassed, left.
d. draped, cuirassed, raising right hand, holding globe in left hand, left.
e. laureate, draped, cuirassed, globe in right hand, spear pointing forward in left hand, right.
f. plain diadem, looking upwards, right.
g. pearl diadem, cuirassed, right.
h. laureate, draped, cuirassed, right.
i. pearl diadem, draped, cuirassed, right.
j. rosette diadem, draped, cuirassed, right.
k. laurel and rosette diadem, draped, cuirassed, right.
l. pearl diadem, right.
m. rosette diadem, right.
n. laureate, looking upwards, right.
o. pearl diadem, looking upwards, right.
p. rosette diadem, looking upwards, right.
q. laurel and rosette diadem, looking upward, right.
r. pearl diadem, helmeted, cuirassed, spear over right shoulder, shield decorated with Christogram on left shoulder, facing.
s. helmeted, draped, cuirassed, holding branch in right hand, spear over left shoulder, right.

All coins are siliquae unless otherwise specified. For a discussion of fourth-century silver denominations and their names, see the Introduction.

CAESAR

		VF	EF
15a	Af R CONSTANTIVS CAESAR, Victory walking l. hldg wreath and palm. Thessalonica T̄S̄Ē. *RIC 216*	300	700

		VF	EF
15b	As last. Heraclea $\overline{\text{SMH}}$. *RIC 146*.	300	700
15c	As last. Constantinople $\overline{\text{CONSA}}$. *RIC 127A*	300	700
15Aa	Af ℞ CONSTANTIVS CAES, as last. Constantinople $\frac{\text{M}}{\text{CONSA}}$. *RIC 128*.	300	700
15Ab	As last. Constantinople $\frac{\text{MI}}{\text{CONSA}}$. *RIC 131B*	300	700
17	Dh ℞ CONSTANTIVS CAESAR, four standards. Siscia $\overline{\text{SIS}}$. *RIC 231* **miliarensis**	650	1,500
17†a	Db ℞ As last. Trier $\overline{\text{SMTR}}$. *RIC 583* **miliarensis**	650	1,500
17†b	As last. Siscia $\overline{\text{SIS}}$. *RIC 232* **multiple?**	650	1,500
17†c	As last. Constantinople $\overline{\text{·CONSA·}}$. *RIC 56* **miliarensis** . .	650	1,500
17†d	Bb ℞ As last. Siscia $\overline{\text{SIS}}$. *RIC 211* **miliarensis**	650	1,500
17†e	Eh ℞ As last. Trier $\overline{\text{SMTR}}$. *RIC 582* **miliarensis**	650	1,500
17†f	Af ℞ As last. Nicomedia $\overline{\text{SMN}}$. *RIC 87* **miliarensis**	750	1,750
18	Ce ℞ As last. Trier $\overline{\text{SMTR}}$. *RIC 584* **miliarensis**	900	2,000
18A	Eh ℞ CONSTANTIVS CAES, as last. Constantinople $\overline{\text{CONSA}}$. *RIC 125* **miliarensis**	650	1,500
19	Af ℞ CONSTANTIVS CAESAR, three palm branches, star above. Rome $\overline{\text{R}}$. *RIC 379* **multiple?**	350	800
19A	Af ℞ CONSTANTIVS NOB CAES, as last. Nicomedia $\overline{\text{N}}$. *RIC 187* .	350	800
75	Cb ℞ FELICITAS ROMANORVM, emperor stg. under arch with three sons. Cyzicus $\overline{\text{SMK}}$. *RIC 43* **miliarensis**	1,000	2,250
75†	Dc ℞ As last but only two sons. Nicomedia $\overline{\text{SMN}}$. *RIC 143* **miliarensis**	1,000	2,250
91a	Dh ℞ GLORIA EXERCITVS, female figure stg l. hldg laurel branch and sceptre, leaning on column. Thessalonica $\overline{\text{TSE}}$. *RIC 220A* **miliarensis**	750	1,750
91b	As last. Constantinople $\overline{\text{·CONSA·}}$. *RIC 57* **miliarensis** . .	750	1,750
91c	As last. Constantinople $\overline{\text{CONSA}}$. *RIC 130* **miliarensis** . .	750	1,750
91d	As last. Constantinople $\overline{\text{C·A}}$ *RIC 134* **miliarensis**	750	1,750
91e	Ah ℞ As last. Thessalonica $\overline{\text{TSE}}$. *RIC 220* **miliarensis** . .	750	1,750
160A	Dh ℞ PRINCIPI IVVENTVTIS, prince in military dress stg. l. hldg. standard and vertical sceptre, standard behind. Sirmium $\overline{\text{SIRM}}$. *RIC 16*	350	800

		VF	EF
250†	Db ℞ VICTORIA CAESARVM Victory advancing l. hldg wreath and palm. Siscia $\overline{\text{SIS}}$. *RIC 213*	250	550

AUGUSTUS

		VF	EF
4a	Gq ℞ CONSTANTIVS AVG, Victory walking l. hldg. wreath and palm. Heraclea $\overline{\text{SMH}}$. *RIC 11*	250	550
4b	G? ℞ As last. Nicomedia $\overline{\text{SMNA}}$. *RIC 3 (confirmation required)*	—	—
4c	Gq ℞ As last. Cyzicus $\overline{\text{SMK·}}$. *RIC 2*	250	550
5†a	Kh ℞ As last, four standards. Trier $\overline{\text{SMTR}}$. *RIC 23* **light miliarensis**	750	1,750

		VF	EF
5†b	Kk ℞ As last. Trier S̄M̄T̄R̄. *RIC 22* **light miliarensis** . .	750	1,750
7	Hi ℞ As last. Arelate P̄C̄ŌN̄. *RIC 243* **heavy miliarensis**. .	750	1,750
8†a	Oi ℞ As last. Arelate P̄C̄ŌN̄. *RIC 244* **heavy miliarensis**. .	750	1,750
8†b	Oj ℞ As last. Arelate P̄C̄ŌN̄. *RIC 245* **heavy miliarensis**. .	750	1,750
8†c	Ok ℞ As last. Arelate P̄C̄ŌN̄. *RIC 246* **heavy miliarensis** .	750	1,750
9a	Ng ℞ As last. Rome *R̄*. *RIC 243* **heavy miliarensis**	750	1,750
9b	As last. Constantinople C̄·Ā. *RIC 131* **heavy miliarensis** . .	750	1,750
9†c	Gm ℞ CONSTANTIVS AVGVSTVS As last. Constantinople C̄·Ā. *RIC 13* **light miliarensis**	850	1,900
9†d	Gq ℞ As last. Constantinople C̄·Ā. *RIC 14* **light miliarensis**	850	1,900
10a	Qk ℞ CONSTANTIVS AVG As last, three palm branches, star above. Siscia S̄ĪS̄ᴗ. *RIC 63*	350	800
10b	As last. Siscia S̄ĪS̄·. *RIC 64*	350	800
10c	Qj ℞ As last. Siscia S̄ĪS̄. *RIC 60*	350	800
10d	As last. Siscia ·S̄ĪS̄·. *RIC 61*	350	800
10e	As last. Siscia S̄ĪS̄ᴗ. *RIC 62*	350	
11	G? ℞ As last. Rome R̄. *RIC 1A (confirmation required)* . .	—	—
11Aa	Gn ℞ CONSTANTIVS AVG, in wreath. Antioch ĀN̄T̄. *RIC 34* . .	400	900
11Ab	Go ℞ As last. Alexandria ĀL̄Ē. *RIC 2*.	400	900
12a	Gp ℞ CONSTANTIVS AVGVSTVS, Victory walking l. hldg. wreath and palm. Constantinople C̄·Ā. *RIC 18*	250	550
12b	Gq ℞ As last. Constantinople. C̄·Ā. *RIC 18A*	250	550
12†c	Gn ℞ As last. Constantinople. C̄·Ā *RIC 17*	250	550
22	Jk ℞ CONSTANTIVS PF AVG, three standards. Thessalonica T̄ĒS̄. *RIC 50* **light miliarensis**	750	1,750

30†	Ji ℞ FEL TEMP REPARATIO VOT XX, Victory stg. r. with foot on globe, inscribing shield supported by kneeling figure. Rome R̄. *RIC 59–60*	225	500
61a	Qk ℞ FELICITAS PERPETVA, Victory walking l. hldg. wreath and trophy. Aquileia ĀQ̄. *RIC 64*	200	450
61b	As last. Aquileia *ĀQ̄. *RIC 67*	200	450
62†a	Oi ℞ As last. Aquileia ĀQ̄·. *RIC 69*	200	450
62†b	Ok ℞ As last. Aquileia ĀQ̄·. *RIC 70*	200	450

		VF	EF
62A	Qk R As last, Victory hldg. wreath and palm. Aquileia $\overline{*AQ}$. *RIC 66*	200	450
65A	Qk R FELICITAS PERPETVA, VOT X MVLT XX, in wreath. Aquileia $\overline{*AQ}$. *RIC 58* **light miliarensis**	750	1,750
65†a	Qk R FELICITAS PERPETVA, VOT XX MVLT XXX in wreath. Aquileia $\overline{AQ}$. *RIC 59* **light miliarensis**	750	1,750
65†b	As last. Aquileia $\overline{AQS}$. *RIC 60* **light miliarensis**	750	1,750
68a	Pj R FELICITAS REIPVBLICE, VOT XV MVLT XX in wreath. Constantinople. $\overline{C\cdot A}$. *RIC 58*	250	550
68†b	Gp R As last. Nicomedia $\overline{SMN}$. *RIC 37*	300	650
70a	Pk R FELICITAS REIPVBLICE, VOT XX MVLT XXX in wreath. Heraclea $\overline{SMH}$. *RIC 40*	250	550

70b	Pj R As last. Constantinople $\overline{C\cdot A}$. *RIC 59*	250	550
70c	As last. Cyzicus $\overline{SMK}$. *RIC 3*	250	550
70d	As last. Cyzicus $\overline{SMKH}$. *RIC 3A*	250	550
70†e	Gq R As last. Nicomedia $\overline{SMN}$. *RIC 38*	300	650
70†f	Gp R As last. Nicomedia $\overline{SMN}$. *RIC 39*	300	650
74†a	Oi R FELICITAS ROMANORVM, emperor and Caesar in mil. dress hldg. spear in r. hand, stg. facing under arch. Aquileia $\overline{AQ}$. *RIC 182* **light miliarensis**	750	1,750

74†b	As last. Sirmium $\overline{SIRM}$ *RIC 11* **light miliarensis**	750	1,750
74†c	As last. Sirmium $\overline{\cdot SIRM\cdot}$. *RIC 13* **light miliarensis** . .	750	1,750
74†d	As last. Nicomedia $\overline{SMN}$. *RIC 77* **light miliarensis** . .	750	1,750
74†e	As last. Nicomedia $\overline{\cdot SMN\cdot}$ *RIC 79* **light miliarensis** . .	750	1,750
74†f	As last. Antioch $\overline{SMAN}$. *RIC 102* **light miliarensis** . .	750	1,750
83	Qk R GAVDIVM POPVLI ROMANI, SIC X SIC XX in wreath. Siscia $\overline{SIS\cup}$. *RIC 48* **heavy miliarensis**	750	1,750
84a	As last. Siscia $\overline{SIS\cup}$. *RIC 42* **multiple**	6,500	13,000
84†b	As last. Siscia $\overline{SIS\cup}$. *RIC 71*	275	600
85a	Ik R As last. Thessalonica $\overline{TES}$. *RIC 44* **multiple** . . .	6,500	13,000
85b	Ij R As last. Thessalonica $\overline{TES}$. *RIC 44 (footnote)* **multiple**.	6,500	13,000
85†c	Jk R As last. Siscia $\overline{SIS\cup}$. *RIC 43* **multiple** . . .	6,500	13,000
85†d	As last. Siscia $\overline{\cdot SIS\cdot}$. *RIC 44* **multiple**	6,500	13,000
86	Ik R As last. Thessalonica $\overline{TES}$. *RIC 76*	6.500	13,000

		VF	EF
87a	Qk ℞ GAVDIVM POPVLI ROMANI, SIC XX SIC XXX in wreath. Siscia ⚜⚜/SISQ. *RIC 150* **heavy miliarensis**	750	1,750
87b	As last. Siscia ⚜⚜/SISᴗ. *RIC 152* **heavy miliarensis**	750	1,750
87†c	Jk ℞ As last. Siscia ‾SIS‾. *RIC 145* **multiple**.	6,500	13,000
87A	Oi ℞ GAVDIVM POPVLI ROMANI, VOTIS XXX MVLTIS XXXX in wreath. Sirmium ·SIRM·. *RIC 10* **heavy miliarensis** . .	750	1,750

		VF	EF
89†a	Ji ℞ GAVDIVM ROMANORVM, VOT XX MVLT XXX inscribed on banner, seated captive either side. Trier T̄R. *RIC 155* **light miliarensis**	750	1,750
89†b	Jj ℞ As last. Trier T̄R. *RIC 154* **light miliarensis**	750	1,750
89†c	Jk ℞ As last. Trier T̄R. *RIC 153* **light miliarensis**.	750	1,750
89A	Jk ℞ As last, but VOT X MVLT XV. Trier T̄R. *RIC 151* **light miliarensis**	750	1,750
89Ba	Ji ℞ As last, but VOT X MVLT XX. Trier T̄R. *RIC 157* **light miliarensis**	750	1,750
89Bb	Jk ℞ As last. Trier T̄R. *RIC 156* **light miliarensis**. . . .	750	1,750
141	Hr ℞ GLORIA ROMANORVM VOT XXX MVLT XXXX, Rome helmeted and Constantinople turreted stg. facing, supporting inscribed shield on short column. Rome R̄. *RIC 232* **multiple** . .	7,500	15,000
141†	Ls ℞ As last. Rome R̄. *RIC 233* **multiple**	7,000	14,000
149†a	Ji ℞ PAX AVGVSTORVM, emperor in mil. dress stg. l. hldg. banner with Chi-rho on banner. Trier T̄R. *RIC 163*.	225	500
149†b	Jj ℞ As last. Trier T̄R. *RIC 162*	225	500
149c	Jk ℞ As last. Trier. T̄R *RIC 161*	225	500
149d	As last. Trier T̄RP. *RIC 170*	225	500
150	Kh ℞ As last. Trier T̄RP. *RIC 31*	225	500
164Aa	Kh ℞ PRINCIPI IVVENTVTIS, emperor in mil. dress stg. r. hldg. spear and globe, spurning captive with l. foot. Trier T̄RP. *RIC 34*	225	500
164Ab	As last. Trier T̄R. *RIC 36*	225	500

		VF	EF
187	Oi ℞ SPES REIPVBLICE, emperor helmeted, in mil. dress stg. l. hldg. globe and spear. Thessalonica T̄ES. *RIC 207* **reduced siliqua**	150	350

		VF	EF

191 Qk ℞ TRIVMFATOR GENTIVM BARBARARVM emperor in mil. dress stg. l. hldg. standard with Chi-rho on banner and transverse spear. Aquileia *AQ. *RIC 48* **multiple** 7,000 14,000

			VF	EF
192a	Ji ℞ As last but circle on banner; emp. resting l. hand on shield. Thessalonica TES. *RIC 84* **heavy miliarensis**		750	1,750
192b	As last. Thessalonica TES. *RIC 84* **heavy miliarensis** . .		750	1,750
192c	Jj ℞ As last. Thessalonica. TES *RIC 83* **heavy miliarensis** .		750	1,750
192d	As last. Thessalonica TES. *RIC 88* **light miliarensis** . . .		750	1,750
192e	Jk ℞ As last. Thessalonica TES. *RIC 82* **heavy miliarensis** .		750	1,750
192f	As last. Thessalonica TES. *RIC 87* **light miliarensis** . . .		750	1,750
192†G	Ik ℞ As last, wreath on banner l. hand empty. Trier TR. *RIC 150* **heavy miliarensis**		750	1,750
193†a	Jk ℞ As last, Chi-rho on banner transverse spear in l. hand. Siscia ·SIS·. *RIC 147* **multiple**.		7,000	14,000
193†b	As last. Sisica SIS. *RIC 146* **multiple**		7,000	14,000
194†a	Ik ℞ As last, standard has wreath on banner, l. hand empty. Trier TR. *RIC 144, 146* **multiple**		7,000	14,000
194†b	Ii ℞ As last, standard has circle on banner, l. hand resting on shield. Thessalonica TES. *RIC 79* **multiple**		7,000	14,000
194†c	Ik ℞ As last. Thessalonica TES. *RIC 78* **multiple**		7,000	14,000
194†d	Id ℞ As last. Thessalonica TES. *RIC 79A* **multiple**. . . .		7,000	14,000
194A	Ik ℞ As last, emperor stg. r., wreath on banner l. hand empty. Trier TR. *RIC 147* **multiple**		7,000	14,000
195	Q? ℞ As last, emperor stg. l., wreath on banner. Trier TR. *RIC — (confirmation required)* **multiple**		—	—
211Aa	Qi ℞ VICTORIA AVGG NN, Victory walking l. hldg. wreath and palm. Arelate PARL. *RIC 64*		125	300
211Ab	Qk ℞ As last. Arelate PARL. *RIC 66*		125	300
211Ac	Jk ℞ As last. Arelate PARL. *RIC 65*		125	300
213†a	Hi ℞ VICTORIA AVGVSTI, Victory walking l. hldg. wreath and palm. Rome R. *RIC 301* **reduced siliqua**		75	185
213†b	Ok ℞ As last. Rome R. *RIC 242*		110	275
213†c	Oi ℞ As last. Rome R. *RIC 241*		110	275
214†a	Qk ℞ As last. Rome R. *RIC 240A*		110	275
214†b	Qi ℞ As last. Rome R. *RIC 240*		110	275
214†c	Kh ℞ As last. Trier TRP. *RIC 27*		110	275
220	Ng ℞ VICTORIA AVGVSTI VOT XXXX, Victory stg. facing, hldg. wreath in r. hand and inscribed shield in l. Constantinople C·A *RIC 132* **heavy miliarensis**		850	1,900
225a	Oi ℞ VICTORIA AVGVSTI N Victory walking l. hldg. wreath and palm. Rome R. *RIC 247*		110	275
225b	As last. Rome *R*. *RIC 248*		110	275
229a	Qj ℞ VICTORIA AVGSTORVM, Victory walking l. hldg. wreath and palm. Siscia SISQ. *RIC 155* **light miliarensis**		650	1,500

		VF	EF
229b	Qk ℞ As last. Siscia $\frac{⚹|}{SISQ}$. *RIC 156* **light miliarensis** . .	650	1,500
229c	As last. Siscia $\frac{⚹|}{SIS\cup}$. *RIC 159* **light miliarensis**	650	1,500
229d	As last. Siscia $\overline{SIS\cup}$. *RIC 160* **light miliarensis**	650	1,500
230	As last. Siscia $\overline{SIS\cup}$. *RIC 162*	125	300
233†a	Qi ℞ As last. Victory hldg. wreath and trophy. Siscia $\overline{SIS\cup}$. *RIC 169, 264*	125	300
233†b	As last. Siscia $\overline{SIS}$. *RIC 266*	125	300
233†c	Qk ℞ As last. Siscia $\overline{SIS\cup}$. *RIC 170*	125	300
233†d	As last. Siscia $\cdot\overline{SIS}\cdot$. *RIC 174*	125	300
234Aa	Qi ℞ As last, Victory hldg. palm and trophy. Siscia $\overline{SIS\cup}$. *RIC 164*.	125	300
234Ab	As last. Siscia $\overline{SIS}$. *RIC 268*	125	300
234Ac	Qk ℞ As last. Siscia $\overline{SIS\cup}$. *RIC 165*	125	300
258A	Qi ℞ VICTORIA DN AVG, Victory walking l. hldg. wreath and palm, spurning captive. Thessalonica $\cdot\overline{TES}\cdot$. *RIC 162*. . .	150	350
259a	Oi ℞ VICTORIA DD NN AVG, Victory walking l. hldg. wreath and palm, one wing visible. Lugdunum $\overline{LVG}$. *RIC 214* **reduced siliqua**	60	150

		VF	EF
259b	Oj ℞ As last but both Victory's wings visible. Lugdunum $\overline{LVG}$. *RIC 211* **reduced siliqua**.	60	150
259c	Ok ℞ As last. Lugdunum $\overline{LVG}$. *RIC 210* **reduced siliqua** .	60	150
259A	Oj ℞ VICTORIA DD NN AVGG, as last. Arelate $\overline{PARL}$. *RIC 69* . .	125	300
263†a	Qk ℞ As last, Victory hldg. wreath and trophy. Lugdunum $\overline{S\overset{*|}{L}G}$. *RIC 34A*	125	300
263†b	Qi ℞ As last. Lugdunum $\overline{S\overset{*|}{L}G}$. *RIC 35*	125	300

		VF	EF
263†c	As last. Thessalonica $\overline{TES}$. *RIC 95*	125	300
263†d	Qj ℞ As last. Thessalonica $\overline{TES}$. *RIC 94*	125	300
263†e	Qk ℞ As last. Thessalonica $\overline{TES}$. *RIC 93*	125	300
266	Ji ℞ As last, Victory hldg. wreath and palm. Trier $\overline{TR}$. *RIC 175*	125	300
267a	Qi ℞ as last. Trier $\overline{TR}$. *RIC 178* **half siliqua**	200	450
267b	Qk ℞ As last. Thessalonica $\overline{TS\epsilon}$. *RIC 40*	125	300
267c	As last. Thessalonica $\overline{TES}$. *RIC 53*	125	300
268a	Ji ℞ As last but captive behind Victory. Rome $\overline{R}$. *RIC 64* . .	125	300

		VF	EF
268b	Jj ℞ As last. Rome $\overline{R}$. *RIC 65* . .	125	300
268c	Jk ℞ As last. Rome $\overline{R}$. *RIC 66* . .	125	300
270	Oi ℞ VICTORIA ROMANORVM, Bene: emperor in mil. dress hldg. spear and globe being cr: Victory. Antioch SMAN. *RIC 103, 181* **light milia:**	750	1,750
275A	Qk ℞ VICTORIAE DN AVG VOT X MVLT X tories stg. facing one another hldg. inscribed wreath. 'AQ, *RIC 56* . .	175	400

| **322†** | Ji ℞ VIRTVS DD NN AVGG, emperor in mil. dress stg. l. hldg. standard with Chi-rho on banner. Trier $\overline{TR}$, *RIC 171* **heavy miliarensis** . . . . | 750 | 1,750 |

| **324A** | Oi ℞ VIRTVS EXERCITVM, soldier stg. l. hldg. inverted spear and resting l. hand on shield. Arelate $\overline{PCON}$. *RIC 289* **light miliarensis** . . . . | 750 | 1,750 |
| **325†** | Jk ℞ VIRTVS EXERCITVS, soldier stg. facing, hldg. vertical spear and resting l. hand on shield. Thessalonica $\overline{TES}$. *RIC 47* **heavy miliarensis** . . . . | 750 | 1,750 |

326a	Oi ℞ As last. Constantinople $\overline{C \cdot A}$. *RIC 100* **light miliarensis**	650	1,500
326b	As last, Cyzicus $\overline{SMK}$. *RIC 41* **light miliarensis**	750	1,750
326c	As last. Cyzicus $\overline{SMKA}$. *RIC 42* **light miliarensis**	750	1,750

| **326†d** | Oi ℞ As last, soldier stg. l. Rome $\overline{R}$. *RIC 238* **light miliarensis** . . . . | 650 | 1,500 |

		VF	EF
326†e	Oj ℞ As last. Rome R̄. *RIC 239* **light miliarensis**	650	1,500
326†f	Oi ℞ As last. Siscia S̄ĪS̄. *RIC 323* **light miliarensis** . . .	650	1,500
326†g	As last. Lugdunum L̄V̄Ḡ. *R ?08* **light miliarensis** . .	650	1,500

		VF	EF
326†h	As last. Arelate P̄C̄ŌN̄. *RIC 252* **light miliarensis**	650	1,500
326†i	Oi ℞ As last, soldier stg. r. Arelate P̄C̄ŌN̄. *RIC 250* **light miliarensis**	650	1,500

		VF	EF
326†j	Oi ℞ As last, soldier stg. facing. T̄ĒS̄. Thessalonica *RIC 160, 203* **light miliarensis**	650	1,500
327†a	Ng ℞ As last, soldier stg. l. Rome R̄. *RIC 245* **light miliarensis**	650	1,500
327†b	As last. Rome *R̄*. *RIC 246* **light miliarensis**	650	1,500
327†c	Ni ℞ As last. Rome R̄. *RIC 244* **light miliarensis**	650	1,500
328A	Ol ℞ As last, three standards. Thessalonica T̄ĒS̄. *RIC 158, 201* **heavy miliarensis**	750	1,750
336Aa	Oi ℞ VOT XXX MVLTS XXXX, in wreath. Rome R̄. *RIC 234* . .	80	200
336A†b	Oi ℞ VOT XXX MVLT XXXX, in wreath. Siscia S̄ĪS̄. *RIC 324* . .	80	200
336A†c	Ol ℞ As last. Siscia S̄ĪS̄. *RIC 325*	80	200
337	Oi ℞ VOT XXXX, in wreath. Constantinople C̄·Ā. *RIC 134* **reduced siliqua**	60	150
338†	Oi ℞ VOTIS V MVLTIS X, in wreath. Arelate P̄C̄ŌN̄. *RIC 262, 294* hybrid: rev. of Julian **reduced siliqua**	—	—
338A	Go ℞ VOTIS XV MVLTIS XX in wreath. Antioch Ā̄N̄T̄. *RIC 35* .	250	550
339a	Ol ℞ VOTIS XX MVLTIS XXX, in wreath. Antioch Ā̄N̄T̄. *RIC 105*	100	250

		VF	EF
339†b	Go ℞ As last. Antioch Ā̄N̄T̄. *RIC 36*	250	550
340a	Ol ℞ VOTIS XXV MVLTIS XXX, in wreath. Constantinople C̄·Ā. *RIC 60*	100	250
340b	As last. Nicomedia S̄M̄N̄. *RIC 40*	100	250
340c	As last. Cyzicus S̄M̄K̄. *RIC 43*	100	250

		VF	EF
340d	As last. Antioch $\overline{\text{ANT}}$. *RIC 106*	100	250
340e	Om R As last. Nicomedia $\overline{\text{SMN}}$. *RIC 41*	100	250
340f	As last. Cyzicus $\overline{\text{SMK}}$. *RIC 44*	100	250
340†g	Oi R As last. Constantinople $\overline{\text{C·A}}$. *RIC 61*	100	250
340†h	As last. Antioch $\overline{\text{ANT}}$. *RIC 107*	100	250
341a	Ol R votis xxx mvltis xxxx. Lugdunum $\overline{\text{LVG}}$. *RIC 180* . .	80	200
341b	As last. Aquileia $\overline{\text{AQ}}$. *RIC 183*	80	200
341c	As last. Thessalonica $\overline{\text{TES}}$. *RIC 163, 205*	80	200
341d	As last. Constantinople $\overline{\text{C·A}}$. *RIC 101*	80	200
341e	As last. Nicomedia $\overline{\text{SMN}}$. *RIC 80*	80	200

342–3a	Oi R As last. Lugdunum $\overline{\text{LVG}}$. *RIC 216* **reduced siliqua** . .	40	100
342–3b	As last. Arelate $\overline{\text{PAR}}$. *RIC 203*	70	175
342–3c	As last. Arelate $\overline{\text{PCON}}$. *RIC 207, 253*	65	160

342–3d	As last. Aquileia $\overline{\text{AQ}}$. *RIC 184*	65	160

342–3e	As last. Sirmium $\overline{\text{SIRM}}$. *RIC 15*	65	160

342–3f	As last. Sirmium $\overline{\cdot\text{SIRM}}$. *RIC 17*	65	160

		VF	EF
342–3g	As last. Sirmium $\overline{\text{SIRM}}$·. *RIC 19*	65	160
342–3h	As last. Sirmium $\overline{\text{SIRM}}$⊍. *RIC 20*	65	160
342–3i	As last. Sirmium ·SIRM·. *RIC 66*	65	160

		VF	EF
342–3j	As last. Constantinople $\overline{\text{C·A}}$. *RIC 102*	65	160
342–3k	As last. Constantinople $\overline{\text{C}\text{\textit{Ɛ}}\text{A}}$. *RIC 104*	65	160

		VF	EF
342–3l	As last. Nicomedia $\overline{\text{SMN}}$. *RIC 81*	65	160

		VF	EF
342–3m	As last. Cyzicus $\overline{\text{SMK}}$. *RIC 44A*.	70	175
342–3n	As last. Antioch ·$\overline{\text{ANTΘ}}$·. *RIC 183*	65	160
342–3o	As last. Antioch ·$\overline{\text{ANT}}$·. *RIC 184*	65	160
342–3p	As last. Antioch $\overline{\text{ANT}}$. *RIC 108*	65	160
342–3q	As last. Arelate $\overline{\text{CON}}$. *RIC 258* **reduced siliqua**	50	125
342–3r	As last. Arelate $\overline{\text{PCON}}$. *RIC 261, 291* **reduced siliqua**	40	100
342–3s	As last. Rome $\overline{\text{R}}$. *RIC 303* **reduced siliqua**	60	150

		VF	EF
342–3t	As last. Siscia $\overline{\text{SIS}}$. *RIC 360* **reduced siliqua**	50	125
342–3u	As last. Sirmium $\overline{\text{SIRM}}$. *RIC 68* **reduced siliqua**	45	110
342–3v	As last. Constantinople $\overline{\text{C·A}}$. *RIC 133* **reduced siliqua**	45	110
342–3w	As last. Nicomedia $\overline{\text{SMN}}$. *RIC 103* **reduced siliqua**	50	125
342–3x	Oj R As last. Constantinople $\overline{\text{C·A}}$. *RIC 103*	65	160
342–3y	As last. Cyzicus $\overline{\text{SMK}}$. *RIC 45*.	70	175

		VF	EF
342–3z	As last. Lugdunum $\overline{\text{LVG}}$. *RIC 217* **reduced siliqua** . . .	40	100
342–3aa	Ok R̅ As last. Arelate $\overline{\text{PCON}}$. *RIC 208, 254*	65	160
342–3bb	As last. Arelate $\overline{\text{CON}}$. *RIC 259* **reduced siliqua**	50	125
342–3cc	As last. Rome $\overline{\text{R}}$. *RIC 235.*	70	175
342–3dd	As last. Rome $\overline{\text{R}}$. *RIC 302* **reduced siliqua** . . ___	60	150
343A	Oi R̅ VOTIS XXXV MVLTIS XXXX, in wreath. Aquileia $\overline{\text{AQ}}$. *RIC 211*		
		100	250

NEPOTIAN
A.D. 350

Nepotianus was the son of Eutropia (step-sister of Constantine I) and was proclaimed emperor in Rome in 350 by opponents of Magnentius. Magnentius suppressed the rebellion within a month. Coins were issued by Neopotian in gold and bronze, but no silver has been recorded.

VETRANIO
A.D. 350

Vetranio was magister peditum of Constans in Illyricum and was proclaimed emperor by his troops in March, 350, shortly after the rebellion of Magnentius in Gaul and the subsequent downfall of Constans. Vetranio was an experienced officer and held Magnentius in check while Constantius II was occupied on the eastern frontier. Constantius later joined him at Naissus where, on 25 December, Vetranio abdicated. His troops proclaimed their allegiance to Constantius and Vetranio was allowed to retire with a generous pension.

Obverse legend
A.   DN VETRANIO PF AVG

Obverse bust
All are laureate, draped, cuirassed, right.

All coins are siliquae unless otherwise stated. For a discussion of fourth-century silver denominations and their names, see the Introduction.

		VF	EF
2A	A R̅ GAVDIVM POPVLI ROMANI, VOT V MVL X in wreath. Siscia. $\frac{\text{X}|\text{F}}{\text{STS}}$		
	RIC 261 **heavy miliarensis**	5,000	10,000
8	A R̅ VICTORIA AVGVSTORVM, Victory walking l. hldg. palm-branch and trophy. Siscia $\overline{\text{SIS}}$. *RIC 269*	2,500	5,500

		VF	EF
9a	A R̅ As last, Victory walking l. hldg. wreath and trophy. Siscia $\overline{\text{SIS}}$ʊ. *RIC 265*	2,500	5,500

		VF	EF
9b	As last. Siscia $\overline{\text{SIS}}$. *RIC 267*	2,500	5,500
10a	A R̨ As last, Victory hldg. wreath and palm. Siscia $\frac{\text{⚹}}{\text{SIS}}$. *RIC 262*		
	light miliarensis	3,500	7,500
10b	As last. Siscia $\frac{\text{⚹}}{\text{SISQ}}$. *RIC 263* **light miliarensis**	3,500	7,500

12A	A R̨ VIRTVS EXERCITVM, emperor in mil. dress stg. facing, hldg. standard with Chi-rho on banner, l. hand resting on shield. Thessalonica $\overline{\text{TSA}}$. *RIC 125* **heavy miliarensis**	4,500	9,000

MAGNENTIUS
A.D. 350–353

Flavius Magnus Magnentius, who was of barbarian origin, was the general chosen by the Gallic court and army to replace Constans, whose rule had become extremely unpopular. He came to power in 350 and was recognized in Gaul, Britain, Spain, Africa, and Italy. Illyricum, however, fell first to Vetranio and soon thereafter to Constantius II. In Italy, Magnentius quickly quelled a revolt by Nepotian in 350. When Magnentius realized he had failed in his bid to be accepted by Constantius as a legitimate ruler, he invaded Illyricum. He was initially successful but decisively defeated at the battle of Mursa in September 351. Constantius had lost too many troops in the battle to be able to use his advantage immediately but Italy and Sicily fell in 352 and in 353 Magnentius was soundly defeated in Gaul and besieged in Lyons. Realizing his days were numbered Magnentius killed his mother and younger brother and then committed suicide.

Obverse legends
A. DN MAGNENTIVS PF AVG.
B. DN MAGNENTIVS AVG.
C. IM CAE MAGNENTIVS AVG.
D. FL MAGNENTIVS PF AVG

Obverse bust
All are draped, cuirassed, right.
All coins are siliquae unless otherwise stated. For a discussion of fourth-century silver denominations and their names, see the Introduction.

		VF	EF
		VF	EF
1A	A R̨ AEQVITAS AVG NOSTRI, Aequitas stg. l. hldg. balance and cornucopiae. Trier $\overline{\text{TR}}$. *RIC 300* **heavy miliarensis** . . .	2,000	4,500
3†a	A R̨ FELICITAS PERPETVA, Victory walking l. hldg. wreath and trophy. Lugdunum $\overline{\text{LVG}}$. *RIC 120*	450	1,000
3†b	D R̨ As last. Aquileia $\overline{\text{AQ}}$. *RIC 146*	450	1,000
3†c	As last. Aquileia $\overline{\text{AQ•}}$. *RIC 139*	450	1,000
3†d	As last. Aquileia $\overline{\text{AQ*}}$. *RIC 140*	450	1,000
3†e	B R̨ As last. Arelate $\overline{\text{PAR}}$. *RIC 163*	500	1,000
3A	A R̨ FELICITAS PERPETVA VOT V MVLT X in wreath. Aquileia $\overline{\text{LXAQ}}$. *RIC 142* **heavy miliarensis**	1,750	4,000

		VF	EF
26A	A ℞ PRINCIPI IVVENTVTIS, emperor in mil. dress walking r. hldg. transverse spear and globe. Trier T̄R̄. *RIC 302* **light miliarensis**	1,750	4,000
34a	A ℞ SECVRITAS REIPVBLICAE, Securitas stg. facing, r. hand touching head. Trier T̄R̄. *RIC 299* **multiple**	9,000	18,000
34†b	C ℞ As last. Trier T̄R̄. *RIC 255* **multiple**	9,000	18,000
35	A ℞ TRIVMFATOR GENTIVM BARBARARVM emperor in mil. dress stg. l., hldg. transverse spear and standard with Chi-rho on banner. Aquileia *TAQ•. *RIC 141* **multiple**	10,000	20,000
65Aa	A ℞ VICTORIAE DD NN AVGG VOT V MVLT X, Victory seated r. on cuirass inscribing wreath held on l. knee. Lugdunum P̄·L̄Ḡ. *RIC 107* **light miliarensis**	1,500	3,500

		VF	EF
65Ab	As last. Arelate P̄ĀR̄. *RIC 160* **heavy miliarensis**	1,500	3,500
65Ac	As last. Aquileia ĀQ̄. *RIC 143* **light miliarensis**	1,500	3,500
65Ad	As last. Aquileia *ĀQ̄. *RIC 144* **light miliarensis**	1,500	3,500
65Ae	As last. Aquileia *ĀQ̄·. *RIC 145* **light miliarensis**	1,500	3,500
66†	A ℞ VICTORIAE DD NN AVG ET CAE VOT V MVL X, two Victories stg. facing one another, hldg. inscribed wreath. Arelate P̄ĀR̄. *RIC 161* **light miliarensis**	1,500	3,500
75	C ℞ VIRTVS AVG NOSTRI, emperor in mil. dress stg. l. hldg. globe and transverse sceptre; kneeling captive before him. Trier T̄R̄. *RIC 257* **light miliarensis**	1,500	3,500
81†	A ℞ VIRTVS EXERCITI, helmeted soldier stg. facing, hldg. spear in r. hand, resting l. hand on shield. Trier T̄R̄. RIC 304 . . .	450	1,000

		VF	EF
82†	C ℞ As last. Trier T̄R̄. *RIC 256, 258*	450	1,000

DECENTIUS
CAESAR A.D. 351–353

Magnus Decentius, the brother of Magnentius, was created Caesar by the latter after the fall of Nepotian, late in 350 or 351. He assisted Magnentius in the defence of Gaul and was responsible for the security of the Rhine frontier. In 353 Poemenius rebelled against Decentius at Trier and closed the city gates against him. Decentius took his own life a few days after the final defeat and suicide of Magnentius.

Obverse legends
A. DN DECENTIVS FORT CAES.
B. DN DECENTIVS NOB CAES.
C. DN DECENTIVS CAESAR.

Obverse busts
a. draped, cuirassed, right.
b. cuirassed, right.

		VF	EF
1†	Aa ℞ AEQVITAS AVG NOSTRI, Aequitas stg. l. hldg. balance and cornucopiae, Trier T̄R̄. *RIC 301* **heavy miliarensis**	3,500	7,500
6	Aa ℞ PRINCIPI IVVENTVTIS, emperor in mil. dress walking r., hldg. transverse spear and globe. Trier T̄R̄. *RIC 303* **light miliarensis**	3,000	6,500
7	Bb ℞ PRINCITI (sic) IVVENTVTIS, as last. Trier T̄R̄. *RIC 298* **light miliarensis**	3,000	6,500

35†	Cb ℞ VICTORIAE DD NN AVG CAE VOT V MVL X, two Victories facing one another holding inscribed wreath. Arelate $\frac{I^{\in}S}{PAR}$. *RIC 162* **light miliarensis**	3,000	6,500

49†	Aa ℞ VIRTVS EXERCITI, helmeted soldier stg. facing, hldg, spear in r. hand, resting l. hand on shield. Trier T̄R̄. *RIC 305* **siliqua**. .	2,000	4,500

CONSTANTIUS GALLUS
CAESAR A.D. 351–354

Flavius Claudius Julius Constantius Gallus, the son of Julius Constantius and Galla, was born in 325. Both he and his half-brother Julian escaped the massacre of the male descendants of Theodora following the death of Constantine I in 337. In 351 Constantius II brought Gallus out of the semi-exile to which he had been condemned, organized his marriage to Constantia and proclaimed him Caesar at Sirmium in March of that year. Gallus was sent to Antioch where he soon proved to be an irresponsible ruler and his regime was characterized by brutality and violence. Constantius had him recalled, stripped of his rank and beheaded in 354.

Obverse legends
A. FL IVL CONSTANTIVS NOB CAES.
B. DN FL CL CONSTANTIVS NOB CAES.
C. DN CONSTANTIVS NOB CAES.
D. DN CONSTANTIVS IVN NOB C.

Obverse busts
a. head, right.
b. draped, cuirassed, right.

All coins are siliquae unless otherwise stated. For a discussion of fourth-century silver denominations and their names, see the Introduction.

	VF	EF
19†a Bb ℞ FELICITAS ROMANORVM, two emperors in mil. dress hldg. spear, stg. facing beneath arch. Nicomedia $\overline{\text{SMN}}$. *RIC 78* **light miliarensis**	1,500	3,500

19†b Ca ℞ As last. Sirmium $\overline{\text{SIRM}}$. *RIC 12* **light miliarensis**	1,500	3,500
19†c As last. Sirmium ·$\overline{\text{SIRM}}$·. *RIC 14* **light miliarensis**	1,500	3,500
20 Cb ℞ GLORIA EXERCITVS, four standards. Nicomedia $\overline{\text{SMN}}$. *RIC 76* **heavy miliarensis**	1,750	4,000
45† Db ℞ VICTORIA CAESARIS, Victory walking l. hldg. palm and trophy. Siscia $\overline{\text{SIS}}$. *RIC 299* .	550	1,250
47A Cb ℞ VICTORIA ROMANORVM, emperor in mil. dress stg. facing, hldg. spear and globe, Victory crowning him with wreath, both beneath arch. Antioch $\overline{\text{SMAN}}$. *RIC 104* **light miliarensis**	1,750	4,000
50a Ba ℞ VIRTVS EXERCITVS, three standards. Cyzicus $\overline{\text{SMK}\Delta}$. *RIC 40* **heavy miliarensis**	1,750	4,000
50†b Ca ℞ As last. Thessalonica $\overline{\text{TES}}$. *RIC 159* **heavy miliarensis** .	1,750	4,000
50†c As last. Arelate KONSA*I*. *RIC 206* **heavy miliarensis** .	1,750	4,000
50†d Cb ℞ As last. Thessalonica $\overline{\text{TES}}$. *RIC 161* **light miliarensis** . .	1,750	4,000
50A Ab ℞ VIRTVS EXERCITVS, helmeted soldier stg. facing, hldg. spear in r. hand and resting l. hand on shield. Thessalonica $\overline{\text{TES}}$. *RIC 140* **light miliarensis**	1,750	4,000
53 Db ℞ VOT V MVLT X, in wreath. Siscia $\overline{\text{SIS}}$. *RIC 326* . .	400	900
53A Cb ℞ VOTIS V, in wreath. Antioch $\overline{\text{ANT}}$. *RIC 109*. . .	400	900
56a Ca ℞ VOTIS V MVLTIS X, in wreath. Aquileia $\overline{\text{AQ}}$. *RIC 185* . .	350	800

		VF	EF
56b	As last. Sirmium $\overline{\text{SIRM}}$. *RIC 16*	325	750
56c	As last. Sirmium $\overline{\cdot\text{SIRM}}$. *RIC 18*	325	750
56d	As last. Thessalonica $\overline{\text{TES}}$. *RIC 164*	350	800
56e	As last. Nicomedia $\overline{\text{SMN}}$. *RIC 83*.	350	800
57†	Ba ℞ As last. Nicomedia $\overline{\text{SMN}}$. *RIC 82*	350	800
58†a	Bb ℞ As last. Constantinople $\overline{\text{C·A}}$. *RIC 105*	350	800
58†b	Db ℞ As last. Siscia $\overline{\text{SIS}}$. *RIC 300*	375	850
61a	Ca ℞ No legend, star within wreath. Lugdunum $\overline{\text{LVG}}$. *RIC 181–2*.	450	1,000
61b	As last. Arelate $\overline{\text{PAR}}$. *RIC 204–5*	450	1,000
61c	As last. Arelate $\overline{\text{PCON}}$. *RIC 210*	450	1,000

61d	As last. Rome $\overline{\text{R}}$. *RIC 237*	450	1,000
61e	As last. Antioch $\overline{\text{ANT}}$. *RIC 110*	450	1,000
61†f	Cb ℞ As last. Arelate. $\overline{\text{PCON}}$. *RIC 209*	450	1,000
62	Ba ℞ As last. Rome $\overline{\text{R}}$. *RIC 236*	450	1,000

JULIAN
CAESAR A.D. 355–360
AUGUSTUS A.D. 360–363

Flavius Claudius Julianus was the half-brother of Constantius Gallus and the son of Julius Constantius and his second wife Basilina. He was born at Constantinople in 332. Spared in the massacre of 337, he and Gallus were banished to a remote estate in Cappadocia. When Gallus was elevated as Caesar Julian was also released from his semi-exile. It was about this time that he experienced a violent reaction against Christianity and became a pagan. In November 355 he was nominated Caesar and sent to Gaul where he proved to be an able general and provincial governor. He waged successful campaigns on the frontier in 357, 358 and 359 and reduced the tax assessed on Gaul by a significant amount. In 360 Constantius demanded that a substantial part of Julian's army should accompany him on his Eastern campaign, but the troops refused to go. Instead they proclaimed Julian Augustus. By the fortuitous death of Constantius soon afterwards civil war was averted and Julian was accepted as undisputed ruler of the whole empire. He instituted a pagan revival and an active anti-Christian policy which was rejected by his chosen capital, Antioch, whose citizens subjected Julian to abuse and ridicule. The emperor was killed during an abortive campaign against the Sassanid Persians in 363 and the pagan revival perished with him.

Obverse legends.

As Caesar
A. FL CL IVLIANVS NOB CAES.
B. FL CL IVLIANVS NOB C.
C. DN CL IVLIANVS NOB CAES.
D. DN IVLIANVS NOB CAES.
E. DN IVLIANVS NOB C.
Eb. DN CL IVLIANVS NC

As Augustus
F. DN FL CL IVLIANVS PF AVG.
G. FL CL IVLIANVS PF AVG.
H. FL CL IVLIANVS PERP AVG.
I. FL CL IVLIANVS PP AVG.
J. FL CL IVLIANVS AVG.
K. DN CL IVLIANVS AVG.
L. DN IVLIANVS PF AVG.

Obverse busts.
a. head, right.
b. draped, cuirassed, right.
c. draped, cuirassed, pearl diadem, right.
d. draped, cuirassed, rosette diadem, right.
e. draped, cuirassed, laurel and rosette diadem, right.
f. cuirassed, right.

All coins are reduced siliquae unless otherwise specified. For a discussion of fourth-century silver denominations and their names, see the Introduction.

CAESAR

		VF	EF
6†	Ab ℞ DN IVLIANVS NOB CAES, three standards. Arelate P̄C̄ŌN̄. RIC 248–9 **heavy miliarensis**	£900	£2,000
7†	Ab ℞ DN IVLIANVS CAES, as last. Arelate PCON. RIC 247 **heavy miliarensis**	900	2,000
63A	Db ℞ VICTORIA ROMANORVM, emperor in mil. dress, stg. facing, Victory hldg. palm crowns him with wreath; both stg. beneath arch. Antioch. S̄M̄ĀN̄. RIC 182 **light miliarensis**	1,000	2,250
73†	Ab ℞ VIRTVS EXERCITVS, helmeted soldier stg. r., hldg. spear in r. hand and resting l. hand on shield. Arelate P̄C̄ŌN̄. RIC 251 **light miliarensis**	900	2,000
74Aa	Ca ℞ VIRTVS EXERCITVS, three standards. Thessalonica T̄ĒS̄. RIC 202 **heavy miliarensis**	900	2,000
74Ab	Cb ℞ As last. Thessalonica T̄ĒS̄. RIC 204 **light miliarensis**.	900	2,000
154a	Db ℞ VOTIS V MVLTIS X, in wreath. Arelate C̄ŌN̄. RIC 260 . .	55	140

		VF	EF
154b	As last. Arelate $\overline{\text{PCON}}$. *RIC 263–5*	50	125
154†c	Eb ℞ As last. Sirmium $\cdot\overline{\text{SIRM}}\cdot$. *RIC 67* **siliqua.**	150	350
154A	Db ℞ VOTIS V, in wreath. Nicomedia $\overline{\text{SMN}}$. *RIC 102A* **siliqua.**	200	450
156	Ca ℞ VOTIS V MVLTIS X, in wreath. Thessalonica $\overline{\text{TES}}$. *RIC 206* **siliqua**	150	350
170†	Ab ℞ No legend, star within wreath. Arelate $\overline{\text{PCON}}$. *RIC 255* **siliqua**	250	550
172a	Db ℞ As last. Arelate $\overline{\text{PCON}}$. *RIC 256* **siliqua**	250	550
172b	As last. Arelate $\overline{\text{PCON}}$. *RIC 257*	200	450

172c	As last. Antioch $\overline{\text{ANT}}$. *RIC 187*.	200	450
172d	As last. Antioch $\cdot\overline{\text{ANT}}\cdot$. *RIC 185* **siliqua**	300	650

172†e	E^{b}f ℞, As last. Rome $\cdot\overline{\text{R}}\cdot$. *RIC —* **siliqua**	300	650

AUGUSTUS

21A	Fc ℞ FIDES EXERCITVVM, two standards with pole between surmounted by wreath on top. Arelate, mintmark unknown. *RIC 305 (confirmation required)* **heavy miliarensis**	–	–
54†a	Ic ℞ VICTORIA AVGVSTI N, Victory warlking l. hldg. wreath and palm. Rome $\overline{\text{R}}$. *RIC 325* **siliqua**	200	450
54†b	Ie ℞ As last. Rome $\overline{\text{R}}$. *RIC 326* **siliqua**	200	450
55A	Ic ℞ VICTORI[AROMAN] ORVM, as last. Siscia $\frac{*}{\text{SIS}}$. *RIC 410* (irregular?).	unique	
58†a	Ic ℞ VICTORIA DD NN AVG. Victory walking l. hldg. wreath and palm, one wing visible. Lugdunum $\overline{\text{LVG}}$. *RIC 215A*. . . .	60	150
58†b	Id ℞ As last. Lugdunum $\overline{\text{LVG}}$. *RIC 215*.	60	150

		VF	EF
58†c	Ic ℞ As last, but both wings visible. Lugdunum L̄V̄G. *RIC 212*	60	150
58†d	Id ℞ As last. Lugdunum L̄V̄G. *RIC 213*	60	150
61†	Jc ℞ VICTORIA PERPETV, Victory walking l. hldg. wreath and palm. Trier T̄R̄. *RIC 366* **half siliqua** . .	250	550
63a	Gc ℞ VICTORIA ROMANORVM, emperor in mil. dress hldg. sceptre and globe, stg. facing being crowned by Victory, both stg. beneath arch. Sirmium *SIRM. *RIC 104* **light miliarensis** .	900	2,000
63†b	As last. Antioch ĀN̄T̄. *RIC 210* **light miliarensis**	1,000	2,250
71A	Lc ℞ VIRTVS EXERCITVM, helmeted solider stg. l. hldg. spear in r., l. resting on shield. Arelate P̄C̄ŌN̄. *RIC 290* **light miliarensis**	800	1,850

		VF	EF
72†a	Fc ℞ VIRTVS EXERCITVS, as last with eagle hldg. wreath in beak, in field to right. Arelate P̄C̄ŌN̄S̄T̄. *RIC 306–8* **light miliarensis**	750	1,750
72†b	Ic ℞ As last, no eagle. Sirmium ·S̄IR̄M̄· *RIC 101* **light miliarensis**	750	1,750
72†c	Hc ℞ As last. Lugdunum L̄V̄G. *RIC 209* **light miliarensis**	750	1,750
142†a	Ic ℞ VOT V MVLT X, in wreath. Lugdunum L̄V̄G. *RIC 229* . .	50	125
142†b	Ie ℞ As last. Lugdunum P̄L̄V̄G*. *RIC 230*	55	140
146a	Ic ℞ VOT X MVLT XX, in wreath. Lugdunum L̄V̄G. *RIC 232* . .	50	125
146b	As last. Lugdunum P̄L̄V̄G. *RIC 233*	45	110
146†c	Ie ℞ As last. Lugdunum L̄V̄G. *RIC 231*	50	125
147†a	Gc ℞ As last. Antioch ĀN̄T̄. *RIC 213–4*	80	200

		VF	EF
148†a	Fc ℞ As last. Lugdunum P̄L̄V̄G. *RIC 234*	45	110
148†b	As last. Lugdunum P̄L̄V̄ḠD̄·(*) *RIC 235*	55	140

		VF	EF
148†c	Fc ℞ As last. Arelate P̄C̄ŌN̄S̄T̄. *RIC 312*	45	110

		VF	EF
148†d	As last. Constantinople $\overline{\text{CP·A}}$. *RIC 159*	70	175
148†e	As last, eagle in medallion in centre of wreath. Arelate $\overline{\text{PCONST}}$. *RIC 309–311*	45	110

		VF	EF
157a	Kc Ŗ VOTIS V MVLTIS X, in wreath. Trier $\overline{\text{TR}}$. *RIC 364* . . .	45	110

		VF	EF
157†b	As last. Trier $\overline{\text{TR}\Psi}$. *RIC 365*	45	110
157†c	As last. Arelate $\overline{\text{PCON}}$. *RIC 296–7*	45	110
159†	Gc Ŗ As last. Sirmium $\overline{\text{SIRM}}$. *RIC 103*	50	125
161†	Lc Ŗ As last. Arelate $\overline{\text{PCON}}$. *RIC 295*	45	110

		VF	EF
163†a	Ic Ŗ As last. Lugdunum $\overline{\text{LVG}}$. *RIC 218*	40	100
163†b	As last. Lugdunum $\overline{\text{PLVG}}$. *RIC 227–8*	40	100
163†c	Id Ŗ As last. Lugdunum $\overline{\text{LVG}}$. *RIC 219*	40	100
163†d	Ic Ŗ As last. Thessalonica $\overline{\text{TES}}$. *RIC 221*	65	160
164†a	As last. Sirmium $\overline{\text{SIRM}}$. *RIC 102*	50	125

		VF	EF
164†b	Jc Ŗ As last. Trier $\overline{\text{TR}}$. *RIC 363*	45	110

		VF	EF
164A	Gc ℞ VOTIS X MVLTIS XX, in wreath. Antioch $\overline{\text{ANT}}$. *RIC 211–12*	80	200
167†a	Kc ℞ VOTIS XXX MVLTIS XXXX in wreath. Arelate $\overline{\text{PCON}}$. *RIC 293* hybrid: rev. of Constantius II	–	–
167†b	Lc ℞ As last. Arelate $\overline{\text{PCON}}$. *RIC 292* hybrid: rev. of Constantius II	–	–

JOVIAN
A.D. 363–364

Flavius Jovianus, comes domesticorum, *was chosen emperor by the army after Julian's unfortunate death during his campaign aginst the Persians in 363. After negotiating a humiliating peace treaty which cost the Romans significant amounts of territory, Jovian withdrew from Persia. Together with his army he went first to Antioch and then westwards, where he died in Asia Minor in February 364. During his brief reign he restored the anti-pagan laws abolished by Julian.*

Obverse legends.
A. DN IOVIANVS PEP AVG.
B. DN IOVIANVS PF AVG.

Obverse bust.
All are
draped, cuirassed, pearl diadem, right.

All coins are reduced siliquae unles otherwise stated. For a discussion of fourth-century silver denominations and their names, see the Introduction.

		VF	EF
4	A ℞ GLORIA ROMANORVM, emperor in mil. dres stg. facing beneath arch, hldg. spear and globe. Antioch $\overline{\text{ANT}}$. *RIC 226* **light miliarensis**	£1,600	£3,750
7†	B ℞ RESTITVTOR REIP, emperor in mil. dress hldg. labarum in r., Victory on globe in l. Arelate $\overline{\text{PCONST}}$. *RIC 328* **light miliarensis**	1,750	4,000
33†a	B ℞ VOT V MVL X, in wreath. Constantinople $\overline{\text{CPA}}$. *RIC 172* . .	100	250
33†b	As last. Constantinople $\overline{\text{CP·A}}$. *RIC 173*	100	250
33Aa	B ℞ VOT V MVLT X in wreath. Arelate $\overline{\text{PCONST}}$. *RIC 329* **siliqua**	250	550

		VF	EF
33Ab	As last. Arelate $\overline{\text{PCONST}}$. *RIC 331–2*	110	275
33Ac	As last. Sirmium $\overline{\text{SIRM}}$. *RIC 117.*	110	275
33Ad	As last. Constantinople $\overline{\text{CP·A}}$. *RIC 174*	100	250

33Ae	As last. Nicomedia $\overline{\text{SMN}}$. *RIC 127*	100	250
33Af	As last. Nicomedia $\overline{\text{SMN}}$. *RIC —* **siliqua**	250	550

33Ag	As last. Antioch $\overline{\text{ANT}}$. *RIC 227.*	100	250
38†	B ℞ VOT X MVLT XX, in wreath. Arelate $\overline{\text{PCONST}}$. *RIC 33* . .	110	275
39†	B ℞ VOTIS V MVLTIS X in wreath. Antioch $\overline{\text{ANT}}$. *RIC 225* **heavy**		
	miliarensis	1,750	4,000

VALENTINIAN I
A.D. 364–375

Flavius Valentinianus was born in 321 into a military family of some distinction, as his father had risen through the ranks to become a general. Valentinian joined the army and became a cavalry officer but was later dismissed on a false charge by Julian and did not serve actively during the years 355 to 363. Jovian recalled him and put him in charge of a Guards regiment, and he was proclaimed emperor in February 364 following his benefactor's death. Shortly thereafter he appointed his younger brother Valens co-emperor and then divided the empire, taking responsibility for the Western portion himself. He concentrated on defending the frontiers and successfully defeated the Alamanni who had invaded Gaul. He also reconstructed frontier fortifications along the Rhine. In 375 Valentinian left Gaul for Pannonia where he planned to retaliate against invaders, but while there he suffered an apoplectic fit and died. He was a conscientious administrator and tried to curb bureaucratic abuses and excessive taxation, but with limited success.

Obverse legends.
A. DN VALENTINIANVS PF AVG.

Obverse busts.
a. pearl diadem, draped, cuirassed, right.
b. pearl diadem, draped, cuirassed, left.
c. pearl diadem, cuirassed, right.
d. rosette diadem, draped, cuirassed, right.
e. rosette diadem, draped, cuirassed, left
f. rosette diadem, cuirassed, right.

All coins are siliquae (= reduced siliquae) unless otherwise stated. For a discussion of fourth-century silver denominations and their names, see the Introduction.

		VF	EF
9†	Aa ℞ GLORIA ROMANORVM, emperor stg. facing <u>under</u> arch, head r., hldg. transverse spear and globe. Antioch ANT. *RIC 4a* **light miliarensis**	£650	£1,500

10†**a**	Aa ℞ As last, two emperors stg. facing, heads turned to<u>wards</u> one another, hldg. labarum in r. hand, globe in l. Siscia ·SIS*. *RIC 3a* **light miliarensis**	650	1,500
10†**b**	Aa ℞ As last, two emperors stg. facing, heads turned to<u>wards</u> one another, hldg. labarum in l. hand, globe in r. Siscia ·SIS*. *RIC 4* **light miliarensis**	650	1,500
10Aa	Aa ℞ As last, two emperors stg. facing under arch, heads turned towards one another, emperor on l. hldg. globe in l. hand, sceptre in r., emper<u>or on r.</u> hldg. globe in r. hand, sceptre in l. Constnatinople CONSA. *RIC 9* **light miliarensis**	700	1,600
10Ab	Ad ℞ As last, two emperors stg. facing under arch, heads turned towards one another, emperor on l. hldg. globe in r. hand, sceptre in l., <u>emperor</u> on r. hldg. sceptre in r. hand, globe in l. Antioch ANT. *RIC 5, 30(2)* **light miliarensis** .	650	1,500
10Ac	As last. Antioch ANT*. *RIC 30(1)* **light miliarensis** . .	650	1,500

		VF	EF
17†	Ac ℞ RESTITVTOR REIP, emperor stg. facing, head r., hldg. Victory on globe and labarum. Rome $\overline{RP}$. *RIC 7a* **light miliarensis**	650	1,500
18–19†a	Aa ℞ As last, emperor stg. facing, head r., hldg. Victory on globe and labarum or standard with cross. Trier $\overline{TR}$. *RIC 2*	700	1,600
18–19†b	As last. Lugdunum $\overline{LVG}$. *RIC 6b(1)*	60	150
19–18†c	As last. Lugdunum $\overline{PLVG}$. *RIC 6a, 6b(2), 6d* . .	60	150
18–19†d	As last. Lugdunum $\overline{PLVG}$·. *RIC 6b(3–4), 6c.* . .	60	150
18–19†e	As last. Arles $\overline{PCONST}$. *RIC 6a(1), 6c(1)*	60	150
18–19†f	As last. Arles $\overline{PCONST}$. *RIC 6a(2)*	60	150
18–19†g	As last. Arles $\frac{OF|I}{CONST}$. *RIC 6a(3–5)*	60	150
18–19†h	As last. Arles $\frac{OF|i}{CONST}$. *RIC 6a(6–8), 6c(2)* . . .	60	150

18–19†i	As last. Arles $\frac{OF|I}{CON}$. *RIC 6a(9–10), 6b*	60	150
18–19†j	As last. Aquileia $\overline{SMAQ}$. *RIC 4a.*	75	185

18–19†k	As last. Thessalonica $\overline{TES}$. *RIC 12a(1)*.	65	160
18–19†l	As last. Thessalonica $\overline{TESA}$. *RIC 12a(2)*	65	160
18–19†m	As last. Constantinople $\overline{CP·A}$. *RIC 12*	80	200
18–19†n	As last. Nicomedia $\overline{SMN}$. *RIC 4a*	65	160
18–19†o	As last. Antioch $\overline{ANT}$. *RIC 7a.*	65	160
22†a	Aa ℞ RESTITVTOR REIPVBLICAE, emperor stg. facing, head r., hldg. labarum or standard and Victory on globe. Lugdunum $\overline{LVG}$. *RIC 5* **light miliarensis**	600	1,350
22†b	Ac ℞ As last. Antioch $\overline{ANTA}$. *RIC 6(1)* **light miliarensis**	600	1,350
22†c	As last. Antioch $\frac{+|}{ANTA}$. *RIC 6(2)* **light miliarensis** . .	600	1,350

		VF	EF
23†	Aa R As last. Nicomedia $\overline{\text{NIK}\in}$. *RIC 5*	650	1,500
34†a	Aa R SALVS REIPVBLICAE, four standards. Lugdunum $\overline{\text{LVG}}$. *RIC 3a* **heavy miliarensis**	700	1,600
34†b	As last. Arles $\overline{\text{PCON}}$*. *RIC 3a* **heavy miliarensis**	700	1,600

35†	Aa R SECVRITAS REIP, two emperors stg., each hldg. labarum and Victory on globe who crowns them. Constantinople CONSPA. *RIC 8* **heavy miliarensis**	750	1,750
36†	Ab R SECVRITAS REIPVBLICAE, Victory stg. l. hldg. wreath and trophy, spurning fallen enemy. Nicomedia $\overline{\text{SMN}}$. *RIC 3a* **light miliarensis**	650	1,500
38Aa	Aa R TRIVMFATOR GENT BARB, emperor stg. facing, head l., hldg. labarum and globe, kneeling captive on l. Siscia ·SISCP. *RIC 8(1)* **multiple**	7,500	15,000
38Ab	As last. Siscia $\overline{\text{SISCP}}$. *RIC 8(2)* **multiple**	7,500	15,000
50	Ac R VICTORIA AVGVSTORVM, Victory advg. r., head l., dragging captive with r. hand, hldg. trophy in l. Rome $\overline{\text{ROMA}}$. *RIC 6a* **heavy miliarensis**	900	2,000

51a	Aa R VICTORIA AVGVSTORVM VOT V MVLT X, Victory stg. r., l. foot on globe, inscribing shield on cippus. Trier $\overline{\text{SMTR}}$. *RIC 24a* **light miliarensis**	550	1,250

51b	As last. Rome $\overline{\text{RP}}$. *RIC 8a(1–4)* **light miliarensis**	500	1,100
51†c	Ab R As last. Trier $\overline{\text{SMTR}}$. *RIC 24b* **light miliarensis** . .	600	1,350
52†a	Aa R VICTORIA AVGVSTORVM VOT X MVLT XV, Victory stg. r., l. foot on globe, inscribing shield on cippus. Arles :S·M·K·A·P. *RIC 13a* **light miliarensis**	550	1,250

		VF	EF
52†b	Af ℞ As last. Arles $\overline{\text{SMKAP}}$. *RIC 13b* **light miliarensis** ..	550	1,250

52A	Ac ℞ VICTORIAS AVGVSTORVM VOT V, two Victories hldg. inscribed shield. Constantinople $\overline{\text{CONSPA}}$. *RIC 10* **light miliarensis**	650	1,500
53A	Ac ℞ VICTORIA DN AVG, emperor stg. l., hldg. Victory on globe and standard, r. <u>foot on</u> kneeling captive, seated captive behind. Constantinople *CONSQ *RIC 32.* **light miliarensis** . . .	700	1,600
53B	Aa ℞ VICTORIA DN AVG VOT X MVLT XX, Victory stg. facing, hldg. wreath and staff surmounted by inscribed shield, kneeling captive on either side. Constantinople $\frac{\cdot\mathscr{P}\cdot\ \ \!\!\ast}{\Psi\overline{\text{CONSAQ}}}$. *RIC 31* **heavy miliarensis**	800	1,850
56A	Aa ℞ VIRTVS EXSERCITI, emperor stg. r., hldg. spear and globe, foot on captive. Constantinople $\frac{\ \ \!\!\ast}{\Psi\overline{\text{CONSAQ}}}$. *RIC 33* **light miliarensis**	600	1,350

58a	Aa ℞ VIRTVS EXERCITVS, emperor stg. facing, <u>head l.</u> hldg. standard in r. hand, resting l. on shield. Trier $\overline{\text{SMTR}}$. *RIC 26a(1)* **light miliarensis.**	550	1,250
58b	As last. Trier $\overline{\text{TRPS}}^{\cdot}$. *RIC 26a(2)* **light miliarensis**. . .	500	1,100
58†c	Ab ℞ As last. Thessalonica $\overline{\text{TES}}$. *RIC 11a* **light miliarensis**.	500	1,100

58†d	Aa ℞ As last, emperor stg. <u>facing</u>, head l., hldg. labarum in r., resting l. on shield. Siscia $\cdot$SISCP. *RIC 10a* **light miliarensis**	500	1,100

		VF	EF
58A	Aa ℞ As last, emperor stg. facing head l., hldg. globe in r. hand, spear in l. Thessalonica TES. *RIC 13*	600	1,350
59	Ad ℞ VIRTVS ROMANI EXERCITVS, emperor stg. facing, head l., hldg. standard with Chi-rho on wreath in r. hand, resting l. on shield. Thessalonica SMTES. *RIC 7* **multiple**	7,500	15,000
69a	Aa ℞ VOT or VOT·V, in wreath. Constantinople CONSPA. *RIC 11f* **argenteus (= pre-reform siliqua)**	125	300
69†b	Ac ℞ As last. Constantinople CONSA. *RIC 11b* **argenteus** .	125	300
69†c	Ad ℞ As last. Constantinople CONSPA. *RIC 11a(1)* **argenteus**	125	300
69†d	As last. Constantinople CONSA. *RIC 11a(2–3), 11g(2)* **argeneus**	125	300
69†e	As last. Constantinople ·CONSPA. *RIC 11g(1)* **argenteus** .	125	300
69Aa	Aa ℞ As last. Constantinople. CP·A *RIC 13a(1–4)*	60	150
69Ab	As last. Constantinople CPA. *RIC 13a(5)*	60	150
69Ac	As last. Constantinople C·A. *RIC 13a(6–7)*	60	150
69Ad	As last. Constantinople CONSA. *RIC 13a(8)*	60	150

		VF	EF
69Ae	As last. Constantinople ·CONSA·. *RIC 13a(9)*	60	150
69A†f	Ad ℞ As last. Constantinople CP·A. *RIC 13g*.	65	160
69B	Aa ℞ VOT V MVL X, in wreath. Thessalonica TES. *RIC 9* **heavy miliarensis**	750	1,750
70†a	Aa ℞ VOT V MVLT X, in wreath. Aquileia SMAQ. *RIC 5* . .	70	175
70†b	As last. Rome RP. *RIC 10b*	60	150
70†c	As last. Constantinople *C·AQ. *RIC 36a*	60	150
70†d	As last. Nicomedia SMN. *RIC 20a*	60	150
70†e	Ad ℞ As last. Constantinople *C·AQ. *RIC 36b(1–3)*. . . .	60	150

		VF	EF
70†f	Aa ℞ VOT V MV·LT X, in wreath. Rome RP. *RIC 10a(1–2)* . .	60	150
70A	Aa ℞ VOT V MVLT X, in wreath. Aquileia SMAQ. *RIC 3a* **heavy miliarensis**	700	1,600
72†a	Aa ℞ VOT V MVLTIS X, in wreath. Nicomedia SMN. *RIC 21a* .	65	160

		VF	EF
72†b	Ad ℞ As last. Nicomedia $\overline{\text{SMN}}$. *RIC 19a* **argenteus** (= **pre-reform siliqua**)	125	300

72Aa	Aa ℞ VOT X MVL XX, in wreath. Antioch $\overline{\text{ANT}}$. *RIC 33a(1)* . .	60	150
72Ab	As last. Antioch $\overline{\text{ANT}}$*. *RIC 33a(2)*	60	150
72Ac	As last. Antioch $\overline{\text{ANT}}^\cup$. *RIC 33a(3)*	60	150
72Ad	As last. Antioch $\overline{\text{AN}}^\cup$. *RIC 33a(4)*	60	150
73†a	Aa ℞ VOT X MVLT XX, in wreath. Siscia $\overline{\text{SISCP}}$. *RIC 12a* . .	70	175
73†b	As last. Constantinople $\overline{\text{C}\mathcal{L}\text{SQ}}$. *RIC 37a*	60	150
73†c	As last. Antioch $\overline{\text{ANT}}$. *RIC 34a(1)*	60	150
73†d	As last. Antioch $\overline{\text{ANT}}$*. *RIC 34a(2)*	60	150
73†e	As last. Antioch $\overline{\text{ANTA}}$. *RIC 34a(3–6)* . .	60	150
73†f	As last. Antioch $\overline{\text{ANTA}}$. *RIC 34a(7)*	60	150
73†g	As last. Antioch $\overline{\text{ANA}}$. *RIC 34a(8)*	60	150
73A	Aa ℞ As last. Constantinople $\overline{\text{CONS}}$. *RIC 34a* **argenteus** (= **pre-reform siliqua**).	125	300
75†	Aa ℞ VOT VX MVLT XX, in wreath. Constantinople $\overline{\text{CONS}}$. *RIC 35* **argenteus**	125	300
75A	Aa ℞ As last. Constantinople $\overline{\text{C}\mathcal{L}\text{S}}$. *RIC 38a*	70	175
77†	Ab ℞ VOTIS V MVLTIS X, in wreath. Trier $\overline{\text{SMTR}}$. *RIC 23a* **heavy miliarensis**	700	1,600
78†a	Aa ℞ As last. Trier $\overline{\text{TRPS}}$. *RIC 23b* **heavy miliarensis** . .	600	1,350
78†b	Ad ℞ As last. Lugdunum $\overline{\text{LVG}}$. *RIC 4* **heavy miliarensis** . .	650	1,500

78†c	Aa ℞ As last. Lugdunum $\overline{\text{S·M·L·A·P}\psi}$. *RIC 16a(1)* **heavy miliarensis**	650	1,500
78†d	Ae ℞ As last. Arles $\overline{\text{SMKAP}}$. *RIC 11a* **heavy miliarensis** . .	650	1,500
78†e	Ad ℞ VOTIS Y MVLTIS X, in wreath. Arles $\overline{\text{SMKAP}}$. *RIC 11c* **heavy miliarensis**	650	1,500

79†a	Aa ℞ VOTIS V MVLTIS X, in wreath. Sirmium $\overline{\text{SIRM}}$. *RIC 2* . .	70	175

		VF	EF
79†b	As last Trier $\overline{\text{TR}}$. *RIC 3*	90	225
80†a	Aa Ɍ VOTIS X MVLTIS XV, in wreath. Lugdunum $\overline{\text{S·M·L·A·P}_{\mathscr{E}}}$. *RIC 17a* **heavy miliarensis**	650	1,500
80†b	Af Ɍ As last. Arles $\overline{\text{SMKAP}}$. *RIC 12* **heavy miliarensis** . .	650	1,500
80A	Aa Ɍ VOTIS XV, MVLTIS XX, in wreath. Siscia $\overline{\cdot\text{SISCP}}$. *RIC 9a* **heavy miliarensis**	600	1,350

81†a	Aa Ɍ VRBS ROMA, Roma seated l. on throne, hldg. spear and Victory on globe. Trier $\overline{\text{TRPS}}$·. *RIC 27a*	55	135
81†b	As last. Lugdunum $\overline{\text{PLVG}}$. *RIC 9a*	65	160
81†c	As last. Rome $\overline{\text{RP}}$. *RIC 11a(1–3)*	55	135
81†d	Aa Ɍ As last, Roma seated l. on throne, hldg. sceptre and victory on globe. Trier $\overline{\text{TRPS}}$. *RIC 27d(2)*	55	135

81†e	As last. Trier $\overline{\text{TRPS}}$·. *RIC 27d(2)*	60	150

MARINA SEVERA

Marina Severa was the first wife of Valentinian I and the mother of Gratian. She was banished by Valentinian after being involved in a fraudulent property deal. No coinage was minted in her name.

JUSTINA

Justina was married while still a young girl to the usurper Magnentius and later became the second wife of Valentinian I and the mother of Valentinian II. Deeply religious, she favoured the Arian sect. When Magnus Maximus invaded Italy in 387 she fled with Valentinian II to Thessalonica where Theodosius agreed to intervene on her behalf in return for the hand of her daughter Galla. She returned to Italy with her two children and died apparently during the war against Maximus. No coinage was minted in her name.

VALENS
A.D. 364–378

Flavius Valens was the youngest brother of Valentinian I, who elevated him to the rank of co-emperor shortly after his own succession in 364. When the brothers divided the empire. Valens was entrusted with the Eastern half. In 365 he lost possession of Constantinople to the usurper Procopius, but the following year defeated his rival and regained his capital. He was a much less forceful and able ruler than his elder brother and his main achievement was to lower taxation by reduced spending. Initially he was successful in his wars with the barbarians but made a serious error when he allowed the Goths to cross the Danube in their flight from the Huns. Once in Roman territory they rebelled against the emperor and Valens mobilized his forces and met them in a pitched battle near Adrianople. The Roman cavalry collapsed in its initial assault and the rest of the army was overrun and suffered heavy casualties. Only a third of the Roman forces survived and the empire never fully recovered from this disaster, in which the emperor himself perished.

Obverse legends.
A. DN VALENS PF AVG.
B. DN VALENS PERF AVG.
C. DN VALENS PER AVG.
D. IMP CE VALENS PF AVG.

Obverse busts.
a. pearl diadem, draped, cuirassed, right.
b. pearl diadem, draped, cuirassed, left.
c. pearl diadem, cuirassed, right.
d. rosette diadem, draped, cuirassed, right.
e. rosette diadem, draped, cuirassed, left.

All coins are siliquae (= reduced siliquae) unless otherwise specified. For a discussion of fourth-century silver denominations and their names, see the Introduction.

		VF	EF
9	Bb ℞ GLORIA ROMANORVM, emperor stg. facing under arch, head r., hldg. transverse spear and globe. Antioch ANT*. *RIC 29a* **light miliarensis**	550	1,250
9†a	Bd ℞ As last. Antioch ANT. *RIC 4b(1)* **light miliarensis**	550	1,250
9†b	As last. Antioch ANTA. *RIC 4b(2–3)* **light miliarensis**	550	1,250
9†c	Be ℞ As last. Antioch ANT*. *RIC 29b* **light miliarensis**	550	1,250
9†d	Cd ℞ As last. Antioch ANA. *RIC 4c* **light miliarensis**	550	1,250
10†	Ba ℞ As last, two emperors stg. facing under arch heads turned towards each other, hldg. vertical sceptre in r. hand, globe in l. Antioch ANT*. *RIC 31* **light miliarensis**	550	1,250

18†	Aa ℞ As last, two emperors stg. facing, heads turned towards each other hldg. labarum in r. hand, globe in l. Siscia •SIS*. *RIC 3b* **light miliarensis**	550	1,250

		VF	EF
27a	Aa ℞ RESTITVTOR REIP, emperor stg. facing, head l. hldg. labarum and Victory on globe. Arles PCONST. *RIC 4* **light miliarensis** . .	600	1,350
27†b	Ac ℞ As last, emperor stg. facing, head r., hldg. labarum and Victory on globe. Rome RP. *RIC 7b* **light miliarensis** . .	600	1,350
28†a	Aa ℞ As last, emperor stg. facing, head r., hldg. labarum or standard with cross in r. hand, and Victory on globe in l. Lugdunum LVG. *RIC 6e(1)*	55	135
28†b	As last. Lugdunum PLVG. *RIC 6e(2), 6f(1–2), 6h*	55	135
28†c	As last. Lugdunum PLVG· *RIC 6f(3–4), 6g*	55	135
28†d	As last. Arles PCONST. *RIC 6d(1–2)*	55	135
28†e	As last. Arles $\frac{*}{\text{PCONST}}$. *RIC 6d(3)*	55	135
28†f	As last. Arles $\frac{|*}{\text{PCONST}}$. *RIC 6d(4)*	55	135
28†g	As last. Arles $\frac{\text{OF|I}}{\text{CONST}}$. *RIC 6d(5–7)*	55	135
28†h	As last. Arles $\frac{|I*}{\text{CONST}}$. *RIC 6d(8–10)*	55	135
28†i	As last. Arles $\frac{\text{OF|II}}{\text{CON}}$. *RIC 6d(11)*	55	135
28†j	As last. Arles PCON. *RIC 6d(12)*	55	135
28†k	As last. Aquileia SMAQ. *RIC 4b*	70	175
28†l	As last. Thessalonica TESA. *RIC 12b*	70	175
28†m	As last. Nicomedia SMN. *RIC 4b*.	60	150
28†n	As last. Antioch ANT. *RIC 7b*	60	150
28†o	As last. Antioch ANT·. *RIC 7c*	60	150
28†p	Ad ℞ As last, emperor stg. facing, head l., hldg. labarum or standard with cross in l. hand, and Victory on globe in r. Thessalonica TES. *RIC 12c*	80	200
44†a	Aa ℞ SALVS REIPVBLICAE, four standards. Lugdunum LVG. *RIC 3b* **heavy miliarensis**	650	1,500
44†b	As last. Arles PCON*. *RIC 3b* **heavy miliarensis**	650	1,500
46A	Ab ℞ SECVRITAS REIPVBLICAE, Victory stg. l. hldg. wreath and trophy, spurning fallen enemy Nicomedia. SMN. *RIC 3b* **light miliarensis** . .	600	1,350
50†	Aa ℞ TRIVMFATOR GENT BARB, emperor stg. facing, head l., hldg. labarum and globe, kneeling captive on his left. Trier TRPS ·. *RIC 22* **multiple**	7,000	14,000
59†	Ac ℞ VICTORIA AVGVSTORVM, Victory advg. r., head l., dragging captive with r. hand, hldg. trophy in l. Rome RP. *RIC 6b* **heavy miliarensis**	800	1,850
60†a	Ac ℞ VICTORIA AVGVSTORVM VOT V MVLT X, Victory stg. r. inscribing shield on cippus, l. foot on globe. Trier SMTR. *RIC 24d* **light miliarensis**	500	1,100

			VF	EF
60†b	Aa ℞ As last. Trier $\overline{\text{SMTR}}$. *RIC 24c* **light miliarense** ..		500	1,100
60†c	As last. Lugdunum $\text{S·M·L·A·}\overline{\text{P}}$. *RIC 18a* **light miliarensis** .		550	1,250

60†d	As last. Rome $\overline{\text{RP}}$. *RIC 8b(1–4)* **light miliarensis**	500	1,100
60A	Aa ℞ VICTORIA AVGVSTORVM VOT X MVLTIS X, as last. Trier $\overline{\text{TRPS}}$. *RIC 25* **light miliarensis**	500	1,100

61A	Aa ℞ VICTORIA AVGVSTORVM VOT X MVLT XV, Victory stg. r., l. foot on globe, inscribing shield on cippus. Arles ·S·M·K·A·P. *RIC 13c* **light miliarensis**	550	1,250
66A	Aa ℞ VICT DD NN AVGG VOT V, two Victories hldg. up inscribed shield. Rome $\overline{\text{RP}}$. *RIC 9* **argenteus?** (= **pre-reform siliqua**)	250	550
66B	Da ℞ VICTORIA DD NN AVG, Victory stg. l. hldg. wreath and palm. Lugdunum $\overline{\text{LVG}}$. *RIC 7*	100	250
71a	Ac ℞ VIRTVS EXERCITVS, emperor stg. facing, head l., hldg. standard in r. hand, resting l. on shield. Trier $\overline{\text{SMTR}}$. *RIC 26c* **light miliarensis**	500	1,100
71†b	Aa ℞ As last. Trier $\overline{\text{SMTR}}$. *RIC 26b(1)* **light miliarensis** . .	500	1,100

71†c	As last. Trier $\overline{\text{TRPS}}$·. *RIC 26b(2), 42a(1)* **light miliarensis**	450	1,000

		VF	EF
71†d	As last. Trier T̄R̄P̄S̄··. *RIC 26b(3)* **light miliarensis** . . .	500	1,100
71†e	As last. Trier T̄R̄P̄S̄. *RIC 42a(2)* **light miliarensis.** . . .	450	1,000
71†f	Aa Ŗ As last, emperor stg. facing, head l., hldg. labarum in r. hand, resting l. on shield. Siscia ·S̄Ī̄S̄C̄P̄. *RIC 10b* **light miliarensis**	500	1,100
72†	Ab Ŗ As last. Thessalonica T̄Ē̄S̄. *RIC 11b* **light miliarensis** .	500	1,100
73†a	Aa Ŗ As last, emperor stg. facing hldg. reversed spear in r. hand, resting l. on shield. Arles P̄C̄Ō̄N̄. *RIC 5(1)* **light miliarensis**	550	1,250
73†b	As last. Arles P̄C̄Ō̄N̄*. *RIC 5(2)* **light miliarensis**	550	1,250
73†c	As last. Thessalonica T̄Ē̄S̄. *RIC 10b* **light miliarensis** . .	500	1,100
73†d	Aa Ŗ As last, emperor stg. facing hldg. spear in r. hand, resting l. on shield. Arles P̄C̄Ō̄N̄. *RIC 2* **multiple**	7,000	14,000
73†e	As last. Thessalonica T̄Ē̄S̄. *RIC 8* **multiple**	7,000	14,000
74†	Aa Ŗ As last, three standards. Nicomedia S̄M̄N̄. *RIC 18* **argenteus** (= **pre-reform siliqua**)	250	550
87†a	Ad Ŗ vot v or vot·v, in wreath. Constantinople C̄Ō̄N̄S̄Ā̄. *RIC 11e(1–3), 11j(1–3)* **argenteus**	125	300
87†b	Ad Ŗ As last. Constantinople C̄Ō̄N̄S̄Ā̄. *RIC 11d(1–5), 11i(1–2)* **argenteus**	125	300
87†c	Aa Ŗ As last. Constantinople C̄Ō̄N̄S̄Ā̄. *RIC 11c, 11h* **argenteus**	125	300
88†a	Aa Ŗ As last. Constantinople C̄P̄·Ā̄. *RIC 13b(1–4) 13d(1–6), 13h, 13i(1)*.	55	135

		VF	EF
88†b	As last. Constantinople C̄·Ā̄. *RIC 13d(7–13), 13i(2–5)* . .	55	135
88†c	As last. Constantinople *C̄·Ā̄. *RIC 13i(6)*	55	135
88†d	As last. Constantinople ·C̄·Ā̄. *RIC 13d(14–15)*	55	135
88†e	As last. Constantinople C̄Ō̄N̄S̄Ā̄. *RIC 13d(16)*	55	135
88†f	As last. Constantinople ·C̄Ō̄N̄S̄Ā̄·. *RIC 13d(17)*	55	135
88†g	As last. Antioch Ā̄N̄T̄··. *RIC 8*	75	185
88†h	Ad Ŗ As last. Constantinople C̄P̄·Ā̄. *RIC 13c*	60	150
88†i	As last. Constantinople *C̄·Ā̄. *RIC 13j*	60	150
90†a	Aa Ŗ vot v mvlt x, in wreath. Aquileia S̄M̄Ā̄Q̄. *RIC 3b* **heavy miliarensis**	600	1,350
90†b	Ba Ŗ As last. Antioch Ā̄N̄T̄·. *RIC 27* **heavy miliarensis** . .	600	1,350
91†a	Aa Ŗ As last. Trier T̄R̄. *RIC 4*	75	185
91†b	As last. Lugdunum L̄V̄Ḡ. *RIC 8(1)*	75	185
91†c	As last. Lugdunum P̄L̄V̄Ḡ. *RIC 8(2)*	75	185
91†d	As last. Rome R̄P̄. *RIC 10d(1–2)*	55	135
91†e	As last. Constantinople *C̄·Ā̄Q̄. *RIC 36c(1–4)*	55	135
91†f	As last. Nicomedia S̄M̄N̄. *RIC 20b*	55	135
91†g	As last. Thessalonica T̄Ē̄S̄. *RIC 14*	70	175

		VF	EF
91†h	Aa Ŗ vot v mv·lt x, in wreath. Rome R̄P̄. *RIC 10c(1–4)* . .	55	135

		VF	EF
91†i	Ad ℞ VOT V MVLT X, in wreath. Constantinople *C•AQ̅. *RIC* 36d(1–3)	55	135
93†a	Aa ℞ VOT V MVLTIS X, in wreath. Nicomedia S̅M̅N̅. *RIC 19b* **argenteus (= pre-reform siliqua)**	125	300
93†b	Ad ℞ As last. Nicomedia S̅M̅N̅. *RIC 19c* **argenteus**	125	300

93†c	Aa ℞ As last. Nicomedia S̅M̅N̅. *RIC 21b.*	60	150

95†a	Aa ℞ VOT X MVLT XV, in wreath. Trier T̅R̅P̅S̅•. *RIC 44a(1)* ..	70	175
95†b	As last. Trier T̅R̅P̅S̅. *RIC 44a(2).*	70	175
95Aa	Ad ℞ VOT X MVL XX, in wreath. Antioch A̅N̅T̅. *RIC 33d* ..	55	135
95Ab	Ba ℞ As last. Antioch A̅N̅T̅. *RIC 33c*	55	135
95Ac	Aa ℞ As last. Antioch A̅N̅T̅. *RIC 33b(1)*	55	135
95Ad	As last. Antioch A̅N̅T̅ᵛ. *RIC 33b(2)*	55	135
95Ae	As last. Antioch A̅N̅T̅••. *RIC 33b(3)*	55	135
95Af	As last. Antioch A̅N̅ᵛ. *RIC 33b(4)*	55	135

96†a	Aa ℞ VOT X MVLT XX, in wreath. Lugdunum L̅V̅G̅. *RIC 19(1)*	65	160
96†b	As last. Lugdunum P̅L̅V̅G̅. *RIC 19(2).*	65	160
96†c	As last. Siscia SISCP. *RIC 12b*	70	175

96†d	As last. Constantinople C R SQ. *RIC 37b*	55	135
96†e	As last. Antioch A̅N̅T̅. *RIC 34b(1)*	55	135
96†f	As last. Antioch •A̅N̅T̅. *RIC 34b(2)*	55	135

		VF	EF
96†g	As last. Antioch $\overline{\text{ANT}}$··. *RIC 34b(3)*	55	135
96†h	As last. Antioch ·$\overline{\text{ANT}}$*. *RIC 34b(4)*	55	135
96†i	As last. Antioch ·$\overline{\text{ANTA}}$. *RIC 34b(5–8)*	55	135
96†j	As last. Antioch ·$\overline{\text{ANTA}}$·. *RIC 34b(9)*	55	135
96†k	As last. Antioch $\overline{\text{AN}}$*. *RIC 34b(10)*	55	135
96†l	As last. Antioch ·$\overline{\text{ANA}}$·. *RIC 34b(11)*	55	135
96†m	As last. Antioch $\overline{\text{AN}}$. *RIC 34b(12)*	55	135
96†n	Ad ℞ As last. Siscia $\frac{\ast}{\text{SISCP}}$. *RIC 12c*	70	175
96†o	As last. Antioch $\overline{\text{ANT}}$. *RIC 34c*	60	150
96†p	Ba ℞ As last. Antioch $\overline{\text{ANT}}$··. *RIC 34d(1)*	55	135
96†q	As last. Antioch $\overline{\text{ANT}}$*. *RIC 34d(2)*	55	135
96†r	As last. Antioch ·$\overline{\text{ANT}}$*. *RIC 34d(3)*	55	135
96†s	As last. Antioch ·$\overline{\text{ANTA}}$. *RIC 34d(4–10)*	55	135
96†t	As last. Antioch ·$\overline{\text{ANA}}$. *RIC 34d(11)*	55	135
96†u	Aa ℞ VOT X MV • LT XX, in wreath. Thessalonica $\overline{\text{TES}}$. *RIC 25* .	70	175
96†v	Aa ℞ VOT X MVLT XX, in wreath. Constantinople $\overline{\text{CONS}}$·. *RIC 34b* **argenteus** (= **pre-reform siliqua**).	125	300
96†w	Bd ℞ As last. Antioch $\overline{\text{ANT}}$*. *RIC 28* **heavy miliarensis** . .	600	1,350
98†a	Aa ℞ VOT XV MVLT XX, in wreath. Siscia $\frac{\ast}{\text{SISCP}}$. *RIC 13a* . .	75	185

98†b	As last. Siscia $\frac{\ast}{\text{SISCP}}$. *RIC 19a(1)*	60	150
98†c	As last. Siscia $\frac{\ast}{\text{SISCPS}}$. *RIC 19a(2)*	60	150
98†d	As last. Siscia $\frac{+}{\text{SISCPS}}$. *RIC 19a(3)*	65	160
100†a	As last. Thessalonica $\overline{\text{T}\cancel{\text{R}}\text{E}}$. *RIC 30a*	70	175

100†b	Aa ℞ VOT VX MVLT XX, in wreath. Constantinople $\overline{\text{C}\cancel{\text{R}}\text{S}}$. *RIC 38b*	70	175
101†a	Aa ℞ VOT XX MVLT XXX, in wreath. Constantinople $\overline{\text{CONCM}}$. *RIC 42bis(1)*	60	150
101†b	As last. Constantinople $\overline{\text{CNCM}}$. *RIC 43 bis(2)*	65	160
102A	Aa ℞ VOTIS V, in wreath. Constantinople *$\overline{\text{C·AQ}}$. *RIC 39a* . .	75	185
103†a	Aa ℞ VOTIS V MVLTIS X, in wreath. Trier $\overline{\text{TRPS}}$·. *RIC 23c* **heavy miliarensis**	550	1,250

		VF	EF
103†b	As last. Lugdunum S·M·L·A·P·☧. *RIC 16b* **heavy miliarensis** . .	600	1,350
103†c	Ad ℞ As last. Arles SMKAP. *RIC 11b* **heavy miliarensis** . .	600	1,350
105†	Aa ℞ VOTIS X MVLTIS XV, in wreath. Lugdunum S·M·L·A·P☧. *RIC 17b* **heavy miliarensis** . .	600	1,350
106†a	Aa ℞ VOTIS X MVLTIS XX, in wreath. Trier TRPS·. *RIC 41a(1)* **heavy miliarensis** . .	550	1,250
106†b	As last. Trier TRPS. *RIC 41a(2)* **heavy miliarensis** . .	550	1,250
107†	Aa ℞ As last. Aquileia AQPS•. *RIC 14a* . .	65	160
108†a	Aa ℞ VOTIS XV MVLTIS XX, in wreath. Siscia •SISCP. *RIC 9b* **heavy miliarensis** . .	550	1,250
108†b	As last. Siscia SISCP . *RIC 16a* **heavy miliarensis** . .	650	1,500

		VF	EF
109†a	Aa ℞ VRBS ROMA, Roma seated l. on throne hldg. sceptre and Victory on globe. Trier TRPS•. *RIC 27e(1), 45(1)* . .	45	110
109†b	As last. Trier TRPS. *RIC 27e(2), 45b(2)* . .	50	125

		VF	EF
109†c	Aa ℞ VRBS ROMA, Roma seated l. on throne hldg. spear and Victory on globe. Trier TRPS•. *RIC 27b, 45a* . .	50	125
109†d	As last. Lugdunum PLVG. *RIC 9b* . .	60	150
109†e	As last. Rome RP. *RIC 11b(1–2)* . .	50	125
109†f	As last. Siscia SISCPS̸. *RIC 20a* . .	70	175

		VF	EF
110†a	Aa ℞ VRBS ROMA, Roma seated l. on cuirass hldg. Victory on globe and reversed spear. Trier TRPS•. *RIC 46a(1)* . .	50	125
110†b	As last. Trier TRPS. *RIC 46a(2)*. . .	55	135
110†c	As last. Aquileia AQPS. *RIC 15a(1)* . .	60	150
110†d	As last. Aquileia AQPS•. *RIC 15a(2)* . .	55	135

		VF	EF
110†e	As last. Aquileia |* AQPS•. *RIC 15a(3)* . .	55	135

162

DOMINICA

Albia Dominica was the wife of Valens and had three children by him. Little is known of her life other than the fact she was an Arian and is said to have converted Valens to the doctrine. No coinage was minted in her name.

PROCOPIUS
A.D. 365–366

Procopius was born c. 326 into a good family and was a distant relative of the Emperor Julian. The latter made him a comes *and in 363 gave him command of a detachment of troops on the Eastern frontier and promised him the succession to the throne. However, he yielded his claim at Jovian's accession and retired to his estates. Valentinian I and Valens regarded him with suspicion and he went into hiding and subsequently made his way to Constantinople. There he won the support of the troops and was proclaimed emperor during Valens' absence on a trip to the East (September, 365). After initial successes he lost military support to Valens and was defeated and executed after a reign of only eight months in May 366.*

Obverse legends.
A.   DN PROCOPIVS PF AVG.

Obverse busts.
a.   pearl diadem, draped, cuirassed, right.
b.   pearl diadem, draped, cuirassed, left.
c.   pearl diadem, cuirassed, right.
d.   rosette diadem, draped, cuirassed, right.

All the silver coins of this reign are siliquae. For a discussion of fourth-century silver denominations and their names, see the Introduction.

		VF	EF
14†a	Ad Ɍ VOT V, in wreath. Cyzicus K̄V̄Ā. *RIC 3b(1–2)*	750	1,750
14†b	Ac Ɍ VOT V or VOT·V, in wreath. Constantinople C̄ · Ā. *RIC 13l*	650	1,500

14†c	Aa Ɍ As last. Constantinople C̄ · Ā. *RIC 13e(1–8), 13k(1–3)* .	600	1,350
14†d	As last. Constantinople · C̄ · Ā. *RIC 13e(9–14), 13k(4–6)*	600	1,350
14†e	As last. Constantinople C̄Ā. *RIC 13e(15)*	600	1,350
14†f	As last. Cyzicus K̄V̄Ā. *RIC 3a(1)*	750	1,750
14†g	As last. Cyzicus S̄M̄K̄Ɫ. *RIC 3a(2)*	750	1,750

14†h	As last. Nicomedia S̄M̄N̄. *RIC 6*	750	1,750
14†i	Ab Ɍ As last. Constantinople C̄ · Ā. *RIC 13f*	900	2,000

GRATIAN
A.D. 367–383

Flavius Gratianus was the elder son of Valentinian I and was elevated to the rank of Augustus in 367, although only seven years of age. He became ruler of the Western Empire following his father's death in 375, and senior emperor three years later on the death of his uncle Valens. Although well educated, he had inherited neither the administrative competence nor the military ability of his father. His devotion to Christianity found expression in the order to remove the statue of Victory from the Roman Senate House, and in the rejection of the title Pontifex Maximus, *the first time this had ever been omitted from the imperial titulature. After the death of Valens in 378 he appointed the general Theodosius to be the Eastern emperor, but relations between the two Augusti were always strained. In 383 Gratian was faced with the rebellion of Magnus Maximus in Britain, and when the usurper invaded Gaul, Gratian immediately marched against him. However, the emperor was abandoned by his commander-in-chief, Merobaudes, and realizing the hopelessness of his position he fled to Lugdunum where he was subsequently killed.*

Obverse legends.
A.   DN GRATIANVS PF AVG.

Obverse busts.
a.   pearl diadem, draped, cuirassed, right.
b.   rosette diadem, draped, cuirassed, right.
c.   rosette diadem, draped, cuirassed, left.
d.   rosette diadem, cuirassed right.

All coins are siliquae unless otherwise specified. For a discussion of fourth-century silver denominations and their names, see the Introduction.

		VF	EF
6†a	Aa ℞ CONCORDIA AVGGG, Constantinopolis seated facing, hldg. sceptre and cornucopiae, r. foot on prow. Trier TRPS. *RIC 55b*	90	225
6†b	As last. Lugdunum LVGPS. *RIC 24a*	70	175
18†	Aa ℞ GLORIA ROMANORVM, Roma seated facing on throne, head l., hldg. globe and reversed spear. Sirmium SMSPV. *RIC 11* .	125	300
20†	Ac ℞ As last, emperor stg. facing under arch, head r., hldg. transverse spear and globe. Antioch ANT*. *RIC 29c* **light miliarensis**	650	1,500
27†	Aa ℞ PERPETVETAS, phoenix stg. l. on globe. Trier TRPS. *RIC 56a* **half argenteus**	300	650

| 36a | Aa ℞ VICTORIA AVGG, Victory advg. l. hldg. wreath and palm. Aquileia AQPS. *RIC 26a* . . . . | 100 | 250 |

36†b	Aa ℞ VICTORIA AVGGG, as last. Rome RP. *RIC 36a* **half siliqua**	300	650
45†	Aa ℞ VICTORIA AVGVSTORVM, as last Trier TR. *RIC 28* **half siliqua**	325	700
45A	Aa ℞ As last. Aquileia AQPS. *RIC 24* **argenteus** (= **pre-reform siliqua**)	250	550

		VF	EF
46†	Aa ℞ VICTORIA AVGVSTORVM VOT V MVLT X, Victory stg. r., l. foot on globe, inscribing shield on cippus. Trier SMTR. *RIC 24e* **light miliarensis**	650	1,500
46A	Ab ℞ As last. Lugdunum S·M·L·A·P℟ *RIC 18b* **light miliarensis**	650	1,500
52†a	Aa ℞ VIRTVS EXERCITVS, emperor stg. facing, head l. hldg. standard in r. hand, resting l. on shield. Trier SMTR. *RIC 26d* **light miliarensis**	600	1,350

		VF	EF
52†b	As last. Trier TRPS·. *RIC 26e, 42b(1)* **light miliarensis** . .	550	1,250
52†c	As last. Trier TRPS. *RIC 42b(2), 53a* **light miliarensis** . .	550	1,250

		VF	EF
52†d	As last. Aquileia AQPS. *RIC 23a* **light miliarensis**	600	1,350
52†e	As last. Rome RP. *RIC 34a(1-3)* **light miliarensis**	600	1,350
53†a	Aa ℞ as last, emperor stg. facing, head l., hldg. labarum in r. hand, resting l. on shield. Aquileia SMAQ·P. *RIC 10* **light miliarense**	650	1,500
53†b	As last. Siscia ·SISCP. *RIC 10c* **light miliarensis**	600	1,350
53†c	As last. Siscia SISCPS. *RIC 23a* **light miliarensis**	650	1,500

		VF	EF
56†a	Aa ℞ VIRTVS ROMANORVM, Roma seated facing on throne, head l., hldg. globe and reversed spear or sceptre. Trier TRPS. *RIC 58a(1)*	55	135
56†b	As last. Trier SMTR. *RIC 58a(2)*	70	175
56†c	As last. Lugdunum LVGPS. *RIC 26*	60	150

		VF	EF
56†d	As last. Aquileia AQPS. *RIC 28a*	55	135

		VF	EF
65†	Aa R̶ VOT V MVLT X, in wreath, Arles $\overline{\text{SMKAP}}$. *RIC 14* **light miliarensis**	650	1,500
66†a	Aa R̶ As last. Siscia $\frac{*}{\text{SISCP}}$. *RIC 11*	75	185
66†b	As last. Constantinople $Æ$ C₽SǪ. *RIC 36e*	65	160
66†c	As last. Nicomedia $\overline{\text{SMN}}$. *RIC 20c*	65	160

66†d	As last. Antioch $\overline{\text{ANT}}$*. *RIC 32*.	65	160
68†	Aa R̶ VOT X MVLT XV, in wreath. Trier $\overline{\text{TRPS}}$. *RIC 44b*. . .	65	160
68A	Aa R̶ VOT X MVLTIS XV, in wreath. Trier $\overline{\text{TR}}$. *RIC 61a* . .	90	225
69†	Aa R̶ VOT X MVLT XX, in wreath. Siscia $\frac{*}{\text{SISCP}}$. *RIC 18*. . .	75	185
70†a	As last. Antioch $\overline{\text{ANT}}$. *RIC 34e, 34f(1)*	65	160
70†b	As last. Antioch · $\overline{\text{ANT}}$. *RIC 34f(2)*	65	160
70†c	As last. Antioch $\overline{\text{ANT}}$ · . *RIC 34f(3)*	65	160
70†d	As last. Antioch $\overline{\text{ANT}}$*. *RIC 34f(4)*	65	160
70†e	As last. Antioch. · $\overline{\text{ANTA}}$. *RIC 34f(5–9)*	65	160
70†f	As last. Antioch $\overline{\text{ANA}}$. *RIC 34f(10)*	65	160
70†g	As last. Antioch · $\overline{\text{ANA}}$. *RIC 34f(11)*	65	160
72a	Aa R̶ VOT XV MVLT XX or MV · LT XX, in wreath. Trier $\overline{\text{TRPS}}$. *RIC 63*	80	200
72b	As last. Siscia $\frac{*}{\text{SISCP}}$. *RIC 13b*	80	200

72c	As last. Siscia $\frac{*}{\text{SISCPS}}$. *RIC 19b(1,3)*	65	160
72d	As last. Siscia $\frac{*}{\text{SISCP⌐}}$. *RIC 19b(2)*	65	160
72e	As last. Siscia $\frac{\text{x}}{\text{SISCPS}}$. *RIC 19b(4)*	65	160
72f	As last. Siscia $\frac{\text{x}}{\text{SISCPS}}$. *RIC 19b(5)*	65	160
72g	As last. Siscia $\frac{·}{\text{SISCPS}}$. *RIC 25*	65	160
73†	Aa R̶ VOT VX MVLT XX or MV · LT XX, in wreath. Thessalonica T₽E *RIC 30b*	75	185

		VF	EF
73A	Aa ℞ VOT XV MVLTIS XX, in wreath. Trier T̄R̄. *RIC 62* . . .	90	225
76†	Aa ℞ VOT XV MVLT XXX, in wreath. Thessalonica. T̄⚹Ē. *RIC 36*	80	200
79a	Aa ℞ VOTIS V, in wreath. Constantinople *C̄·A̅Q̅. *RIC 39b* . .	70	175
79†b	Ab ℞ As last. Constantinople *C̄·A̅Q̅. *RIC 37c.*	70	175
80a	Aa ℞ VOTIS V or Ꙩ MVLTIS X, in wreath. Trier T̄R̄P̄S̄. *RIC 23e* **heavy miliarensis**.	650	1,500
80†b	As last. Trier S̄M̄T̄R̄. *RIC 23d* **heavy miliarensis**	700	1,600
80†c	As last. Lugdunum S̄·M̄·L̄·A̅·P̄ꙅ *RIC 16c(1)* **heavy miliarensis**	700	1,600
80†d	As last. Lugdunum ·S̄·M̄·L̄·A̅·P̄ꙅ *RIC 16c(2)* **heavy miliarensis**	700	1,600
80†e	Ad ℞ As last. Arles S̄M̄K̄A̅P̄. *RIC 11d* **heavy miliarensis** . .	700	1,600
81†a	Aa ℞ VOTIS X MVLTIS XX, in wreath. Trier T̄R̄P̄S̄·. *RIC 41b(1)* **heavy miliarensis**.	650	1,500
81†b	As last. Trier T̄R̄P̄S̄. *RIC 41b(2)* **heavy miliarensis** . . .	650	1,500
82†	As last. Aquileia A̅Q̅P̄S̄·. *RIC 14b.*	70	175
83†a	Aa ℞ VOTIS XV MVLTIS XX, in wreath. Trier T̄R̄P̄S̄. *RIC 52* **heavy miliarensis**.	700	1,600
83†b	As last. Siscia S̄I̅S̄C̄P̄ꙅ. *RIC 16b* **heavy miliarensis** . . . ·	750	1,750

86†a	Aa ℞ VRBS ROMA, Roma seated l. on throne hldg. sceptre and Victory on globe. Trier T̄R̄P̄S̄ · . *RIC 27f(1), 45c(1)* . . .	50	125
86†b	As last. Trier T̄R̄P̄S̄. *RIC 27f(2), 45c(2)*	55	135

86Aa	Aa ℞ As last, Roma seated l. on throne hldg. spear and Victory on globe. Trier T̄R̄P̄S̄ · . *RIC 27c.*	55	135
86Ab	As last. Rome R̄*P̄. *RIC 35a(1–5)*	55	135
86Ac	As last. Siscia S̄I̅S̄C̄P̄ꙅ. *RIC 20b*	75	185

87†a	Aa ℞ As last, Roma seated l. on cuirass hldg. Victory on globe and reversed spear. Trier T̄R̄P̄S̄ · . *RIC 46b(1)*	55	135
87†b	As last. Trier T̄R̄P̄S̄. *RIC 46b(2), 64a*	55	135
87†c	As last. Lugdunum L̄V̄ḠP̄S̄. *RIC 27*	60	150
87†d	As last. Aquileia A̅Q̅P̄S̄. *RIC 15b(1)*	60	150

					VF	EF
87†e	As last. Aquileia $\overline{\text{AQPS}}$ · . *RIC 15b(2)* . .	. .	. .	. .	60	150
87†f	As last. Aquileia $\overline{\text{AQPS}}$ · . *RIC 15b(3)* . .	. .	. .	. .	60	150

CONSTANTIA

Constantia was the posthumous daughter of Constantius II, by Faustina, and later became the wife of Gratian whom she married c. 374. Little is known of her life other than that when Procopius decided to go to Constantinople in 365, to make his bid for the throne, he took Constantia and her mother with him to ensure the loyalty of the troops. No coinage was minted in her name.

168

VALENTINIAN II
A.D. 375–392

Flavius Valentinianus was the younger son of Valentinian I by his second wife, Justina. He was proclaimed emperor at the age of four following his father's death, and initially was under the protection of his half-brother, Gratian, his residence being in Illyricum. He was still too young to exercise effective power when, at the age of twelve, he became Senior Augustus after the death of Gratian. His court was established at Milan, where his mother managed his affairs. When Magnus Maximus invaded Italy in 387 Valentinian II fled, but after the defeat of the usurper by Theodosius, Valentinian was re-established in the West. However, his weak character was dominated by his general Arbogast, and being unable to assert his authority his frustration probably led him to commit suicide (May, 392).

Obverse legends.
A. DN VALENTINIANVS PF AVG.
B. DN VALENTINIANVS IVN PF AVG.

Obverse busts.
a. pearl diadem, draped, cuirassed, right.
b. pearl diadem, draped, cuirassed, left.
c. rosette diadem, draped, cuirassed, right.

All coins are siliquae unless otherwise specified. For a discussion of fourth-century silver denominations and their names, see the Introduction.

		VF	EF
17†	Ac ℞ GLORIA ROMANORVM, emperor stg. facing, head l. hldg. sceptre in r. hand, resting l. on shield. Constantinople CON. *RIC 84* **heavy miliarensis**	700	1,600

18†	Aa ℞ As last, but emperor hldg. standard in r. Lugdunum LVGPS. *RIC 40* **light miliarensis**	650	1,500
19†a	Ac ℞ As last, emperor stg. facing, head l., raising r. hand, hldg. globe in l. Aquileia AQPS. *RIC 56a* **light miliarensis**	650	1,500
19†b	Ab ℞ As last. Constantinople CON. *RIC 85a* **light miliarensis**	700	1,600
25†	Ba ℞ PERPETVETAS, phoenix stg. l. on globe. Trier TRPS. *RIC 56b* **half argenteus**	300	650
35	Aa ℞ TRIVMFATOR GENT BARB, emperor stg. facing, head l., hldg. labarum and globe, kneeling captive on his l. Rome RP. *RIC 32* **multiple**	7,500	15,000
39†a	Ba ℞ VICTORIA AVGGG, Victory advg. r., hldg. wreath in either hand. Trier TRPS. *RIC 54* **argenteus?** (= **pre-reform siliqua**)	300	700
39†b	Aa ℞ As last, Victory advg. r., hldg. wreath in either hand. Siscia SISCP. *RIC 17*	100	250

39A	Ba ℞ VICTORIA AVGG, Victory advg. l., hldg. wreath and palm. Aquileia AQPS. *RIC 26b*	110	275

			VF	EF
40†a	Ba ℞ VICTORIA AVGGG, as last. Trier $\overline{\text{TRPS}}$. *RIC 43, 57a* . .		60	150
40†b	As last. Lugdunum $\overline{\text{LVGPS}}$. *RIC 25*		70	175
40†c	As last. Aquileia $\overline{\text{AQPS}}$. *RIC 27a*		65	160
41†a	Aa ℞ As last. Trier $\overline{\text{TRPS}}$. *RIC 57b*		75	185
41†b	As last. Aquileia $\overline{\text{AQPS}}$. *RIC 27b*		70	175

42†	As last. Rome $\overline{\text{RP}}$. *RIC 36b* **half siliqua**.		300	700
49A	Aa ℞ VICTORIA AVGVSTORVM, Victory advg. r., head l., dragging captive with r. hand, hldg. trophy in l. Rome $\overline{\text{RP}}$. *RIC 33b–c* **heavy miliarensis**		750	1,750
55A	A? ℞ As last, emperor carrying trophy on shldr, dragging captive, r. Thessalonica $\overline{\text{TES}}$. *RIC 57a* **light miliarensis** . .		900	2,000

58†a	Ba ℞ VIRTVS EXERCITVS, emperor stg. facing, head l., hldg. standard in r., resting l. on shield. Trier $\overline{\text{TRPS}}$. *RIC 42c* **light miliarensis**		550	1,250

58†b	As last. Aquileia $\overline{\text{AQPS}}$. *RIC 23b* **light miliarensis**		600	1,350
58†c	Aa ℞ As last. Trier $\overline{\text{TRPS}}$. *RIC 53b, 93a* **light miliarensis** .		600	1,350
58†d	As last. Lugdunum $\overline{\text{LVG}}$. *RIC 41(1)* **light miliarensis** . .		600	1,350
58†e	As last. Lugdunum $\overline{\text{LVG}}$·. *RIC 41(2)* **light miliarensis** . .		600	1,350
58†f	As last. Rome $\overline{\text{RP}}$. *RIC 34b(1–3)* **light miliarensis**		600	1,350
60†a	Aa ℞ VIRTVS ROMANORVM, Roma seated facing, head l., on throne, hldg. globe and reversed spear. Milan $\overline{\text{MDPS}}$. *RIC 12a*		80	200

		VF	EF
60†b	As last. Aquileia $\overline{\text{AQPS}}$. *RIC 28c, RIC 41a*	60	150
60†c	Ba Ŗ As last. Aquileia $\overline{\text{AQPS}}$. *RIC 28b*.	65	160
61†	Aa Ŗ As last, Roma seated l. on cuirass hldg. Victory on globe and reversed spear. Trier $\overline{\text{TRPS}}$. *RIC 94a*	60	150
66†a	Ba Ŗ VOT V MVLT X, in wreath. Trier $\overline{\text{TRPS}}$. *RIC 59a* . . .	90	225
66†b	As last. Constantinople $\overline{\text{CONS}}$•. *RIC 51a*	90	225

66†c	Aa Ŗ As last. Siscia $\overline{\text{SISCP}}$. *RIC 24a*	65	160
66†d	As last. Thessalonica T ₽E. *RIC 29*	75	185
67A	Ba Ŗ VOT V MVLTIS X, in wreath. Trier $\overline{\text{TR}}$. *RIC 60* . .	100	250
67B	Ba Ŗ VOTIS V MVLTIS X, in wreath. Aquileia $\overline{\text{AQPS}}$•. *RIC 13a* .	75	185
71†a	Aa Ŗ VOT X MVLT XX, in wreath. Milan $\overline{\text{MDPS}}$. *RIC 14a* . .	80	200
71†b	As last. Thessalonica $\overline{\text{TES}}$. *RIC 58a*	90	225
71†c	As last. Constantinople $\overline{\text{CONS}}$·. *RIC 77a*	75	185
71†d	Aa Ŗ VOT X MV·LT XX, in wreath. Rome $\overline{\text{RP}}$. *RIC 62a*. . . .	85	210
71†e	As last. Constantinople $\overline{\text{CONS}}$. *RIC 77f*	75	185
71†f	Ac Ŗ As last. Constantinople $\overline{\text{CONS}}$·. *RIC 77g*	75	185
74Aa	Aa Ŗ VOT XV MVLT XX, in wreath. Lugdunum $\overline{\text{LVG}}$·. *RIC 42* argenteus	350	800
74Ab	As last. Siscia $\overset{*}{\text{SISCPS}}$. *RIC 19c(1)*	75	185
74Ac	As last. Siscia $\overset{*}{\text{SISCP}\varsigma}$. *RIC 19c(2)*	75	185

74A†d	Aa Ŗ VOT XV MVL XX, in wreath. Lugdunum $\overline{\text{LVG}}$•. *RIC—* argenteus	350	800
76†a	Aa Ŗ VRBS ROMA, Roma seated l. on cuirass, hldg. Victory on globe and reversed spear (sometimes without barb). Trier $\overline{\text{TRPS}}$. *RIC 95a*	75	185

76†b	As last. Lugdunum $\overline{\text{LVGPS}}$. *RIC 43a(1)*	65	160

		VF	EF
76†c	As last. Lugdunum $\overline{\text{LVGP}}$. *RIC 43a(2–3)*	65	160
76†d	As last. Lugdunum $\overline{\text{LVG}}$·. *RIC 43a(4)*	65	160

76†e	Ba Ŗ As last. Trier $\overline{\text{TRPS}}$. *RIC 46c, 64b*	70	175
76†f	As last. Aquileia $\overline{\text{AQPS}}$. *RIC 15c*	70	175
76†g	As last. Aquileia $\overline{\text{AQPS}}$·. *RIC 15d(1)*	65	160

76†h	As last. Aquileia $\overset{|*}{\overline{\text{AQPS}}}$·. *RIC 15d(2)*	65	160
76†i	As last. Aquileia $\overset{|*}{\cdot\overline{\text{AQPS}}}$·. *RIC 15d(3)*	70	175

76Aa	Aa Ŗ As last, Roma seated l. on throne hldg. spear and Victory on globe. Rome $\overline{\text{R}^*\text{P}}$. *RIC 35b*	65	160
76Ab	As last. Rome $\overline{\text{RP}}$. *RIC 53a*	70	175
76Ac	As last. Siscia $\overline{\text{SISCPS}}$. *RIC 20c(1)*	75	185
76Ad	As last. Siscia $\overline{\text{SISCP}}$ʃ. *RIC 20c(2)*	75	185

172

THEODOSIUS I, THE GREAT
A.D. 379–395

Flavius Theodosius was the son of Count Theodosius, a renowned frontier general who was executed in 375 for reasons which are not altogether clear. His father's disgrace and death forced the younger Theodosius into retirement, but he was recalled by Gratian after the death of Valens and made Eastern emperor. Theodosius came to terms with the Goths by allowing them to settle within Roman territory in return for supplying military units. He also settled the Eastern frontier problem. He did little to oppose the usurpation of Magnus Maximus in the West until the latter invaded Italy, but then he moved against him and put a speedy end to the rebel regime (August, 388). He was also forced to deal with the usurpation of Eugenius, in 392, which he accomplished in equally summary fashion in the late summer of 394. Just four months after this success Theodosius died of natural causes at Milan. He was the last emperor to exercise effective authority over both the eastern and western divisions of the Empire.

Obverse legend.
A. DN THEODOSIVS PF AVG.

Obverse busts.
a. pearl diadem, draped, cuirassed, right.
b. pearl diadem, draped, cuirassed, left.
c. rosette diadem, draped, cuirassed, right.

All coins are siliquae unless otherwise specified. For a discussion of fourth-century silver denominations and their names, see the Introduction.

		VF	EF
4a	Aa ℞ CONCORDIA AVGGG, Constantinople seated facing, head r., hldg. sceptre and cornucopiae, r. foot on prow. Trier TRPS. *RIC* 55a, 83a	65	160
4b	As last. Lugdunum LVGPS. *RIC 24b*	75	185

4c	As last. Aquileia AQPS. *RIC 25*	70	175
17†	Ab ℞ GLORIA ROMANORVM, emperor stg. facing, head l., raising r. hand, hldg. globe in l. Milan MDPS. *RIC 25a* **light miliarensis**.	700	1,650
26†	Aa ℞ PERPETVETAS AVG, phoenix stg. l. on globe. Trier TRPS. *RIC 56c* **half argenteus**.	300	650
29†	Aa ℞ RESTITVTOR REIPVBLICE, emperor stg. facing, head l., hldg. labarum in r. hand, resting l. on shield. Thessalonica TES. *RIC 56* **multiple**	8,000	16,000
32	Aa ℞ SPES ROMANORVM, Victory advancing l. hldg. wreath and palm. Rome RP. *RIC 66* **half siliqua**	300	650
34†	Aa ℞ TRIVMFATOR GENT BARB, emperor stg. facing, head l., hldg. labarum and globe, kneeling captive on his l. Rome RP. *RIC 52a* **multiple**	7,000	14,000
35	Aa ℞ VICTORIA AVGG, Victory advg. l. hldg. wreath and palm. Aquileia AQPS. *RIC 26c*	110	275

	VF	EF
40a Aa ℞ VICTORIA AVGGG, as last. Milan $\overline{MD}$. *RIC 33a, 38a* **half siliqua** .	250	550
40b As last. Aquileia $\overline{AQPS}$. *RIC 57a* **half siliqua** . .	275	600
40c As last. Rome $\overline{RP}$. *RIC 36c* **half siliqua**. .	300	650
47A Aa ℞ VICTORIA AVGVSTORVM, Victory advg. r., head l. dragging captive with r. hand, hldg. trophy in l. Rome $\overline{RP}$. *RIC 33d* **heavy miliarensis** . .	750	1,750
47B A? ℞ As last, emperor carrying trophy on shldr., dragging captive, r. Thessalonica $\overline{TES}$. *RIC 57b* **light miliarensis**. . .	900	2,000
55†a Aa ℞ VIRTVS EXERCITVS, emperor stg. facing, head l., hldg. standard in r., resting l. on shield. Trier. $\overline{TRPS}$. *RIC 53c, 93b* **light miliarensis** . .	600	1,350

55†b As last. Rome $\overline{RP}$. *RIC 34c* **light miliarensis**	650	1,500
55†c Aa ℞ As last, but emperor hldg. labarum in r. Siscia $\overline{SISCP\varsigma}$. *RIC 23b* **light miliarensis**	700	1,650

56†a Aa ℞ VIRTVS ROMANORVM, Roma seated facing on throne hldg. globe and reversed spear. Trier $\overline{TRPS}$. *RIC 58b(1), 84* . .	70	175
56†b At last. Trier $\overline{SMTR}$. *RIC 58b(2), 71c*	70	175
56†c As last. Milan $\overline{MDPS}$. *RIC 12b*	75	185

56†d As last. Aquileia $\overline{AQPS}$. *RIC 28d, 41b*	60	150
57†a Aa ℞ As last, Roma seated l. on cuirass, hldg. Victory on globe and reversed spear. Trier $\overline{TRPS}$. *RIC 94b, 106a*	60	150

57†b As last. Milan $\overline{MDPS}$. *RIC 32a*	75	185

	VF	EF
64†a Aa ℞ VOT V MVLT X, in wreath. Trier T̄R̄P̄S̄. *RIC 59b*	90	225
64†b As last. Siscia S̄ĪS̄C̄P̄ʃ. *RIC 24b*	65	160
64†c As last. Constantinople C̄ŌN̄S̄·. *RIC 51b*	90	225

67†a Aa ℞ VOT X MVLT XX, in wreath. Milan M̄D̄P̄S̄. *RIC 14b* . .	80	200
67†b As last. Thessalonica T̄ĒS̄. *RIC 58b*	80	200
67†c As last. Constantinople C̄ŌN̄S̄·. *RIC 77b*	75	185
67†d As last. Constantinople C̄ŌN̄S̄. *RIC 87a*	70	175
67†e Ac ℞ As last. Thessalonica T̄ĒS̄. *RIC 58c*	80	200
67†f As last. Constantinople C̄ŌN̄S̄·. *RIC 77c*	75	185
67Aa Aa ℞ VOT X MV·LT XX, in wreath. Rome R̄P̄. *RIC 62b*	75	185
67Ab As last. Constantinople C̄ŌN̄S̄·. *RIC 77h*	75	185
67Ac Ac ℞ As last. Constantinople C̄ŌN̄S̄·. *RIC 77i*	75	185
67B Aa ℞ VOT X MVLTIS XV, in wreath. Trier T̄R̄. *RIC 61b*	90	225

71†a Aa ℞ VRBS ROMA, Roma seated l. on throne, hldg. spear and Victory on globe. Rome R̄*P̄. *RIC 35c*	65	160
71†b As last. Rome R̄P̄. *RIC 53b*	70	175
72†a Aa ℞ As last, Roma seated l. on cuirass, hldg. Victory on globe and reversed spear (sometimes without barb). Trier T̄R̄P̄S̄. *RIC 64c, 95b*	75	185

72†b As last. Lugdunum L̄V̄ḠP̄S̄. *RIC 43b(1)*	65	160
72†c As last. Lugdunum L̄V̄ḠS̄. *RIC 43b(2)*	70	175
72†d As last. Lugdunum L̄V̄ḠN̄. *RIC 43b(3)*	75	185
72†e As last. Lugdunum L̄V̄Ḡ··. *RIC 43b(4)*	80	200
72A Aa ℞ As last, but cippus beneath Victory on globe. Lugdunum L̄V̄ḠP̄S̄. *RIC 43d*	90	225

AELIA FLACCILLA

Aelia Flavia Flaccilla was the first wife of Theodosius I and the mother of Arcadius and Honorius. Noted for her charitable works and her piety, she predeceased her husband in 386.

Obverse legend.
AEL FLACCILLA AVG.

Obverse bust.
pearl diadem, draped, right.

		VF	EF
8† R No legend, Chi-rho in wreath. Constantinople $\overline{\text{CONS}}$·.			
RIC 78 **siliqua**	. . . .	2,500	5,500

MAGNUS MAXIMUS
A.D. 383–388

Magnus Maximus was related to Count Theodosius, father of Theodosius I. He served in the army in Britain and Africa and was eventually made commander of the British army. In July 383, his troops proclaimed him emperor and he moved into Gaul where he defeated Gratian, who had been abandoned by his commander-in-chief, Merobaudes. Magnus Maximus remained undisturbed in Gaul until 387, but his action in invading Italy in that year, while initially successful, forced Theodosius I to act. The Eastern army marched on Italy and Maximus surrendered at Aquileia, in August 388, and was later put to death.

Obverse legend.
DN MAG MAXIMVS PF AVG.

Obverse bust.
pearl diadem, draped, cuirassed, right.

All coins are siliquae unless otherwise specified. For a discussion of fourth-century silver denominations and their names, see the Introduction.

	VF	EF
1† R CONCORDIA AVGGG, Constantinopolis seated facing, hldg. sceptre and cornucopiae, l. foot on prow. Trier $\overline{\text{TRPS}}$. *RIC 83b–c* . .	200	450
9A R VICTORIA AVGG, Victory advg. l. hldg. wreath and palm. London $\overline{\text{AVGPS}}$. *RIC 3*	650	1,500

| 16† R VICTORIA AVGVSTORVM, as last. Aquileia $\overline{\text{AQPS}}$. *RIC 53a* . . | 150 | 350 |

	VF	EF

19a ℞ VIRTVS EXERCITVS, emperor stg. facing, head l., hldg. labarum in r. hand, resting l. on shield. Trier T̄R̄P̄S̄. *RIC 82* **light miliarensis** . .   1,750   4,000

19b As last. Lugdunum L̄V̄ḠS̄. *RIC 31* **light miliarensis**. .   1,850   4,250

20†a ℞ VIRTVS ROMANORVM, Roma seated facing on throne, head l., hldg. globe and reversed spear. Trier T̄R̄P̄S̄. *RIC 84b(1), 84c* .   70   175

20†b As last. Trier T̄P̄R̄S̄. *RIC 84b(2)*. .   100   250

20†c As last. Milan M̄D̄P̄S̄. *RIC 19a* . .   80   200

20†d As last. Aquileia A̅Q̅P̅S̅. *RIC 54a* . .   125   300

22A ℞ VOT V MVLT X, in wreath. London A̅V̅G̅P̅S̅. *RIC 4* . .   650   1,500

22B ℞ VOTIS V MVLTIS X, in wreath. Trier T̄R̄P̄S̄. *RIC 80* **heavy miliarensis** . .   2,000   4,500

23† ℞ VOTIS V MLTIS X (sic), in wreath. Trier T̄R̄P̄S̄. *RIC 81* **heavy miliarensis** . .   2,000   4,500

FLAVIUS VICTOR
A.D. 387–388

Flavius Victor was the son of the usurper Magnus Maximus and was proclaimed emperor by his father while still a young child. He apparently remained behind in Gaul when Maximus invaded Italy and, after the latter's defeat in 388, the unfortunate boy-emperor was executed by Arbogast, the general of Theodosius.

Obverse legend.
DN FL VICTOR PF AVG.

Obverse bust.
pearl diadem, draped, cuirassed, right.

The silver coins of this reign are all siliquae. For a discussion of fourth-century silver denominations and their names, see the Introduction.

		VF	EF
4†	℞ VICTORIA AVGVSTORVM, Victory walking l., hldg. wreath and palm. Aquileia AQPS. *RIC 53b*	550	1,250

6Aa	℞ VIRTVS ROMANORVM, Roma seated facing on throne, head l., hldg. globe and reversed spear. Trier. TRPS. *RIC 84d(1)* . .	350	800
6Ab	As last. Trier TPRS. *RIC 84d(2)*.	350	800

6Ac	As last. Milan MDPS. *RIC 19b*	275	600

6Ad	As last. Aquileia AQPS. *RIC 54b*	400	900

EUGENIUS
A.D. 392–394

Flavius Eugenius was proclaimed emperor by the general Arbogast, in August 392, to replace Valentinian II who had probably committed suicide three months before. Eugenius had been a professor of rhetoric and a court official of the middle rank, a respectable background that was unlikely to pose any real threat to Arbogast's supreme power in the West. Eugenius and his general invaded Italy in 393 and this action finally provoked Theodosius I to take retaliatory measures. The folowing year, 394, the Eastern emperor and his army marched on Italy and achieved a total victory over the usurpers at the Battle on the Frigidus. Eugenius was put to death and Arbogast took his own life rather than face the wrath of Theodosius.

Obverse legend.
DN EVGENIVS PF AVG.

Obverse bust.
pearl diadem, draped, cuirassed, right.

All coins are siliquae unless otherwise specified. For a discussion of fourth-century silver denominations and their names, see the Introduction.

		VF	EF
2†a	℞ GLORIA ROMANORVM, emperor stg. facing, head l., hldg. standard in r. hand, resting l. on shield. Trier TRPS. *RIC 104* **light miliarensis**	2,500	5,500
2†b	As last. Milan MDPS. *RIC 31a* **light miliarensis**	500	1,100
6A	℞ VICTORIA AVGGG, Victory walking l., hldg. wreath and palm. Milan MD *RIC 33b* **half siliqua**	500	1,100

13†	℞ VIRTVS EXERCITVS, emperor stg. facing, head l., hldg. standard in r. hand, resting l. on shield. Trier TRPS. *RIC 105* **light miliarensis**	2,500	5,500

14†a	℞ VIRTVS ROMANORVM, Roma seated l. on cuirass, hldg. Victory on globe and reversed spear. Trier TRPS. *RIC 106d*	350	800

14†b	As last. Milan MDPS. *RIC 32c*	400	900

	VF	EF

17†   ℞ VOT V MVLT X, in wreath. Milan $\overline{\text{MDPS}}$. *RIC 30* **heavy miliarense**   3,500   7,500

18A   ℞ VRBS ROMA, Roma seated l. on cuirass hldg. Victory on globe and reversed spear. Lugdunum $\overline{\text{LVGPS}}$. *RIC 46*   400   900

ARCADIUS
A.D. 383–408

Flavius Arcadius was the elder son of Theodosius I and Aelia Flaccilla. At the age of six he was proclaimed Augustus in Constantinople and he succeeded to the Eastern throne after Theodosius I's death at Milan in 395. He was never successful in holding effective power in his own hands, rather he was ridiculed for allowing his ministers to lead him 'like an ox'. He was lethargic by nature, halting of speech and totally incapable of leading his armies or directing government. Effective power lay first with the Praetorian Prefect, Rufinus, and later with the Eunuch Eutropius. After Arcadius' marriage to Eudoxia she quickly dominated him, and in consequence manipulated imperial policy as well, but following her death in 404 power passed into the hands of the Praetorian Prefect Anthemius. The feeble emperor expired in his palace in 408, at the age of 31, and was succeeded by his young son Theodosius II.

Obverse legends.
A.   DN ARCADIVS PF AVG.
B.   DN ARCAPIVS PF AVG.

Obverse busts.
a.   pearl diadem, draped, cuirassed, right.
b.   pearl diadem, draped, cuirassed, left.
c.   rosette diadem, draped, cuirassed, right.

All coins are siliquae unless otherwise stated. For a discussion of fourth- and fifth-century silver denominations, see the Introduction.

N.B. The RIC coverage of the imperial coinage at present ends at the death of Theodosius I in 395. The tenth volume, which is still in preparation, will include all the subsequent issues, down to the fall of the Western Empire in 476, and the commencement of the Byzantine coinage in the East, under Anastasius I. The absence of RIC references for post-395 issues has been offset as far as possible by the addition of citations, where appropriate, to Count Jean Tolstoi's *Monnaies Byzantines* (St. Petersburg, 1913–14); Francesco Gnecchi's *I Medaglioni Romani* (Milan, 1912); and J. Sabatier's *Description générale des Monnaies byzantines* (Paris, 1862).

	VF	EF

3a   Aa ℞ GLORIA ROMANORVM, emperor stg. facing. head l., raising r. hand, hldg. globe in l. Milan $\overline{\text{MDPS}}$. *RIC 25b* **light miliarensis**   650   1,500

3b   As last. Aquileia $\overline{\text{AQPS}}$. *RIC 56b* **light miliarensis** . .   650   1,500

3†c   Ab ℞ As last. Constantinople $\overline{\text{CON}}$. *RIC 85b* **light miliarensis**   700   1,650

3A   Aa ℞ As last, emperor stg. facing, head l., hldg. standard with cross on banner in r. hand, and resting l. on shield. Milan $\overline{\text{MDPS}}$. *RIC 31b* **light miliarensis**   700   1,650

		VF	EF
4a	Aa ℞ TRIVMFATOR GENT BARB, emperor stg. facing, head l., hldg. labarum in r., globe in l., to his right a kneeling captive. Rome $\overline{\text{RMPS}}$. **multiple**	7,000	14,000
4b	As last. Rome $\overline{\text{RP}}$. *RIC 52b* **multiple**	7,500	15,000
25A	Aa ℞ VICTORIA AVGG, Victory advg. l. hldg. wreath and palm. Milan $\overline{\text{MD}}$. **half siliqua**	200	450
26a	Aa ℞ VICTORIA AVGGG, as last. Milan $\overline{\text{MD}}$. *RIC 39a* **half siliqua**	200	450
26b	As last. Aquileia $\overline{\text{AQPS}}$. *RIC 57b* **half siliqua**	200	450
26c	As last. Rome $\overline{\text{RM}}$. **half siliqua**	200	450
26Aa	Aa ℞ VIRTVS EXERCITVS, emperor stg. facing, head l., hldg. reversed spear in r. hand, resting l. on shield. Milan $\overline{\text{MDPS}}$. *Sab. 7* **light miliarensis**	700	1,650
26Ab	As last. Ravenna $\overline{\text{RVPS}}$. *Sab. 7* **light miliarensis**	700	1,650
26Ac	As last. Rome $\overline{\text{RMPS}}$. *Sab. 7* **light miliarensis**	700	1,650
27a	Aa ℞ VIRTVS ROMANORVM, Roma seated l. on cuirass hldg. Victory on globe and reversed spear or sceptre. Trier $\overline{\text{TRPS}}$. *RIC 106b*	60	150

| **27b** | As last. Milan $\overline{\text{MDPS}}$. *RIC 32b* . . . . | 60 | 150 |

| **27c** | As last. Rome $\overline{\text{RMPS}}$. . . . . | 70 | 175 |
| **27d** | As last. Aquileia $\overline{\text{AQPS}}$. . . . . | 80 | 200 |

27†e	Ba ℞ As last. Trier $\overline{\text{TRPS}}$. *RIC 106c*	65	160
27A	Aa ℞ As last, Roma seated facing, head l., on throne, hldg. globe and reversed sceptre. Aquileia $\overline{\text{AQPS}}$. *RIC 41c*	100	250
27B	Aa ℞ VOT V MVLT X, in wreath. Milan $\overline{\text{MDPS}}$. *RIC 13* . .	65	160

| **27C** | Aa ℞ VOT X MVLT XV, in wreath. Milan $\overline{\text{MDPS}}$. *RIC 27a* . . | 70 | 175 |

	VF	EF
28†a Aa ℞ VOT X MVLT XX, in wreath. Milan $\overline{\text{MDPS}}$. *RIC 24* **heavy miliarensis** .	750	1,750
28†b As last. Rome $\overline{\text{RMPS}}$. **heavy miliarensis**	750	1,750
28†c As last. Ravenna $\overline{\text{RVPS}}$. *Gnecchi pl. 37,8* **heavy miliarensis** .	750	1,750
28Aa As last. Thessalonica $\overline{\text{TES}}$. *RIC 58d* . .	80	200
28Ab As last. Constantinople $\overline{\text{CONS·}}$. *RIC 77d*	70	175
28Ac As last. Constantinople $\overline{\text{CONS}}$. *RIC 87b* .	70	175
28A†d Ac ℞ As last. Constantinople $\overline{\text{CONS}}$*. . .	85	210
28A†e As last. Constantinople $\overline{\text{CONS·}}$. . .	85	210
28A†f Aa ℞ VOT X MV·LT XX, in wreath. Rome $\overline{\text{RP}}$. *RIC 62e* . .	85	210

28Ba Aa ℞ VRBS ROMA, Roma seated l. on cuirass, hldg. Victory on globe and reversed spear. Trier $\overline{\text{TRPS}}$. *RIC 95c Sab. 25* . .	65	160

28Bb As last. Lugdunum $\overline{\text{LVGPS}}$. *RIC 43c Sab. 25*. .	65	160
28C Aa ℞ As last, Roma seated l. on throne hldg. spear and Victory on globe. Rome $\overline{\text{RP}}$. *RIC 53c* . .	80	200

EUDOXIA

Aelia Eudoxia was the daughter of the Frank Bauto and was brought up in Constantinople. In April 395 she married the Emperor Arcadius and bore him five children in rapid succession: Flaccilla, Pulcheria, Arcadia, Theodosius II and Marina. In 400 she was proclaimed Augusta but she died at Constantinople only four years later. She was renowned for her beauty, her forcefulness of character and her piety.

Obverse legend.
AEL EVDOXIA AVG.

Obverse bust.
rosette diadem, draped, right.

		VF	EF
1	R̸ Chi-rho in wreath. Constantinople $\overline{\text{CONS}}$. **heavy miliarensis**	4,500	9,000
2	R̸ Cross in wreath. Constantinople $\overline{\text{CONS}}$*. **siliqua** *Tol. 145*	550	1,200

HONORIUS
A.D. 393–423

Flavius Honorius was the younger son of Theodosius I and Aelia Flaccilla. He was proclaimed Augustus by Theodosius I in 393 and eventually succeeded as Western emperor in January 395 on the death of his father. He never held more than nominal power, as effective control lay with the general Stilicho whose daughter Honorius married. Stilicho also claimed he was the guardian of Arcadius, the Eastern emperor, and this led to a rupture between the Eastern and Western halves of the empire. During Honorius' reign barbarian invaders overran Gaul and Spain and he was plagued by the usurpations of Constantine III (407–411) and Jovinus (411–413) in Gaul, and of Maximus in Spain (409–411). Alaric's invasions of Italy and the realization of his own vulnerability led Honorius to remove his court to Ravenna in 402, where he was safe amidst the marshes. Thanks to the competence of his general Constantius, the barbarian threat was temporarily held in check, the usurpations were put down, and large parts of Gaul and Spain were recovered for the empire though Roman control of the island province of Britain was permanently lost. Honorius died in 423 leaving no heir.

Obverse legend.
A. DN HONORIVS PF AVG.

Obverse busts.
a. pearl diadem, draped, cuirassed, right.
b. pearl diadem, draped, cuirassed, left.
c. pearl diadem, draped, cuirassed, right, right hand raised, hiding Victory on globe in left.

All coins are siliquae unless otherwise stated. For a discussion of fourth- and fifth-century silver denominations and their names, see the Introduction.

		VF	EF
12	Aa ℞ GLORIA ROMANORVM, Roma seated facing on <u>throne</u>, head l., hldg. globe in r. and spear in left. Ravenna RVPS. **half siliqua**	250	550
17†	Ac ℞ As last, emperor nimbate in mil. dres, stg. facing in a chariot drawn by six horses raising r. hand, hldg. globe in left. Constantinople CONOB with objects depicted between the N and O which may be rings and a strong box. *Gnecchi pl. 36,15* **multiple**	12,500	25,000
18	Aa ℞ As last, emperor nimbate, stg. facing, head l., hldg. sceptre in r. hand, resting l. on shield. Constantinople CON *Gnecchi pl. 37,2* **heavy miliarensis**	750	1,750
19	Aa ℞ As last. Constantinople CON. *Gnecchi pl. 37,1* **light miliarensis**	700	1,650

19A	Ab ℞ As last, emperor nimbate, stg. facing, head l., raising r. hand, hldg. globe in l. Constantinople CON. **light miliarensis**	650	1,500
31	Aa ℞ SALVS REIPVBLICAE, Victory walking l. hldg. wreath. Rome? **half siliqua**	250	550

		VF	EF
34a	Aa ℞ TRIVMFATOR GENT BARB, emperor stg. facing, head l., hldg. labarum in r. hand and globe in l., on his right a kneeling captive. Milan $\overline{\text{MDPS}}$. *Gnecchi p. 82,4* **multiple**	7,000	14,000
34b	As last. Rome $\overline{\text{RMPS}}$. *Gnecchi pl. 37,4* **multiple**	7,000	14,000
34c	As last. Ravenna $\overline{\text{RVPS}}$. *Gnecchi pl. 37,5* **multiple**	7,000	14,000
35a	Aa ℞ VICTORIA AVGG, Victory walking l. hldg. wreath and palm. Milan $\overline{\text{MD}}$. **half siliqua**	200	450

35b	As last. Ravenna $\overline{\text{RV}}$. **half siliqua**	200	450
36	Aa ℞ As last, Roma seated l., hldg. Victory on globe and reversed spear. Ravenna $\overline{\text{PSRV}}$. **half siliqua**	225	500
38†a	Aa ℞ VICTORIA AVGGG, Victory walking l. hldg. wreath and palm. Milan $\overline{\text{MD}}$. *RIC 38b, 39b* **half siliqua**	200	450
38†b	As last. Rome $\overline{\text{RM}}$. **half siliqua**	200	450
41A	Aa ℞ VICTORIA AAVGGG, Roma seated l. on throne hldg. reversed spear in l. hand, and Victory on globe in right. Arelate $\overline{\text{CONT}}$.	125	300
56A	Aa ℞ VIRTVS EXERCITVM, emperor in mil. dress stg. facing, head l., hldg. reversed spear or sceptre in r. hand, resting l. on shield. Milan $\overline{\text{MDPS}}$. **light miliarensis**	700	1,650
57a	Aa ℞ VIRTVS EXERCITVS, as last. Milan $\overline{\text{MDPS}}$. **light miliarensis**	700	1,650

57b	As last. Rome $\overline{\text{RMPS}}$. **light miliarensis**	700	1,650
57c	As last. Ravenna $\overline{\text{RVPS}}$. **light miliarensis**	700	1,650
57a	Aa ℞ VIRTVS ROMANORVM, as last. Ravenna $\overline{\text{RVPS}}$. **?heavy miliarensis**	750	1,750
59†a	Aa ℞ As last, Roma seated l. on cuirass, hldg. Victory on globe and reversed spear or sceptre. Trier $\overline{\text{TRPS}}$.	90	225

| **59†b** | As last. Milan $\overline{\text{MDPS}}$. *RIC 32c* . . . . | 65 | 160 |

| **59†c** | As last. Rome $\overline{\text{RMPS}}$. . . . . | 80 | 200 |

		VF	EF
59†d	As last. Ravenna $\overline{\text{RVPS}}$.	80	200
59†e	As last. Aquileia $\overline{\text{AQPS}}$.	85	210
62†a	As R̩ VOT V MVLT X, in wreath. Milan $\overline{\text{MDPS}}$. *Gnecchi p. 83,9* **heavy miliarensis**.	750	1,750
62†b	As last. Milan $\overline{\text{MDPS}}$. **light miliarensis**	700	1,650
62†c	As last. Ravenna $\overline{\text{RVPS}}$. *Gnecchi p. 83,8* **light miliarensis** . .	700	1,650

63†	Aa R̩ VOT V MVLT X, in wreath. Milan $\overline{\text{MDPS}}$. *RIC 26* . . .	70	175
63A	Aa R̩ VOT X MVLT XV, in wreath. Milan $\overline{\text{MDPS}}$. *RIC 27b* . .	80	200
64a	Aa R̩ VOT X MVLT XX, in wreath. Milan $\overline{\text{MDPS}}$. *Gnecchi p. 83,10* **heavy miliarensis**.	750	1,750
64b	As last. Rome $\overline{\text{RMPS}}$. **heavy miliarensis**	750	1,750
64c	As last. Ravenna $\overline{\text{RVPS}}$. **heavy miliarensis**	750	1,750
65†a	As last. Constantinople $\overline{\text{CONS}}$. *RIC 87c*	75	185
65†b	As last. Constantinople $\overline{\text{CONS}}$*.	85	210
66a	Aa R̩ VOT XV MVLT XX, in wreath. Rome $\overline{\text{RMPS}}$. *Gnecchi pl. 37,3* **heavy miliarensis**.	750	1,750
66b	As last. Constantinople $\overline{\text{CONS}}$*. **heavy miliarensis**. . . .	750	1,750
67	As last. Constantinople $\overline{\text{CONS}}$*.	85	210
70a	Aa R̩ VRBS ROMA, Roma seated l. on cuirass hldg. Victory on globe and reversed spear. Rome $\overline{\text{RMPS}}$.	125	300
70b	As last. Ravenna $\overline{\text{RVPS}}$.	110	275
70†c	Aa R̩ As last, but Roma is seated l. on throne. Ravenna $\overline{\text{RVPS}}$.	110	275
70†d	As last. Milan $\overline{\text{MDPS}}$.	125	300

186

GALLA PLACIDIA

Galla Placidia was born in 388, the daughter of Theodosius I and his second wife Galla, and thus the half-sister of Arcadius and Honorius. In 410 she was taken prisoner by the Visigoths after their capture of Rome and taken by them to Gaul in 412. In 414 she married the Visigothic King Athaulfus and bore him a son who died in infancy. She was restored to the Romans after the murder of Athaulfus by King Vallia in 416. Her second husband was the 'patricius' Flavius Constantius (who became Augustus for a few months in 421) and by him she had two children, Justa Grata Honoria and Placidius Valentinianus (III). Although Placidia and Honorius were very close after her husband's death, they later quarrelled and she departed with her children to Constantinople. The Eastern Emperor Theodosius II championed the cause of Placidia and her son against Honorius' successor, the usurper Johannes, and with his defeat and death in 425 Placidia assumed the reins of government in the West, where she acted as regent for her six-year-old son Valentinianus III. She lost her political influence in the latter part of her son's reign and spent her final years erecting holy buildings in Ravenna. She died at Rome in 450.

Obverse legends.

A.   DN GALLA PLACIDIA PF AVG.
B.   DN GALL PLACIDIA PF AVG.

Obverse bust.

a.   pearl diadem, draped, right.

		VF	EF
5†	Aa ℞ SALVS REIPVBLICAE, Victory seated r. on cuirass inscribing a chi-rho on shield resting on her knee. Ravenna RVPS. **siliqua** .	900	2,000

		VF	EF
16a	Aa ℞ No legend, Chi-rho in wreath. Ravenna RV. **half siliqua**.	750	1,750
16b	Ba ℞ As last Ravenna RV. **half siliqua**	750	1,750
16c	Aa As last. Aquileia AQ. **half siliqua** *forgery*		
18†	Aa ℞ No legend, cross in wreath. Aquileia AQMPS. **siliqua** *forgery*		

THEODOSIUS II
A.D. 402–450

Theodosius II, the son of Arcadius and Aelia Eudoxia, was born in 401 and proclaimed emperor in 402. He succeeded to the throne of the Eastern half of the empire in 408, on his father's death, and married Aelia Eudocia (Athenais) in 421, by whom he had three children. His interests were primarily intellectual and religious; he was the moving force behind the collection of imperial legislation which bears his name, the Codex Theodosianus. The second half of his reign was dominated by the threat of Attila and the Huns. The barbarians invaded the Eastern empire after Theodosius failed to pay an agreed indemnity in 435, and sacked Singidunum, Sirmium, Naissus, and Serdica. Theodosius died in 450 as a result of a hunting accident in which he fell from his horse.

Obverse legend.
DN THEODOSIVS PF AVG.

Obverse busts.
a. pearl diadem, draped, cuirassed, right.
b. pearl diadem, draped, cuirassed, left.

All coins are siliquae unless otherwise stated. For a discussion of fifth-century silver denominations and their names, see the Introduction.

	VF	EF
20† Aa ℞ GLORIA ROMANORVM, emperor nimbate, stg. facing, head l., hldg. sceptre in r., resting l. on shield. Constantinople *⁄CON. *Tol. 68* **heavy miliarensis**	700	1,650

20A Ab ℞ As last, emperor nimbate stg. facing head l., raising r. hand, hldg. globe in left. Constantinople *⁄CON. **light miliarensis**	450	1,000

20B Aa ℞ VOT X MVLT XX, in wreath. Constantinople CONS*.	150	350
20C Aa ℞ VOT XV MVLT XX, in wreath. Constantinople CONS*. *Tol. 71*	175	400

20D Aa ℞ VOT XX MVLT XXX, in wreath. Constantinople CONS*. *Tol. 72*	150	350

		VF	EF

20E Aa Ŗ vot xxx mvlt xxxx, in wreath. Constantinople $\overline{\text{CONS}}$*.
Tol. 74 . . . . 175 400

21 Aa Ŗ vot mvlt xxxx, in wreath. Constantinople $\overline{\text{CONS}}$*. *Tol.
75* 125 300

22†a Aa Ŗ vrtvs romanorvm (sic), Roma seated l. hldg. Victory on
globe and reversed spear. Trier $\overset{*}{\text{TRPS}}$. **half siliqua** 200 450

22†b Aa Ŗ As last, emperor stg. facing, head l., hldg. standard in r.,
globe in left. Trier $\overline{\text{TRPS}}$. **half siliqua** 225 500

22†c Aa Ŗ virtvs romanorum, as last. Trier $\overline{\text{TRPS}}$. **half siliqua** . 225 500

CONSTANTINE III
A.D. 407–411

Flavius Claudius Constantinus was proclaimed emperor by the British legions in 407, in succession to the ephemeral usurpers Marcus and Gratian. He quickly crossed over to Gaul and by the summer of 408 he had established his capital at Arles, had seized control of Spain and proclaimed his son Constans Caesar. In 409 he sent an embassy to Honorius claiming he had been forced to accept the purple. The emperor, who was having severe difficulties at the time coping with Alaric, sent him an imperial robe as a sign of temporary recognition. However, in 411 Constantine III was besieged by Honorius' general Constantius and surrendered; he and his younger son Julianus were murdered on their journey to the court of Honorius at Ravenna, and the usurper's head, mounted on a pole, was placed on public display in the city.

Obverse legend.
DN CONSTANTINVS PF AVG.

Obverse bust.
pearl diadem, draped, cuirassed, right.

The silver coins recorded for this reign are all siliquae. For a discussion of fifth-century silver denominations and their names, see the Introduction.

		VF	EF

4a Ŗ victoria aavggg, Roma seated l. on throne hldg. Victory on
globe and reversed spear. Trier $\overline{\text{TRMS}}$. £350 £750

4b As last. Lugdunum $\overline{\text{SMLD}}$. 250 550
4c As last. Lugdunum $\overline{\text{LDPV}}$ *(confirmation required)*. . . . 300 650

		VF	EF
4d	As last. Arelate $\overline{\text{SMAR}}$. . .	275	600
4e	As last. Arelate $\overline{\text{KONT}}$. . .	275	600
4f	As last. Arelate $\frac{+|}{\text{KONT}}$. . .	350	750
4g	As last. Arelate $\frac{*|}{\text{KONT}}$. . .	350	750
4h	As last. Arelate $\overline{\text{CONT}}$. . .	300	650

4A   R As last but Rome seated l. on cuirass. Trier $\overline{\text{TRMS}}$. .   . .   375   800

7a   R VICTORIA AAAVGGGG, as last but Roma seated l. on throne. Lugdunum $\overline{\text{LDPV}}$. .   . .   300   650

7b	As last. Lugdunum $\overline{\text{SMLD}}$. .	275	600
7c	As last. Lugdunum $\overline{\text{LDPS}}$ (*confirmation required*). . .	300	650
8	Aa R No legend, cross with A and ω under its arms. Lugdunum $\overline{\text{SMLD}}$. **half siliqua** *?forgery* . .		

CONSTANS II
A.D. 409–411

Constans was the eldest son of Constantine III. He was created Caesar by his father in 408 and sent to Spain to deal with resistance from supporters of Honorius. Having accomplished this he left the general Gerontius in charge of affairs in the province. Shortly before his father entered Italy, late in 409 or early in 410, Constans was elevated to the rank of Augustus, but in 411 he was attacked and killed at Vienne by Gerontius, who was supporting his own nominee to the throne, Maximus.

Obverse legend.
DN CONSTANS PF AVG.

Obverse bust.
pearl diadem, draped, cuirassed. right.

The silver coins recorded for this reign are all siliquae. For a discussion of fifth-century silver denominations and their names, see the Introduction.

		VF	EF
1a	R VICTORIA AAVGGG, Roma seated l. on cuirass(?) hldg. Victory on globe and reversed spear. Arelate $\overline{\text{KONT}}$.	1,500	3,500
1b	As last. Lugdunum $\overline{\text{LDPV}}$. (*confirmation required*)	1,500	3,500

PRISCUS ATTALUS
A.D. 409–410 and 414–415

Priscus Attalus, a native of Asia, was sent by Honorius to Rome in 409 to fill the office of City Prefect. Late in the same year the Visigothic King Alaric, who was besieging Rome, had him proclaimed emperor, and he acted as a puppet of the barbarians until he was deposed in the summer of 410. Following the capture and sack of Rome (August, 410) the Visigoths made peace with Honorius, but Attalus remained in the Gothic camp. After Alaric's death, Attalus accompanied his successor, Athaulfus, into Gaul and urged him to join forces with the usurper Jovinus, but the alliance soon collapsed. In 414 Attalus was again proclaimed emperor by the Visigoths, but they abandoned him when they moved into Spain the following year. He later fell into the hands of Honorius who had him mutilated and then exiled him to the Lipari islands.

Obverse legend.
PRISCVS ATTALVS PF AVG

Obverse busts.
a. pearl diadem, draped, cuirassed, right.
b. pearl and rosette diadem, draped, cuirassed, right.
c. rosette diadem, draped, cuirassed, right.

All coins are siliquae unless otherwise stated. For a discussion of fifth-century silver denominations and their names, see the Introduction.

		VF	EF
5	Ab ℞ INVICTA ROMA AETERNA, Roma seated facing on throne, hldg. Victory on globe and reversed spear. Rome RMPS. *Gnecchi pl. 37, 6–7.* **multiple**.	25,000	50,000

		VF	EF
7a	Aa ℞ As last, Roma seated l. on cuirass, hldg. Victory on globe and reversed spear. Rome PST.	1,250	3,000
7b	As last. Rome PST*.	1,250	3,000
9A	Aa ℞ VICTORIA AVGG, Roma seated l. on cuirass, hldg. Victory on globe and reversed spear. Rome SRV.	1,500	3,500

		VF	EF
10A	Aa ℞ VICTORIA ROMANORVM, Victory advg. R., hldg. trophy over r. shldr., and shield with Chi-rho. Rome $\frac{*}{\overline{PST}}$? **heavy milliarensis**	6,000	12,500
11†	As last, Victory advancing l. hldg. wreath in l. hand, palm over r. shldr. Rome $\frac{*}{\overline{PST}}$. *Gnecchi pl. 83, 3.* **light millarensis** . .	6,000	12,500
12†	Aa ℞ As last, Victory advancing l. hldg. wreath and palm. Rome $\frac{*}{\overline{PST}}$	1,500	3,500
16	Ac ℞ VOT V MVLT X, in wreath. Rome $\overline{PST}$.	1,500	3,500

MAXIMUS
A.D. 409–411

In 409 Gerontius, a general of Constantine III and Constans, who had been left in charge of Spain with part of the Gallic army, rebelled against his imperial masters. He decided to nominate his own candidate for the throne, and his choice fell on a certain Maximus, who may have been a relative. Gerontius ordered Maximus, who seems to have been a nonentity, to remain in Spain while he pursued Constans into Gaul, where he attacked and killed the young emperor at Vienne. Gerontius then besieged Constantine III at Arles but was forced to flee to Spain when his troops abandoned him in favour of Honorius' general Constantius, who had been sent to quell the Gallic uprising. After the death of Gerontius in 411 Maximus was deposed by the Gallic troops, and is said to have retired into private life in Spain.

Obverse legend.
DN MAXIMVS PF AVG.

Obverse bust.
pearl diadem, draped, cuirassed, right.

The silver coins recorded for this reign are all siliquae. For a discussion of fifth-century silver denominations and their names, see the Introduction.

		VF	EF
1a	℞ VICTORIA AAVGGG, Roma seated l. on cuirass, hldg. Victory on globe and reversed spear. Barcelona $\overline{SMB}$. *forgery*		

		VF	EF
1b	℞ VICTORIA AVGGG, as last. Barcelona $\overline{SMBA}$.	1,250	3,000

JOVINUS
A.D. 411–413

Jovinus was a native of Gaul and is said to have been of noble birth. He was proclaimed Augustus in 411 and received support from Burgundians, Alamans, Franks, and Alans. In 412 he elevated his brother Sebastian to the rank of co-emperor, but the following year his fortunes took a turn for the worse. He was besieged by Athulfus, who had previously favoured him but was now in alliance with Honorius, and after Jovinus surrendered he and his brother Sebastian were murdered while being escorted to Honorius.

Obverse legend.
DN IOVINVS PF AVG.

Obverse bust.
pearl diadem, draped, cuirassed, right.

All coins are siliquae unless otherwise specified. For a discussion of fifth-century silver denominations and their names, see the Introduction.

		VF	EF
2†a	℞ REŚTITVTOR REIP, Roma seated l. on throne, hldg. Victory on globe and reversed spear. Arelate $\overline{\text{KONT}}$. **argenteus (=pre-form siliqua)** *?forgery*	650	1,500

2†b	As last. Arelate $\overline{\text{KONT}}$.	400	900
2†c	As last. Lugdunum $\overline{\text{SMLD}}$. .	450	1,000
2†d	℞ As last, Roma seated l. on cuirass (?), hldg. Victory on globe on reversed spear. Arelate $\overline{\text{KONT}}$	450	1,000

4†a	℞ VICTORIA AVGG, Roma seated l. on throne hldg. Victory on globe and reversed spear or sceptre. Trier $\overline{\text{TRMS}}$.	450	1,000
4†b	As last. Lugdunum $\overline{\text{SMLD}}$. .	400	900

4†c	As last. Lugdunum $\overline{\text{SMLDV}}$.	400	900
4†d	℞ As last Roma seated l. on cuirass (?) hldg. Victory on globe and sceptre. Lugdunum $\overline{\text{SMLDV}}$.	450	1,000
8	Aa ℞ No legend, cross with A and ω under its arms. Lugdunum $\overline{\text{SMLD}}$. **half siliqua** *?forgery*.		

194

SEBASTIAN
A.D. 412–413

Sebastian was the brother of the usurper Jovinus and was proclaimed co-emperor in 412, despite the opposition of Athaulfus who, up until this time, had been a supporter of Jovinus. Athaulfus, now acting on behalf of Honorius, proceeded to besiege Jovinus and both he and Sebastian were captured in 413. The deposed usurpers both met violent ends while on their journey to the court of Honorius.

Obverse legend.
DN SEBASTIANVS PF AVG.

Obverse bust.
pearl diadem, draped, cuirassed, right.

The only coin recorded for this reign is a silver siliqua. For a discussion of fifth-century silver denominations and their names, see the Introduction.

		VF	EF
1	R VICTORIA AVGG, Roma seated l. on throne, hldg. Victory on globe and reversed spear. Arelate $\overline{\text{KONT}}$. .	2,750	6,000

CONSTANTIUS III
A.D. 421

Flavius Constantius was an Illyrian, from Naissus, who joined the army under Theodosius I and had a distinguished military career. In 411 Honorius appointed him commander in the war to recover Gaul from Constantine III, which he achieved after a brief but successful campaign. He then attacked the Visigoths forcing them to leave Gaul and cross the Pyrenees into Spain. In 415 he captured the usurper Priscus Attalus, who had been abandoned by the Goths, and the following year the Visigothic war ended with the accession of a new king and the return of Galla Placidia to her brother Honorius. Constantius married Placidia in 417 and they had two children, Justa Grata Honoria and Placidus Valentinianus, later Valentinian III. Constantius III was proclaimed Augustus in the West in 421 by Honorius, but was never recognized in the East. He died of natural causes after holding office for only six months, thus averting a possible civil war between East and West. No authentic silver coins in the name of Constantius III have yet been identified.

JOHANNES
A.D. 423–425

Little is known of the early life of Johannes, other than that he followed a career in the civil service and rose to become principal secretary to Honorius. After the death of the emperor in 423 he seized power in the West. Although he sent an embassy to Constantinople he was not recognized by the Eastern Emperor Theodosius II, who supported the claims of Galla Placidia and the young Placidius Valentinianus against him. Johannes was in a weak position militarily, so when the Eastern army entered northern Italy in 425 he was able to offer little resistance, and was soon captured and put to death.

Obverse legend.
DN IOHANNES PF AVG.

Obverse bust.
pearl and rosette diadem, draped, cuirassed, right.

For a discussion of fifth-century silver denominations and their names, see the Introduction.

		VF	EF
3	R VICTORIA AVGG, Victory advg. l. hldg. wreath and palm. Ravenna $\overline{RV}$. **half siliqua**	1,250	2,750
4A	R VICTORIA AVGGG, emperor in mil. dress stg. facing, head r., hldg. standard with banner in r. hand, Victory on globe in l., l. foot on captive. Ravenna $\frac{R|V}{COMOB}$. *Confirmation required. Probably a forgery in silver of a gold solidus.*		

9	R VRBS ROMA, Roma seated l. hldg. Victory on globe and sceptre. Ravenna $\overline{RVPS}$. **siliqua**	1,500	3,500

PULCHERIA

Aelia Pulcheria was born in 399, the daughter of Arcadius and Aelia Eudoxia and the sister of Theodosius II. She played a prominent role in the education and training of her brother and was instrumental in selecting his bride. In 414 she was proclaimed Augusta, playing a dominant role in administering affairs of state from the time she was fifteen years old. She remained single by choice throughout most of her life and persuaded her sisters to do likewise. After her brother died in 450 she supported Marcian as his successor and entered into a form of marriage with him. Pulcheria died in July, 453, leaving all her possessions to the poor.

Obverse legend.
AEL PVLCHERIA AVG.

Obverse bust.
pearl diadem, draped, right.

For a discussion of fifth-century silver denominations and their names, see the Introduction.

	VF	EF
10a R No legend, cross in wreath. Constantinople $\overline{\text{CONS}}$*. *Tol. pl. 7, 45.* **siliqua**	450	1,000
10⁺b As last. Constantinople $\overline{\text{CONS}}$*. *Tol. pl. 7, 47.* **half siliqua** . .	500	1,100
10A R SAL REI PVI (sic), in wreath. Constantinople $\overline{\text{CONS}}$*. *Tol.* — **half siliqua**	550	1,200

EUDOCIA (ATHENAIS)

Aelia Eudocia was an Athenian, the daughter of the sophist Leontius, a pagan, and originally called Athenais. After her father's death she went to Constantinople to press her claims to her inheritance. While living there with a paternal aunt, she was seen by the Empress Pulcheria, the sister of Theodosius II, who decided she would be a suitable consort for the emperor. In order for the marriage to take place, the bride had to become a Christian, and it was on this occasion that she changed her name from Athenais to Eudocia. She married Theodosius II in 421 and their union resulted in three children: Licinia Eudoxia, Flaccilla, and Arcadius. Two years after the wedding she was granted the title Augusta. She was not only well educated but extremely beautiful and the author of several literary works. She outlived her husband by a decade and devoted much of her later years to the erection of churches and monasteries.

Obverse legends.
A.　AEL EVDOCIA AVG.
B.　AEL EVDOXIA AVG.

Obverse bust.
pearl diadem, draped, right.

All the silver coins in the name of Eudocia are siliquae. For a discussion of fifth-century silver denominations and their names, see the Introduction.

	VF	EF
4 Aa R No legend, cross in wreath. Constantinople $\overline{\text{CONS}}$*. *Tol. pl. 6, 98*	450	1,000
5 Aa R No legend, Chi-rho in wreath. Constantinople $\overline{\text{CONS}}$*.	550	1,200

VALENTINIAN III
A.D. 425–455

Placidius Valentinianus was the son of Constantius III and Galla Placidia and the brother of Justa Grata Honoria. After his mother quarrelled with Honorius she took him and his sister with her to Constantinople. Following the death of Honorius in 423 Theodosius II supported his cousin's claim to the throne, and furnished him with an army which overthrew the usurper Johannes and installed Valentinian III on the Western throne, under his mother's regency. The new emperor was betrothed to Theodosius II's daughter Licinia Eudoxia and the marriage took place in 437. After 433 the influence of Placidia over Valentinian yielded to Aetius, his commander-in-chief and the most able general which the Empire possessed. During his reign Valentinian was forced to accept the settlement of the Vandals in Africa, and the treachery of his sister Honoria ultimately resulted in the invasion of Italy by the Huns in 452. In the light of these failures Valentinian was persuaded to assassinate Aetius in 454, but was himself murdered the following year by two of Aetius' bodyguards who wished to avenge him.

Obverse legends.
A. DN VALENTINIANVS PF AVG.
B. DN PLA VALENTINIANVS PF AVG.

Obverse busts.
a. pearl diadem, draped, cuirassed, right.
b. rosette diadem, draped, cuirassed, right.

All coins are siliquae unless otherwise stated. For a discussion of fifth-century silver denominations and their names, see the Introduction.

		VF	EF
2†**Bb**	℞ GLORIA ROMANORUM, helmeted soldier stg. l., hldg. long cross. Ravenna RVPS	450	1000
11a	Ba ℞ VICTORIA AVGG, Victory advg. l. hldg. wreath and palm. Rome RM. **half siliqua**	400	900
11b	As last. Ravenna RV. **half siliqua**	400	900
11†c	Bb ℞ As last. Rome RM. **half siliqua**	400	900
32†a	Aa ℞ VRTVS ROMANORVM (sic), emperor stg. facing, head l., hldg. standard in r., globe in left. Trier TRPS. **half siliqua** . .	450	1,000
32†b	Aa ℞ VIRTVS ROMANORVM, as last. Trier TRPS **half siliqua** . .	350	1,200
33†	Aa ℞ VIRTVS ROMANORVM, Roma seated facing, head l. hldg. globe in r. hand, spear in l. Trier TRPS.	550	1,200

34	Aa ℞ VRTVS ROMANORVM (sic), Roma seated l. on throne, hldg. Victory on globe and reversed spear. Trier ⁎TRPS. **half siliqua**	400	900
41A	Aa ℞ VOT XX MVLT XXX, in wreath. Constantinople CONS*. . .	500	1,100

	VF	EF
46†a Bb ℞ vʀʙs ʀᴏᴍᴀ, Roma seated l. on cuirass hldg. Victory on globe and sceptre. Ravenna $\overline{\text{RVPS}}$..	500	1,100
46†b Ba ℞ As last. Rome $\overline{\text{RMPS}}$. .	500	1,100
46†c Aa ℞ As last. Ravenne $\overline{\text{RVPS}}$.	500	1,100

	VF	EF
46A Bb ℞ vʀʙɪs ʀᴏᴍᴀ, Roma seated l. hldg. Victory on globe and inverted spear or sceptre. Rome $\overline{\text{RMPS}}$. . .	550	1,200

	VF	EF
48A Bb ℞ No legend, Chi-rho in wreath. Ravenna $\overline{\text{RV}}$. **half siliqua**	450	1,000
59† Ba ℞ No legend, cross in wreath. Ravenna $\overline{\text{RV}}$. **half siliqua** . .	400	900

HONORIA

Justa Grata Honoria, born c. 418, was the daughter of Constantius III and Galla Placidia and the sister of Valentinian III. In about 449 she was discovered to be involved in a love-affair with the manager of her estates who apparently had aspirations to imperial power. As a result she was expelled from the palace and in addition to being kept under guard she was also betrothed to a trustworthy senator for whom she had no affection. Her reaction was to send a message to Attila, King of the Huns, asking him to avenge her and sending him a ring as evidence of her good faith. Attila chose to interpret the ring as a sign that they were betrothed and sent envoys to Valentinian III demanding Honoria as his bride and half of the Western empire as a dowry. This led to an invasion of Italy by the Huns in 452 which caused considerable devastation to a number of the principal cities. Fortunately, Attila died the following year and Honoria herself, soon afterwards, in 454. No silver coinage was minted in her name.

MARCIAN
A.D. 450–457

Marcian was the son of a soldier and himself chose a military career, rising to high rank under Theodasius II and eventually becoming a senator. Despite the relative obscurity of his origins he was proclaimed emperor at Constantinople in 450, having been the favoured candidate of the Empress Pulcheria who married him to legitimize the succession. He refused to pay tribute to Attila and the Huns, and the threat of invasion was only averted by the timely death of the barbarian king in 453. Marcian ruled the Eastern Empire wisely until his death, by natural causes in 457. His reign is chiefly remembered for the famous Fourth Ecumenical Council which was convened at Chacedon in 451 and laid down the principles of the Orthodox Faith.

Obverse legend.
DN MARCIANVS PF AVG.

Obverse busts.
a.   pearl diadem, draped, cuirassed, right.
b.   pearl diadem, draped, cuirassed, left.

All coins are siliquae unless otherwise stated. For a discussion of fifth-century silver denominations and their names, see the Introduction.

		VF	EF
10A	Aa ℞ GLOR ORVS TERRHR (sic), emperor nimbate, stg. facing, head l., hldg. sceptre in r. hand, resting l. on shield. Thessalonica $\overline{\text{TESOP}}$. *Tol.*— **heavy miliarensis**	2,500	5,500

10Ba	Aa ℞ GLORIA ROMANORVM, emperor nimbate, stg. facing, head l., hldg. spear in r., resting l. on shield. Constantinople $\overline{\text{CON}}$. *Tol.*— **heavy miliarensis**.	2,000	4,500
10Bb	As last. Constantinople $\overline{\text{CON}}$. *Tol.*— **heavy miliarensis** . .	2,000	4,500
10C	Ab ℞ As lAST, EMPEROR NIMBATE, STG. FACING, HEAD L., RAISING R. HAND, HLDG. GLOBE IN LEFT. Constantinople $\overline{\text{CON}}$. *Tol.*— **light miliarensis**	1,750	4,000
10Da	Aa ℞ SAL REI PPI (sic), in wreath. Constantinople $\overline{\text{CONS}}$*. *Tol. 23*	400	900

10Db	As last. Constantinople $\overline{\text{CONS}}$*. *Tol.*— **half siliqua**. . . .	350	800

		VF	EF

10E   Aa R̶ sal rei pvi (sic), in wreath. Constantinople $\overline{\text{CONS}}$*. *Tol.*
    24   400   900

10F   Aa R̶ vot mvlt xxxx, in wreath. Constantinople $\overline{\text{CONS}}$*. *Tol.*
    25   400   900

LICINIA EUDOXIA

Licinia Eudoxia, the daughter of Theodosius II and Eudocia, was born in 422. She was soon betrothed to Valentinian III and they married in 437, two daughters, Eudocia and Placidia, being the result of the union. She was proclaimed Augusta at Ravenna c. 439 and seems to have kept the title until her death. After the murder of Valentianian III in 455, his successor, Petronius Maximus, forced the widowed empress to marry him to legitimize his position, but this outrage caused her to appeal to the Vandal king Gaiseric to rescue her and avenge her late husband. Being more than happy to answer such an appeal, Gaiseric sacked Rome in 455 and took Eudoxia and her two daughters back to Africa with him. After seven years had elapsed Gaiseric finally agreed to send Eudoxia and Placidia to Constantinople, but only after Eudoxia's other daughter, Eudocia, had consented to marry his son Huneric. Eudoxia spent the remainder of her life in the city of her birth, Constantinople, whilst her daughter Placidia married the future Western Emperor Anicius Olybrius.

No silver coinage was minted in the name of Licinia Eudoxia.

PETRONIUS MAXIMUS
A.D. 455

Petronius Maximus was deeply implicated in the assassination of Valentinian III, in March 455, and seized the throne on the day following the murder. He had previously had a long and distinguished civil career and had held the posts of City Prefect and Praetorian Prefect. On his accession, he forced Valentinian III's widow, Eudoxia, to marry him in order to strengthen his claim to the throne. She, however, countered by summoning Gaiseric and the Vandals to help her. After a reign of only eleven weeks Maximus was killed in the city streets while attempting to flee from the Vandals as they approached Rome.

No silver coinage appears to have been minted in his name.

AVITUS
A.D. 455–456

Avitus was born in Gaul into a senatorial family and studied law as a young man. He paid a visit to the Visigothic court about 425 and was thereafter favoured by Theodoric. He pursued a distinguished military career in Gaul, serving under Aetius, and in 439 became Praetorian Prefect of his native province. After giving up the prefecture he retired to his country estates until Attila and the Huns invaded Gaul in 451, when he emerged from retirement to urge Theodoric to join with Aetius and the Romans against the common enemy. He was appointed Magister Militum by Petronius Maximus in 455 and was sent as an envoy to the Visigoths. After the death of Petronius Maximus, Avitus was persuaded by the Goths and the Gauls to become emperor. However, he was greatly disliked in Rome, and in the following year he was defeated and deposed by the general Ricimer. He was created bishop of Placentia, but died not long afterwards.

Obverse legend.
DN AVITVS PF AVG.

Obverse bust.
pearl diadem, draped, cuirassed, right.

For a discussion of fifth-century silver denominations and their names, see the Introduction.

		VF	EF
9	℞ VRBIS ROMA, Roma seated l., hldg. Victory on globe and reversed spear. Rome RMPS. **siliqua** *(confirmation required)*	2,500	5,500

MAJORIAN
A.D. 457–461

Flavius Julius Valerius Majorianus served in the army under Aetius and saw active service in Gaul c. 447–448. Subsequently he retired from the army but was recalled by Valentinian III to appease Aetius' troops following their general's assassination. Appointed Magister Militum in 457, later the same year he was proclaimed emperor, nearly six months after the downfall of Avitus. He sent a small army against the Alamanni in 457 and defeated them. In 460 he organized a large force to attack the Vandals in Africa, but by treachery Gaiseric succeeded in destroying most of the Roman fleet before it had even left harbour, and Majorian was forced to abandon the expedition and make peace. As a result of this disaster the emperor's authority was undermined, and he was arrested by the general Ricimer and executed in northern Italy in 461.

Obverse legends.
A. DN MAIORANVS PF AVG.
B. DN MAIORIANVS (N reversed in name).
C. DN MAIORIANVS AVG.

Obverse bust.
pearl diadem, helmeted, draped, cuirassed, right, spear pointing forward.

For a discussion of fifth-century silver denominations and their names, see the Introduction.

		VF	EF
8†a	Ba ℞ VICTORIA AVG, Victory stg. l. hldg. long cross. Ravenna(?)⊥. **siliqua** *(barbarous?)*	1,500	3,500
8†b	Ca ℞ CC VIT (sic), As last. Mint? **`**`** **half siliqua** *(barbarous)* . .	1,250	2,750
8†c	Ca ℞ As last. Mint? **`*.*`** **half siliqua** *(barbarous)*	1,250	2,750
13	Aa ℞ VOTIS MVLTIS, emperor stg. facing in mil. dress hldg. spear and shield. Ravenna(?) ⊥. **half siliqua** *forgery*		

202

LEO I
A.D. 457–474

Leo, a native of Dacia, was a soldier of considerable experience who reached the rank of tribune, though he had had little formal education. Despite the obscurity of his origins he succeeded Marcian on the throne of the Eastern Empire in 457, thanks to the support of Aspar who hoped to control policy by using him as a puppet. Leo remained under Aspar's domination for ten years and it was only after he began to promote the interests of the Isaurian chieftain Zeno, who became his son-in-law in 467, that Leo's independence began to increase. He intervened actively in the affairs of the Western Empire by appointing Anthemius, and later Julius Nepos, as emperors but he never succeeded in dominating the West. His campaign against the Vandals failed because its commander Basiliscus, the brother-in-law of the emperor, lost the whole of his fleet through his own incompetence. Despite the assassination of Aspar in 470 Leo continued to experience difficulties with his Gothic federates, but he had laid the foundation of the freedom of the Eastern Empire from Germanic domination. He died of natural causes in 474, having named his infant grandson, Leo II, as his successor.

Obverse legends.
A.   DN LEO PERPET AVG.
B.   DN LEO PERPET AV.
C.   DN LEO PERPETVVS AVG.

Obverse busts.
a.   pearl diadem, draped, cuirassed, right.
b.   pearl diadem, draped, cuirassed, left.
c.   rosette diadem, draped, cuirassed, right.

For a discussion of fifth-century silver denominations and their names, see the Introduction.

		VF	EF
11†	Aa ℞ GLOR ORVS TERRRHL (sic), emperor nimbate, stg. facing, head l., hldg. spear in r. hand, resting l. on shield. Thessalonica $\frac{*|}{THSOB}$. *Sab. 11 Tol. 23* **heavy miliarensis**	2,000	4,500

11Aa	Aa ℞ GLORIA ROMANORVM, emperor nimbate, stg. facing, head l., hldg. spear in r. hand, resting l. on shield. Constantinople $\frac{*|}{CON}$. *Sab. — Tol —* **heavy miliarensis**	1,500	3,500
11Ab	As last. Constantinople $\frac{*|}{CONOB}$ *Sab. — Tol. —* **heavy miliarensis**	1,500	3,500
11B	Ab ℞ As last, emperor nimbate, stg. facing, head l., raising r. hand, hldg. globe in left. Constantinople $\frac{*|}{CON}$. *Sab. — Tol. —* **light miliarensis**	1,250	2,750

	VF	EF

11Ca Ba ℞ SAL REI PPI (sic), in wreath. Constantinople $\overline{\text{CONS}}$*.
Tol. — **?half siliqua** 275 600

11Cb Aa ℞ SAL REI PPI (sic), in wreath. Constantinople $\overline{\text{CONS}}$*.
Tol. 25 **half siliqua.** 250 550

11Cc As last. Constantinople $\overline{\text{CONS}}$*. *Tol.* — **quarter siliqua** . . 225 500

12†a Aa ℞ SAL REI PVI (sic), in wreath. Constantinople $\overline{\text{CONS}}$*.
Tol. 24 **half siliqua.** 300 650

12†b As last. Constantinople $\overline{\text{ƆONƧ}}$*. *Tol.* — **siliqua** 300 650

12A As last. Constantinople $\overline{\text{CONS}}$*. *Tol.* — **half siliqua.** 275 600

12B Aa ℞ VOT XXXV MVLT XXXX, in wreath. Constantinople $\overline{\text{CONS}}$**.
Sab. 1 *Tol.* 22 **multiple** *(doubtful, confirmation required)*

12C Bc ℞ No legend, Chi-rho in wreath. Rome $\overline{\text{RM}}$. *Tol.* — **half
siliqua** 350 750

VERINA

Aelia Verina was the wife of the Emperor Leo I, the sister of Basiliscus, and the mother-in-law of Zeno. She bore Leo two daughters, Ariadne and Leontia, the elder of whom married the Isaurian chieftain Tarasicodissa in 467, whereupon he changed his name to Zeno. Verina was opposed to Zeno's elevation, following the deaths of Leo I and Leo II, and conspired with her brother Basiliscus to overthrow him, thus forcing Zeno to temporarily abandon his capital and to live in exile in Isauria (475–6). Some years later she was implicated in the revolt of Leontius against Zeno, and she eventually died in the Isaurian fortress of Papyrius in the autumn of 484.

It appears that no silver coinage was minted in the name of Verina, though issues in gold and in bronze are known.

LIBIUS SEVERUS
A.D. 461–465

Libius Severus, sometimes known as Severus III, was apparently a native of Lucania and was proclaimed emperor by the general Ricimer in 461, about four months after the death of Majorian. He was never recognized by the government of the Eastern Empire, nor did he exercise any real power, since this was firmly in the hands of Ricimer. He died at Rome in November 465, an event scarcely noticed by his contemporaries.

Obverse legends.
A. DN LIB SEVERVS PF AVG.
B. DN LIB SEVERVS P AVG.
C. DN LIB SEVERVS PF AV.

Obverse bust.
rosette diadem, draped, cuirassed, right.

For a discussion of fifth-century silver denominations and their names, see the Introduction.

		VF	EF
15	Aa ℞ VRBIS ROMA, Roma seated l. on cuirass, hldg. Victory and reversed spear. Rome $\overline{\text{SMPS}}$. **siliqua**	1,250	2,750
16†a	Aa ℞ No legend, Chi-rho in wreath. Rome $\overline{\text{RM}}$. **half siliqua** .	750	1,750

16†b	Ba ℞ As last. Rome $\overline{\text{RM}}$. **half siliqua**	750	1,750
16†c	Ca ℞ As last. Rome $\underset{\text{RM}}{|}$. **half siliqua**	750	1,750

ANTHEMIUS
A.D. 467–472

Anthemius was born in Constantinople and married Aelia Marcia Euphemia, the daughter of the Emperor Marcian, by whom he had one daughter and four sons. He adopted a military career, and was made Magister Militum by his father-in-law. He successfully campaigned against a band of Ostrogoths in Illyricum and later defeated a group of Huns who had seized Serdica. In 467 Leo I chose him to fill the vacant Western throne and sent him with an army to Italy where he was proclaimed Augustus. Anthemius gave his daughter Alypia in marriage to the general Ricimer in the hope of conciliating him, but Ricimer had no intention of surrendering his authority in the West. Finally, in 472, Ricimer set up a rival emperor, Olybrius, and in the ensuing conflict Anthemius was slain by Ricimer's nephew, Gundobaudes.

Obverse legends.
A. DN ANTHEMIVS PF AVG.
B. DN ANTHEMIVS PERPET AVG.

Obverse busts.
a. pearl diadem, draped, cuirassed, right.
b. rosette diadem, draped, cuirassed, right.

All the silver coins recorded for this reign are half siliquae. For a discussion of fifth-century silver denominations and their names, see the Introduction.

		VF	EF
19†a Aa ℞ No legend, Chi-rho in wreath. Rome $\overline{\text{RM}}$.		1,250	2,750

		VF	EF
19†b Ba ℞ As last. Rome $\overline{\text{RM}}$.		1,250	2,750
19†c Ab ℞ As last. Rome $\overline{\text{RM}}$.		1,250	2,750
19†d Aa ℞ As last. Milan? ⊥ *forgery?*			

EUPHEMIA

Aelia Marcia Euphemia, the only daughter of Marcian, was married to Anthemius in 453. She bore him four sons and one daughter and was probably made Augusta on her husband's accession to the Western throne in 467. Her fate, following Anthemius' downfall in 472, is unknown.

Obverse legend.
DN AELIAE MARCIAE EVFIMI AVG.

Obverse bust.
pearl diadem, draped, right.

For a discussion of fifth-century silver denominations and their names, see the Introduction.

	VF	EF
3† ℞ VRBIS ROMA, Roma seated facing on throne, head l., hldg. Victory on globe in r. hand, sceptre in left. Rome $\overline{\text{RMPS}}$. **siliqua**	3,000	6,500

OLYBRIUS
A.D. 472

Anicius Olybrius was an aristocrat and one of the leading members of the Roman senate. In 455 he escaped to Constantinople when the Vandals attacked Rome, and seven years later he married Placidia, the younger daughter of Valentinian III, who had just been released from captivity in Carthage. In consequence of his marriage to Placidia, and that of Huneric to Eudocia (her sister), Olybrius was related to the Vandal King Gaiseric. After the death of Majorian in 461 Gaiseric supported Olybrius' claim to the Western throne, but Ricimer preferred the weak-willed Libius Severus. In 472 Leo I sent him to Italy to mediate between Ricimer and Anthemius, but instead he was proclaimed emperor by the general and succeeded the murdered Anthemius. However, he died of dropsy after ruling little more than six months.

It appears that no silver coinage was minted in his name.

GLYCERIUS
A.D. 473–474

Glycerius became Comes Domesticorum *in the West in 472, under the Emperor Olybrius. The following year he was proclaimed Augustus at Ravenna, at the instigation of Gundobaudes, the nephew and successor of Ricimer, but Glycerius never received recognition from the East. Instead, the government of Constantinople ordered Julius Nepos, the military governor of Dalmatia, to invade Italy and overthrow the usurper. Deserted by his patron Gundobaudes, Glycerius gave up without a struggle and was dethroned at Portus, near the mouth of the Tiber.*

Obverse legend.
DN GLYCERIVS PF AVG.

Obverse bust.
pearl diadem, draped, right.

		VF	EF
4†	R VICTORIA AVGGG, Victory advancing l., raising r. hand holding wreath. Rome R̄M. *?forgery*	1,500	3,500

JULIUS NEPOS
A.D. 474–475

Julius Nepos, son of Nepotianus, was the nephew of Marcellinus who, as Magister Militum in Dalmatia, had personal control of the area from 454 to 468. On the death of Marcellinus the administration of Dalmatia passed into the hands of Nepos. In 474 he was put in command of an army by Leo I, with orders to attack Italy and depose the usurper Glycerius, a task which he successfully accomplished. He was then proclaimed emperor at Rome, in June 474, and for the last time in Roman history Eastern and Western Augusti reigned in unison. His failure to win the support of the Western troops, largely barbarian, was to prove his downfall, since he had to promote a Western general as commander. In 475 Orestes was appointed Magister Militum by Nepos and within a few months had raised the standard of revolt and had elevated to imperial rank his own young son, Romulus. Nepos, realizing the hopelessness of his position, fled back to Dalmatia in August 475 and remained there as an emperor in exile until his assassination five years later.

Obverse legend.
DN IVL NEPOS PF AVG.

Obverse bust.
pearl diadem, draped, cuirassed, right.

For a discussion of fifth-century silver coins and their names, see the Introduction.

		VF	EF
13†	R VRBIS ROMA, Roma seated facing on throne, hldg. sceptre and Victory on globe. Ravenna R̄V̄P̄S̄. **siliqua** .	1,500	3,500

		VF	EF
15a	R No legend, turreted figure stg. l., r. foot on prow, hldg. sceptre in r. hand, and cornucopiae in left. Ravenna R̲|V̲. **half siliqua** .	1,000	2,250
15†b	As last. Rome R̲|M̲. **half siliqua** . .	1,100	2,500

LEO II
A.D. 473–474

Leo II was the grandson of Leo I, and the son of Zeno and Ariadne. He was appointed Augustus while still a very young child, in 473, and after the death of Leo I, early in the following year, the sickly Leo II was persuaded to crown his own father Augustus and co-emperor. The unfortunate boy-emperor died of natural causes just nine months later.
No silver coins were minted in his name.

ZENO
A.D. 474–491

Flavius Zeno was an Isaurian by birth, and changed his name from Tarasicodissa after his arrival in Constantinople in 466. He brought documents incriminating Ardabur (Aspar's son) in treasonous relations with the Persians. Ardabur was dismissed and Leo, anxious to rid himself of Aspar's domination, promoted Zeno and gave him his daughter Ariadne's hand in marriage (467). Zeno is said to have been implicated in the murder of Aspar in 471 and supported Leo in the troubles which followed the assassination. He was proclaimed emperor by his son Leo II after the death of Leo I in 474, reigning jointly with him for ten months. Zeno was sole ruler from November 474 until his death in 491, except for the brief period of the usurpation of Basiliscus (475–476), which he spent in exile in Isauria. As an emperor he was mild, indolent, in many respects weak and not especially popular. He died of natural causes in 491.

Obverse legends.
A. DN ZENO PERP AVG.
B. DN ZENO PERP AG.
C. DN ZENO PERP F AV.
D. DN ZENO PERP F AVG. (*the Ns are backwards*)

Obverse bust.
pearl diadem, draped, cuirassed, right.

All coins are half siliquae unless otherwise stated. For a discussion of the fifth-century silver denominations and their names, see the Introduction.

		VF	EF
9A	Aa ℞ GLOR ORVS TARRAR (sic), emperor nimbate, stg. facing, head l., hldg. spear in r., resting l. on shield. Thessalonica $\frac{*}{\text{THSOB}}$. *Tol.*— (?) **heavy miliarensis**	2,250	5,000
9B	Aa ℞ SRI REI RVL (sic) in wreath. Constantinople $\overline{\text{CONOS*}}$. *Tol.* --	300	650
10	Aa ℞ TOV VIM V MTI (sic) in wreath. Constantinople $\overline{\text{CONS*}}$. *Sab. 10 Tol. 34* **siliqua**	350	750
10A	Aa ℞ VOT V M2 ITI2 (sic), in wreath. Constantinople $\overline{\text{CONS*}}$. *Tol. 33* **siliqua**	350	750

11†a	Ba ℞ No legend, turreted figure stg. l., r. foot on prow, hldg. sceptre in r. hand, cornucopiae in left. Milan $\underline{\text{M}|\text{D}}$. *Tol.*— . .	275	600
11†b	Aa ℞ As last. Milan $\underline{\text{M}|\text{D}}$. *Tol. 58.*	250	550
11†c	As last. Milan $\underline{\text{M}|\Delta}$. *Tol.*—.	275	600
12	As last. Ravenna. $\underline{\text{R}|\text{V}}$. *Tol. 60*	300	650

		VF	EF
13a	Aa R No legend, eagle stg. facing on prow, head l., wings spread in circle, cross over head. Milan ⊥. *Tol.—*	250	550
13†b	Ba R As last. Milan ⊥. *Tol.—*	275	600
13†c	Aa R As last but eagle is not stg. on a prow. Milan ⊥. *Tol. 61.* .	250	550
14†	Ca R No legend, eagle stg. left, head r., wings spread, cross over head. Ravenna ⊥. *Tol. 62*	275	600
15†	Da R No legend, Victory stg. l. hldg. wreath and palm. ?Mint ⊥. *Sab. 15 Tol. 64*	350	750

15A	Aa R No legend, Chi-rho in wreath. Milan C̄M̄. *Tol.—* . . .	350	750

ARIADNE

Aelia Ariadne was the eldest daughter of the Emperor Leo I and Verina, and was born prior to her father's elevation to the purple. In 467 she was married to Zeno and the union resulted in the birth of a son, Leo II, who was proclaimed Augustus in 473, briefly reigning with his father after Leo I's death in 474. She fled with Zeno to Isauria when Basiliscus revolted and took possession of the capital, remaining with him there for twenty months before returning to Constantinople in October 476. When Zeno died in 491 Ariadne selected his successor, Anastasius, and married the new emperor to legitimize his position. She died in 515, toward the end of Anastasius' reign.

No silver coins were minted in her name.

210

BASILISCUS
A.D. 475–476

Basiliscus was the brother of the Empress Verina, wife of Leo I, and thus enjoyed a highly influential position as the brother-in-law of the emperor. He adopted a military career, and commanded forces against the Goths in Thrace, between 464 and 467/8, and was later given the command of the campaign against the Vandals in 468. The African expedition ended in disaster, as Basiliscus lost the whole of his fleet prior to engagement with the enemy, and he retired in disgrace to Heraclea. Upon the accession of Zeno in 474 Basiliscus plotted to overthrow him and succeeded in forcing him into exile in Isauria. Basiliscus was proclaimed emperor by Verina and reigned for twenty months, but his unpopularity soon led to his downfall. Upon Zeno's return to Constantinople, in 476, Basiliscus surrendered and he and his family were banished to Cappadocia, imprisoned in a dried-up reservoir, and allowed to starve to death.

Obverse legends.
A. DN BASILISCVS PF AVG.
B. DN BASILISCVS P AVG.

Obverse bust.
pearl diadem, draped, cuirassed, right.

For a discussion of fifth-century silver denominations and their names, see the Introduction.

	VF	EF
7A Aa R GLORIA ROMANORVM, emperor nimbate, stg. facing, head l., hldg. spear in r. hand resting l. on shield. Constantinople $\frac{*}{CON}$.		
Tol. — **heavy miliarensis.**	3,500	7,500

9A Ba R No legend, turreted figure stg. l., r. foot on prow, hldg. sceptre in r. hand, cornucopiae in l. Ravenna R|V. *Tol. pl. 11, 87* **half siliqua**	550	1,250

ZENONIS

Aelia Zenonis, the wife of Basiliscus, was proclaimed Augusta by him in 475, during his short-lived revolt against Zeno. She bore him a son Marcus, who was created Caesar, and other children about whom little is known. When Basiliscus surrendered, Zenonis and her children accompanied him into exile in Cappadocia where they all starved to death after being imprisoned in a dried-up reservoir. No silver coins were minted in her name.

ROMULUS AUGUSTUS
A.D. 475–476

Romulus Augustus, nicknamed Augustulus, the last Roman emperor in the West, was set up as a puppet ruler by his father Orestes, the Master of Soldiers, who had driven out the legitimate Emperor Julius Nepos. A few months later Odoacer, leader of the German mercenaries, rebelled against Orestes and established the first barbarian kingdom in Italy. Romulus was deposed but allowed to live because of his extreme youth and beauty. He retired to a relative's estate in Campania where he spent the remainder of his days as a private citizen.

Obverse legend.
DN ROMVL AVGVSTVS PF AVG.

Obverse bust.
pearl diadem, draped, cuirassed; right.

For a discussion of fifth-century silver denominations and their names, see the Introduction.

		VF	EF
8	R No legend, turreted figure stg. l., r. foot on prow, hldg. sceptre in l., and cornucopiae in r. Ravenna R|V. **half siliqua**	2,000	4,500

INDEX OF ISSUERS